FRACTURE MECHANICS
Current Status, Future Prospects

INTERNATIONAL SERIES ON THE
STRENGTH AND FRACTURE OF MATERIALS AND STRUCTURES
Series Editor: D. M. R. TAPLIN, D.Sc., D.Phil., F.I.M.

OTHER TITLES IN THE SERIES

EASTERLING	Mechanisms of Deformation and Fracture
HAASEN, GEROLD and KOSTORZ	Strength of Metals and Alloys (ICSMA5) (3 Volumes)
MILLER and SMITH	Mechanical Behaviour of Materials (ICM3) (3 Volumes)
TAPLIN	Advances in Research on the Strength and Fracture of Materials (6 Volumes)

Related Pergamon Journals

Engineering Fracture Mechanics
Fatigue of Engineering Materials and Structures
International Journal of Mechanical Sciences
Journal of Mechanics and Physics of Solids
Materials Research Bulletin
Progress in Materials Science

FRACTURE MECHANICS
Current Status, Future Prospects

Proceedings of a Conference held at Cambridge University
16 March 1979

Editor

R. A. SMITH

Cambridge University, England

Organised by

Cambridge University Engineering Department
in conjunction with
the Society of Environmental Engineers

PERGAMON PRESS

TORONTO · OXFORD · NEW YORK · SYDNEY · PARIS · FRANKFURT

208237

CANADA	Pergamon of Canada, Suite 104, 150 Consumers Road, Willowdale, Ontario M2J 1P9, Canada
U.K.	Pergamon Press Ltd., Headington Hill Hall, Oxford OX3 0BW, England
U.S.A.	Pergamon Press Inc., Maxwell House, Fairview Park, Elmsford, New York 10523, U.S.A.
AUSTRALIA	Pergamon Press (Aust.) Pty. Ltd., P.O. Box 544, Potts Point, N.S.W. 2011, Australia
FRANCE	Pergamon Press SARL, 24 rue des Ecoles, 75240 Paris, Cedex 05, France
FEDERAL REPUBLIC OF GERMANY	Pergamon Press GmbH, 6242 Kronberg-Taunus, Pferdstrasse 1, Federal Republic of Germany

British Library Cataloguing in Publication Data

Fracture Mechanics: Current Status, Future Prospects
(Conference), Cambridge University, 1979
Fracture mechanics. - (International series on
the strength and fracture of materials and
structures).
1. Fracture mechanics - Congresses
I. Title II. Smith, R A III. University of
Cambridge, *Engineering Department*
IV. Society of Environmental Engineers
V. Series
620.1'126   TA409   79-40769
ISBN 0-08-024766-0

In order to make this volume available as economically and as rapidly as possible the authors' typescripts have been reproduced in their original forms. This method unfortunately has its typographical limitations but it is hoped that they in no way distract the reader.

Printed and bound in Great Britain by
William Clowes, Beccles and London.

CONTENTS

INTRODUCTION

The last decade or so has seen a tremendous increase in the number of tools available for engineers to deal with cracked structures in a quantitative manner. The main reason is probably due to the acceptance of the "stress intensity factor" as a characterising similitude parameter which properly accounts for the applied mechanics near crack tips in many cases of practical interest. It was in order to review both these cases, and those situations where the stress intensity factor is not applicable, that the programme of the meeting at which these papers were presented was formulated.

One need not look far to justify increasing the literature of the subject. At one level, some of this material which was properly considered "research" some half a dozen years ago, has slipped down through the various syllabi, to a stage where it is now being taught to our first year general engineering students here in Cambridge. On the other hand, the interest from the potential users in industry is tremendous - exemplified by the industrial origin of some 80% of the 160 or so delegates to our symposium "Fracture Mechanics - Current Status, Future Prospects".

The "Current Status" of fracture mechanics is reviewed in the first three papers - in an ascending order of characteristic size interest. The introductory paper by Ashby, concentrates on the micromechanisms of material separation, whilst Pook and Smith develop the applied mechanics background of elastic fracture mechanics, which uses the stress intensity factor to quantify both fracture and fatigue crack growth. The advantages of these approaches to an industry which has to live with cracked components is then illustrated in the paper from Neate and his colleagues.

The "Future Prospects" consists of reviews of areas of considerable current debate. A new method of obtaining stress intensity factors is developed by Cartwright and Rooke, Dover looks at the random load problem so important in aircraft and marine oil-rig loadings, whilst Lidiard looks at a topic of increasing importance in this era of increasing public awareness and product liability legislation - probabalistic fracture mechanics.

High temperature applications, with their associated non-linear difficulties are reviewed by Tomkins, Beaumont looks at the attempts to apply fracture mechanics to an increasingly important class of engineering materials, composites, whilst the final paper from Wells develops some thoughts on elastic and elastic/plastic criteria.

I hope readers will find the contents of this volume both interesting and useful - I further hope they might enjoy reading the papers and approach their fracture prevention work with enthusiasm! I certainly have enjoyed the close collaboration with the authors that the production of this book necessitated and I thank them most sincerely. The tidying up of endless pieces of paper, including the final one on which these words are written, has been performed cheerfully and skilfully by Miss D.J. Cooke, to whom I extend my grateful thanks.

R.A. Smith
Cambridge University Engineering Department
March 1979

MICROMECHANISMS OF FRACTURE IN STATIC AND CYCLIC FAILURE

M. F. Ashby

Cambridge University Engineering Department, Trumpington Street, Cambridge CB2 1PZ, U.K.

Abstract

A solid may fail by any one of a number of competing micromechanisms of fracture: cleavage, ductile fracture, rupture, intergranular creep fracture, and so on. The over-all behaviour, for a given material and stress state, can be summarised as a *fracture-mechanism map:* a diagram with stress as one axis and temperature as the other, showing the field of dominance of each mechanism. Such maps are constructed by assembling and analysing fracture observations and data for the material. They give an overview of the micromechanisms by which the material may fail, and help identify the one most likely to be dominant in a given experiment, or an engineering application. They further help in identifying the mechanism of crack-advance likely to be dominant in the monotonic or cyclic loading of cracked materials.

1.   Introduction

If a cylindrical bar of a crystalline solid is pulled in tension, it may fail in one of several ways (Fig. 1). It may, for example, neck down until the cross-section locally goes to zero. At low temperatures it may fail, instead, by cleavage, or by a brittle intergranular fracture; or it may fail in a ductile manner. And at high temperatures, it may fail by various sorts of creep fracture, some transgranular, some intergranular. A single material – tungsten, for example – can show all these modes of failure. It would be useful to have some idea of the conditions under which each appears, and of how these conditions might change if the tungsten were alloyed, or were subjected to a stress state other than that of simple tension.

The answers to these questions determine how a crack will propagate, under a static or a cyclic load. The stress state at the tip of a propagating crack differs from that in a cylindrical tensile specimen, but – as far as we know at present – no new mechanisms of separation appear there. The ranges of dominance of individual mechanisms are shifted somewhat by this altered stress-state, but the mechanisms themselves do not change; and it is the mechanism which determines whether the material is tough or brittle, or how fast (under given loading conditions) a fatigue crack propagates through it.

1

BROAD CLASSES OF FRACTURE MECHANISM

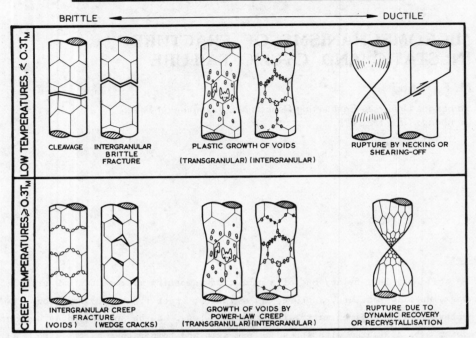

Fig. 1   The simplest classification of fracture mechanisms. The upper row re-
                fers to low temperatures ($< 0.3\ T_M$) where plastic flow does not depend
                strongly on temperature or time; the lower row refers to the tempera-
                ture range ($> 0.3\ T_M$) in which materials creep. The mechanisms are
                described in Section 2.

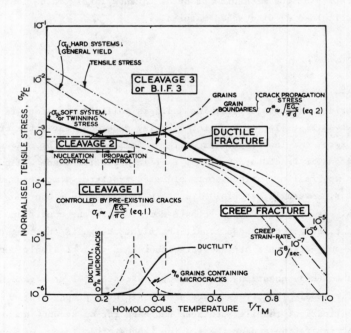

Fig. 2   The definition of the three cleavage, or intergranular brittle fracture
                (I.B.F.) fields. A totally brittle failure from a pre-existing flaw,
                well below general yield, is called Cleavage 1 or I.B.F.1. An almost
                totally brittle failure from a crack nucleated by slip or twinning,
                below general yield, is called Cleavage 2 or I.B.F.2. A cleavage
                or brittle boundary failure after general yield, and with measurable
                strain-to-failure, is called Cleavage 3 or I.B.F.3.

We approach the problem in the following way. The range of dominance of the more easily recognised mechanisms - cleavage, for instance - can be determined by experiment. The field of stress and temperature, or of strain and temperature, in which each mechanism appears can be displayed in an appropriate diagram[1,2]. In this paper, the results of such experiments are plotted on axes of (normalised) tensile stress and temperature - though other possibilities (stress and time; strain and temperature) exist. Before presenting the results, the mechanisms of fracture will be reviewed briefly.

2.   Micromechanisms of Fracture

2.1 *Fracture of the Ideal Strength*

The stress which will overcome the interatomic forces in a perfect crystal, causing it to separate on a plane normal to the stress axis, defines its upper limiting strength. The many calculations[3,4,5] of it are in general agreement: at an adequate level of accuracy, it is

$$\sigma_{IDEAL} = (\frac{2E\gamma_s}{\pi b})^{\frac{1}{2}} \approx \frac{E}{10} \tag{2.1}$$

where γ_s is the surface free energy, E is Young's Modulus; and b is the atomic size. Fracture occurs when the maximum principal stress, σ_n, exceeds σ_{IDEAL}. The ideal strength appears as a horizontal line, coincident with the top of the diagram, in the later figures.

2.2 *Cleavage and Brittle Intergranular Fracture*

Almost all crystalline solids fail by cleavage if the temperature is sufficiently low; certain f.c.c. metals* and their alloys appear to be the only exceptions.

Brittle solids - those in which plasticity at low temperatures is limited - generally contain small cracks because of abrasion or corrosion or as growth defects (Fig. 3a). Such cracks may propagate at a stress which is lower than that required for slip on any slip system. Fracture then occurs without general plasticity, at the nominal stress

$$\sigma_f \approx (\frac{EG_c}{\pi a})^{\frac{1}{2}} \tag{2.2}$$

where 2a is the pre-existing crack length, E is Young's Modulus, and G_c is the toughness. Since the stress is less than the yield stress of even the softest system, no general plasticity is possible, (though there may be local plasticity at the crack tip). We call this field *"Cleavage 1"*. Within it, the strength of the solid is determined by the largest crack it contains.

If pre-existing cracks are small or absent, then the stress can reach the level required to initiate slip or twinning (Fig. 3b). Either can generate internal stresses which can nucleate cracks[6]. We have called this regime of slip or twin-nucleated

---

* Al, Cu, Ag, Au, Pt, Pb and Ni do not cleave; Ir and Rh do.

M. F. Ashby

CLEAVAGE

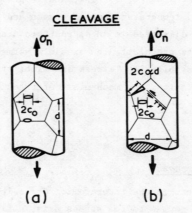

Fig. 3 (a)   Brittle solids contain incipient cracks of length 2 C_o.

(b)   Cracks can be generated by slip. Their length, 2c, often scales as the
grain size. Either sort of crack may propagate to give a cleavage fracture.

DUCTILE, AND TRANSGRANULAR CREEP, FRACTURE.

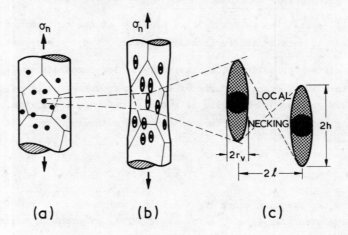

Fig. 4 (a)   Ductile fracture, and transgranular creep fracture requires either that
holes pre-exist or that they nucleate at inclusions which concentrate
stress.

(b)   The holes elongate as the specimen is extended.

(c)   They link, causing fracture, when their length, 2h, is about equal to
their separation $(2l - 2r_v)$.

cracking *"Cleavage 2"* [7] to distinguish it from cleavage from pre-existing flaws
(Cleavage 1). Cracks nucleated in this way generally have a length which is proportional to the grain size, d, because this is the wavelength of the internal
stresses. If the twinning stress, or the flow stress on the easiest slip system
(σ_y) exceeds the value

$$\sigma^* \approx \left(\frac{EG_c}{\pi d}\right)^{\frac{1}{2}} \tag{2.3}$$

a crack propagates as soon as it forms, and cleavage fracture occurs at the micro-
yield stress, σ_y. But if $\sigma^* > \sigma_y$, then cracks nucleated by slip or twinning will not
immediately propagate, and the stress will have to be raised further, leading to fracture within the Cleavage 2 field. The field can be regarded as one of cleavage preceed-
ed by micro-plasticity. The fracture is brittle, with negligible ductility (< 1 %).

As the temperature is raised, the flow stress falls (Fig. 2) until general
plasticity or creep preceeds failure - which may, nevertheless, be by cleavage.
We have called this regime *"Cleavage 3"* [7] to distinguish it from the regimes of completely brittle fracture (Cleavage 1 and 2). Within this field, substantial plastic
strain (1 - 10 %) preceeds fracture, and this plasticity is sufficient to blunt small
pre-existing cracks, effectively raising G_c. General plasticity or (often) grain
boundary sliding then nucleates a larger grain boundary crack, or causes a pre-
existing crack to grow in a stable manner, until its increased length, coupled
with the higher stress caused by work-hardening, cause it to propagate unstably as a
cleavage crack.

In many metals and ceramics there is a delicate balance between the stress required to cause a crack to propagate by cleavage and that required to cause brittle
separation along grain boundaries: small changes in impurity content, texture or temperature can cause the crack path to switch from the one to the other; and a mixed
trans- and intergranular fracture is often observed. Both fracture paths are associated with low energy absorption (G_c = 1 to 100 J/m^2). When the fracture path is
transgranular, following cleavage planes, we will refer to it as *"Cleavage (1, 2 or
3)"*. When, instead, it follows the grain boundaries, we shall refer to it as *"Brittle
Intergranular Fracture (1, 2 or 3)"* or simply as *"B.I.F. (1, 2 or 3)"*.

2.3 *Ductile Fracture at Low Temperature*

When they do not cleave, polycrystalline solids may fail in a ductile, transgranular way. Holes nucleate at inclusions; further plasticity makes them grow;
and, when they are large enough, or when the specimen itself becomes mechanically
unstable, they coalesce, and the material fractures (Fig. 4).

Consider nucleation first. A hard inclusion (Fig. 4a) disturbs both the elastic
and plastic displacement field in a deforming body[8,9,10,11,12]. The disturbance
concentrates stress at the inclusion, this stress building up as the plastic strain
increases, until the inclusion either parts from the matrix, or fractures[12].

Having nucleated in this way, the holes grow until they coalesce to give a fracture path. Void growth in simple tension is understood, at least approximately[13,14].

A spherical void concentrates stress, and because of this, it elongates at first at a rate which is about twice that of the specimen itself. As it extends it becomes ellipsoidal and grows more slowly, until, when very elongated, it extends at the same rate as the specimen itself. Finally, some critical strain is reached at which plasticity becomes localised, the voids coalesce, the fracture follows with almost no further elongation (Fig 4b and c).

The physics underlying this localisation of flow is not completely clear. Thomason[15,16] and Brown and Embury[17] both use a critical distance of approach of the growing voids as a criterion for coalescence. Although their models differ in detail, both require that a local slip-line field can be developed between adjacent voids — a condition that is met when the void height, 2h, is about equal to its separation from its neighbours:

$$2h = \alpha(2l - 2r_v)$$

where α is a constant of order unity. If the voids elongate at a rate which, on average, is faster by a factor of C than the rate of extension of the specimen itself, $(1 < C < 2)$, then the true strain required for coalescence is

$$\varepsilon_g = \frac{1}{C} \ln\{\alpha(\frac{2l - 2r_v}{2r_v})\}$$

$$\approx \frac{1}{C} \ln\{\alpha(\frac{1}{f_v^{\frac{1}{2}}}) - 1)\} \tag{2.4}$$

where f_v is the volume fraction of inclusions.

It should be recognised that this description fails to include the effects of macroscopic instabilities: necking, or the formation of zones of concentrated shear. It is a serious omission, since the onset of necking is known to influence both the nucleation and growth of holes, and localised shear can cause holes to coalesce, giving failure by "void sheeting". Yet, as Brown and Embury[17] have shown, an equation with the form of eq. 2.4 reasonably describes data from a number of alloys which fail in a fully ductile way.

Ductile fracture usually follows a transgranular path. But if the density of inclusions, or of pre-existing holes is higher on grain boundaries than it is within the grains, then the fracture path may follow the boundaries, giving a fibrous, or ductile intergranular fracture, as sketched in Fig. 1.

2.4 *Transgranular Creep Fracture*

At temperatures above $0.3\ T_M$, metals creep: the flow stress now depends on strain-rate, often approximating a power-law

$$\dot{\varepsilon} = B(\frac{\sigma_n}{\sigma_o})^n \tag{2.5}$$

where B and n are material parameters.

Several new fracture mechanisms now appear. One - the subject of this section - is merely the adaptation to the creep regime of low-temperature ductile fracture: holes nucleate at inclusions within the grains and grow as the material creeps, until they coalesce to give a transgranular fracture path.

Although the stages of fracture parallel those described for ductile fracture (Fig. 4), their progress is modified in two ways. First, since the material is creeping, the stresses within it tend to be lower than before, and nucleation may thereby be postponed to larger strains. And second, the strain-rate dependence of creep can stabilise flow and thereby postpone the coalescence of voids.

Both Ductile Fracture and Transgranular Creep Fracture allow comparable, large ductilities.

2.5 *Intergranular, Creep-Controlled, Fracture*

At lower stresses, and longer times-to-fracture, a transition from a transgranular to an intergranular fracture is observed. Within this new regime, grain boundaries slide, wedge-cracks or voids grow on boundaries lying roughly normal to the tensile axis, and a proportionality is found[18] between the time-to-fracture, t_f, and the reciprocal of the steady-state strain-rate, $\dot{\varepsilon}_{ss}$:

$$t_f \dot{\varepsilon}_{ss} = C_{MG} \tag{2.6}$$

where C_{MG} is a constant. This strongly suggests that the fracture is still directly controlled by power-law creep, not by some new process (such as boundary diffusion). Yet the shapes of the grain-boundary voids or cracks strongly suggest that the local diffusion contributes to their growth

In certain instances, this behaviour can be explained if the nucleation of voids or cracks is controlled by grain-boundary sliding, which, in turn, is limited by power-law creep[19]. But this explanation is tenable only if the nucleation stage consumes almost all the life of the specimen, and the growth stage occupies a small part only of the life. A much more general explanation[20,21] is that the voids, when small, grow by local diffusion, but the rate of diffusion is controlled by power-law creep in the surrounding grains. Void or crack growth is then a result of coupled diffusion and power-law creep, as illustrated in Fig. 5.

The figure shows voids growing by diffusion. But the diffusion field of one cavity extends less than half way to the next, so that there remains a ligament of material between the voids which must deform if they are to grow. Each void is contained in a cage of creeping material (shaded), the deformation of which controls the rate of cavity growth.

Fracture by one or other sort of coupled diffusion and power-law creep accounts for almost all intergranular creep fractures. But at very low stresses and high temperatures, the diffusion fields of the growing voids overlap, and the containing cage of power-law creeping material disappears. The resulting regime of pure-diffusional growth, which can be regarded as a special limiting case of the mechanism described above, is discussed in the next section.

INTERGRANULAR, CREEP CONTROLLED, FRACTURE

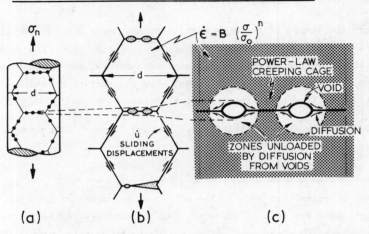

Fig. 5 (a)(b) Grain boundary sliding stimulates the nucleation of grain boundary voids.

(c)   The voids grow by diffusion, but the diffusion fields of neighbouring voids do not, in general, overlap, so that each void is contained within a cage of power-law creeping material.

DIFFUSIONAL VOID GROWTH

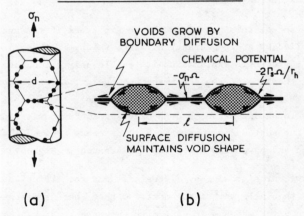

Fig. 6 (a)(b) Voids which lie on boundaries which carry a tensile stress can grow by the diffusion transport of matter from the perifery of the void onto the boundary plane, by grain boundary diffusion. Rapid surface diffusion or vapour transport is required within the void to maintain its near-spherical shape; if this is suppressed, the void becomes crack-like. This mechanism is the limiting case of that shown in Fig. 5 when the diffusion fields of the growing voids overlap.

2.6 *Pure Diffusional Fracture*

When the temperature is high enough to permit diffusion, and the stress so low that power-law is negligible, holes on grain boundaries in stressed solids can grow by diffusion along[22,23,24] (Fig. 6). The tensile traction, σ_n, acting across a grain boundary, lowers the chemical potential of atoms or ions there by the amount, $\sigma_n \Omega$. If the chemical potential difference $(\sigma_n \Omega - 2\Gamma_s \Omega / r_h)$ between sites on the boundary and those on the void surface is negative, then matter flows out of the holes (usually by grain boundary diffusion) and deposits onto the boundary causing the grains on either side to move apart. Although pure diffusional fracture is encountered in laboratory tests only rarely, we have no reason to doubt that this physical process is a correct description of void growth when power-law creep is absent.

There are certian complicating factors. Voids do not always maintain their equilibrium near-spherical shape. The faster they are caused to grow, and the larger they become, the greater must be the rate of surface redistribution if equilibrium is to be maintained. The void shape is then determined by the balance between the growth rate and the rate of surface redistribution[25,26]: they become flatter and more penny-shaped as the stress is raised, until a change of mechanism (to that described in sections 2.5 or 2.4) takes place.

2.7 *Rupture*

If no other fracture mechanism intervenes, a material pulled in tension ultimately becomes mechanically unstable. Deformation becomes localised in a neck or shear band and continues until the cross-section has gone to zero, when the material is said to rupture. The strain-to-rupture depends on the strain at which localisation starts, and, through this, on the work-hardening characteristics and strain-rate sensitivity of the material[27].   And it depends, also on the further strain required to make the initial neck grow until the cross section has become zero; this, too, depends on the strain-rate sensitivity of the material[28].

Rupture obviously involves large reductions in area. For present purposes, it can be thought of as the tensile failure mode which appears when all other modes are suppressed. It requires either that the nucleation of internal voids is suppressed; or (if they nucleate) that they do not coalesce. It is commonly observed at high temperatures (> 0.6 T_M) when dynamic recovery recrystallisation suppresses void nucleation (Fig. 7).

3.   Fracture Mechanism Maps

3.1 *General Features of the Maps*

Fig. 8 is a fracture map for commercial purity Nickel. It shows, on axes of normalised stress and temperature, the fields of dominance of each mechanism of fracture: Ductile Fracture, Transgranular Creep Fracture, Intergranular Creep Fracture, Rupture, and so forth. No distinction is drawn between the two mechanisms of Intergranular Creep Fracture (pure diffusional growth and growth by coupled diffusion and power-law creep) because of the experimental difficulty in distinguishing them; however, a

RUPTURE WITH DYNAMIC RECRYSTALLISATION

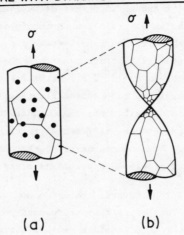

Fig. 7 (a)(b) Rupture at high temperatures is observed in all f.c.c. metals and most of their alloys. It is generally associated with dynamic recovery or recrystallisation.

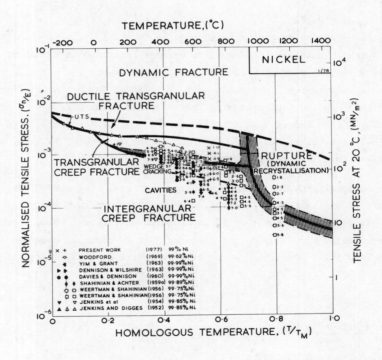

Fig. 8   A fracture-mechanism map for round bars of commercially pure nickel tested in tension. The axes are nominal tensile stress, σ_n, divided by Young's Modulus, E, and homologous temperature, T/T_M. The map shows four fields corresponding to four modes of failure. Individual tests are marked by symbols, and (for creep tests) labelled with the logarithm, to the base 10, of the time-to-fracture in secs ($\log_{10} t_f$). Solid symbols mean that the fracture was identified as intergranular. Shading indicates a mixed mode of fracture. (The references, in order, are:[2,37-44].)

boundary separating the regime of wedge-cracking from that of grain-boundary void growth is shown whenever data makes it possible, and this boundary is a rough indicator of the change of mechanism.

The maps are based, in part, on our own experiments and on an exhaustive analysis of previously published work[2,7].

3.2 *Method of Construction of the Maps*

The procedure[2] is as follows. First, we assemble the available tensile and creep data for the given material. We then tabulate the *homologous temperature*, T/T_M, and the *normalised tensile stress*, σ_n/E, where σ_n is the nominal stress in a creep or tensile test*, and E is Young's Modulus, adjusted to the temperature of the test, together with the *time-to-fracture*, t_f, and *strain-to-fracture*, ε_f. The data are from the sources listed in the figures. The normalising parameters (T_M and E(T)) are listed in Table 1.

Second, we assign, where possible, a *mechanism of failure* to each datum. This is usually based on fractographic observations, though it can sometimes be inferred from sudden changes in ε_f or in t_f. The information is then plotted in the way shown in Fig. 8. The axes are σ_n/E and T/T_M; each datum is plotted as a symbol identifying the investigator and (where possible) the mode of failure, and is labelled with the logarithm of the time-to-fracture, $\log_{10} t_f$.

Finally, boundaries are drawn separating blocks of data with a given mode of failure. Although the data sometimes conflict, and certain points cannot be assigned a mechanism, we have found, in constructing maps for over 30 metals and ceramics, that there is little difficulty in doing this in a way which is consistent with fractographic evidence. The maps are truncated at a stress level corresponding to a strain-rate of about 10^6/sec (times-to-failure of about 10^{-6} sec). Above this line, loading and the subsequent deformation are dynamic and involve the propagation of elastic and plastic waves through the material. The region is labelled *Dynamic Fracture*, although it must be remembered that fast fracture can occur in cracked solids at stress levels which are far lower than this.

There are, of course, difficulties and ambiguities in a study of this sort. There is the influence of purity: strictly, a diagram applies to one purity of metal, or composition of alloy, with one grain size and in one state of heat-treatment. Specimen shape is important: rupture is favoured in thin sheet, for instance, because the conditions are more nearly those of plane stress (where possible, we have selected data from round bars, tested in tension, with a ratio of diameter to gauge length of 1:7 or greater). In spite of these difficulties, we have found that the general form of the diagrams is reproducible.

---

*Creep fracture data refer to tests at constant load; σ_n is the load divided by the initial area of cross section. Tests at lower temperatures were at constant displacement rate; here σ_n is the ultimate tensile stress.

TABLE 1. NORMALISING PARAMETERS

MATERIAL	T_M(K)	REFERENCE	YOUNG'S MODULUS (MPa)	REFERENCE
NICKEL	1726	Metals Handbook (1961)[29]	$E = 2.10 \times 10^5 [1 - (T - 300) \times 3.7 \times 10^{-4}]$	Alers et al (1960)[31] Armstrong and Brown (1964)[32]
TUNGSTEN	3683	Metals Handbook[29]	$E = 4.16 \times 10^5 [1 - (T - 300) \times 1.0 \times 10^{-4}]$	Lundy et al[33] Koster[34]
MAGNESIUM	923	Metals Handbook[29]	$E = 4.52 \times 10^4 [1 - (T - 300) \times 4.4 \times 10^{-4}]$	Metals Handbook[29]
Al_2O_3	2323	Amer. Inst. Phys. Handbook[30]	$E = 3.89 \times 10^5 [1 - (T - 300) \times 1.6 \times 10^{-4}]$	Teffe[35]
H_2O	273	Amer. Inst. Phys. Handbook[30]	$E = 7.66 \times 10^3 [1 - (T - 300) \times 9.9 \times 10^{-4}]$	Bass et al[36]

4.   Maps for Metals and Ceramics

This section describes fracture maps for 6 metals and ceramics. Each is chosen because it typifies the class of material to which it belongs.

4.1 *The F.C.C. Metals: Commercially Pure Nickel (Fig. 8)*

Fig. 8, for commercially pure nickel, is typical of fracture maps for many f.c.c. metals and alloys[2]. It shows four mechanism-fields. At high stresses and low temperatures, nickel fails by Ductile Fracture (section 2.3). As the temperature is raised, the metal starts to creep, and, in the range of temperature and stress indicated in the figure, it fails by a Transgranular Creep Fracture (Section 2.4). The fracture mechanism is identical with that of Ductile Fracture, but the dominant mode of plasticity causing hole-growth and linkage has changed: it is power-law creep, not glide-plasticity. The boundary between these two fields simply shows where power-law creep becomes the dominant mode of flow.

Below this field lies a field of Intergranular Creep Fracture (section 2.5 and 2.6). Specimens stressed in this regime fail because holes or wedge-cracks nucleate and grow on grain boundaries (often those carrying the largest normal traction) until they link, reducing the cross section of the specimen until plasticity causes the remaining ligaments to fail. Such samples show little or no necking, and may fail after very small strains. The transition is a gradual one: within the shaded band, a mixed mode of fracture - part transgranular, part intergranular - is observed.

As the temperature is raised further, strain-induced grain growth and dynamic recrystallisation accompany the creep test (section 2.7). The result is a broad transition to Rupture: necking to a point or chisel edge.

Alloying alters the extent and position of the fields[2]. A stable dispersion suppresses dynamic recrystallisation, and thereby inhibits Rupture (although very pure metals may rupture even at room temperature). Both a dispersion and a solid solution raise the overall stress levels and tend to make the Intergranular Creep Fracture field expand at the expense of the others. This progression seems to be a systematic one, observed in all the alloy systems examined so far.

4.2 *The B.C.C. Metals: Tungsten (Fig. 9)*

Fig. 9 describing commercially pure tungsten, is typical of maps for many b.c.c. refractory metals[7]. If they are pre-cracked, or contain flaws, these materials fail at low temperatures by Cleavage 1, without any detectable general plasticity, (though, of course, there may be plasticity at the crack tip). More usually, twinning or slip nucleates cracks which propagate either by cleavage, or along the grain boundaries leading to Cleavage 2 or Intergranular Brittle Fracture 2 (I.B.F.2).

As the temperature is raised, the flow stress falls rapidly and general yield preceeds fracture. The fracture toughness tends to rise and higher stresses are required to initiate an unstable cleavage crack. All b.c.c. metals show a hump in the fracture stress (or U.T.S.) in this temperature range, and fail by Cleavage 3 or I.B.F. 3, with measurable ductility (1 to 10 %). The extent of this field depends on grain size and interstitial impurity content.

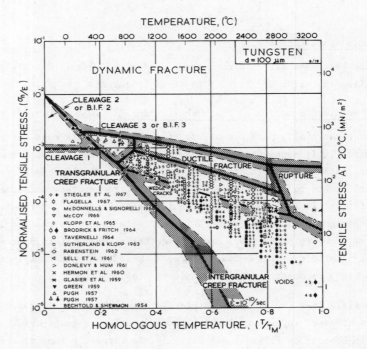

Fig. 9   A fracture-mechanism map for tungsten tested in tension. The map shows
                three modes of cleavage at low temperatures; and other fields resemble
                those of f.c.c. metals[1]. (The references, in order, are:([45-61]).)

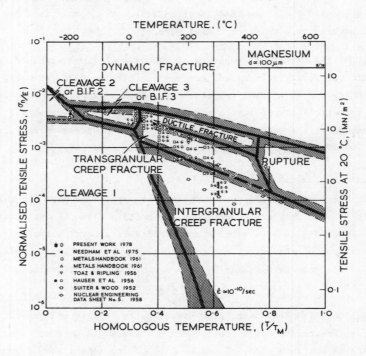

Fig. 10   A map for commercially pure magnesium. The fields lie at higher nor-
                malised stresses than do those for b.c.c. metals. (The references, in
                order, are:([7, 62-67]).)

As the temperature is increased further, there is a transition to a fully ductile fracture; in recrystallised b.c.c. metals, it occurs at about 0.3 T_M. At slightly higher temperatures, creep becomes appreciable, and at high stresses, fracture is by Transgranular Creep Fracture.

At low stresses and high temperatures, the fracture mechanism changes to Intergranular Creep Fracture. Wedge cracks or cavities form on the grain boundaries and grow in size and number with creep strain, finally linking to give a fracture path along the grain boundary. Wedge cracking is typical of the low temperature (0.5 T_M) high stress ($\frac{\sigma_n}{E} \simeq 10^{-4}$) section of the Intergranular Creep Fracture Field; cavities form at higher temperatures and lower stresses. Ideally, we would wish to subdivide the field to show this, but the data are rarely complete enough to permit it.

At temperatures above 0.8 T_M, failure is by Rupture, apparently a consequence of dynamic recovery, recrystallisation and grain growth.

There are slight differences between the b.c.c. refractory metals. Tantalum, for instance, has the least tendency to cleave; chromium has the greatest. But on the broad scales of the figures, these differences are slight, and the b.c.c. refractory metals form a well-defined class with remarkably similar maps.

4.3 *The Hexagonal Metals: Magnesium (Fig 10)*

Fig. 10, a map for commercially pure magnesium, typifies metals with h.c.p. structure[7]. If they contain cracks or flaws, these materials fail at low temperatures by Cleavage 1. More usually, basal slip or twinning nucleates small cracks which propagate, either by Cleavage or by Intergranular Brittle Fracture, or by a combination of both, giving a mixed mode of fracture. This field is labelled "Cleavage 2" or "IBF 2". As the temperature is raised, the fracture stress becomes greater than the yield strength and general plasticity preceeds fracture, although it is still of cleavage or brittle intergranular type (Cleavage 3 or I.B.F. 3).

All the hexagonal metals we examined[7] show a transition to a completely ductile mode of fracture, with large ductility, at above 0.3 T_M. At rather higher temperatures (about 0.35 T_M), they start to creep, failing by Transgranular Creep Fracture at high stresses and Intergranular Creep Fracture at low. The commercial purity materials fail by rupture above 0.8 T_M, and the alloys, too, showed this mode of failure, though at a slightly higher temperature.

At low temperatures, the fracture behaviour of hexagonal metals resembles that of ceramics (discussed in the next section). At higher temperatures, more slip systems become available and they behave like f.c.c. metals. On the normalised scales used to plot the maps, the h.c.p. metals are significantly stronger than b.c.c. metals, both at low temperatures and at high. We have noted, however, that h.c.p. metals and alloys are particularly prone to Intergranular Creep Fracture, perhaps because the difficult non-basal slip means that grain boundary sliding is not as readily accommodated by general plasticity as it is in b.c.c. and f.c.c. metals.

4.4 *The Refractory Oxides: Alumina, Al₂O₃ (Fig. 11)*

Fig. 11 for commercially pure alumina is typical of the maps for many oxides. Commercial materials are often flawed, and fail, at low temperatures, by Cleavage 1. If flaws are avoided, failure occurs when twinning or microslip nucleates cracks; these propagate by cleavage or by grain boundary fracture (Cleavage 2 or I.B.F. 2), still with negligible ductility.

Additional slip systems (Table 3) appear and general plasticity or creep becomes possible above 0.45 T_M. Over a wide range of temperature and stress, failure is by Brittle Intergranular Fracture 3, or, occasionally, Cleavage 3. As the temperature is raised further, strain-induced grain growth and dynamic recrystallization accompany the creep test. This permits added plasticity and causes a broad transition to a transgranular creep failure, or in extreme cases, to rupture. At high temperatures and low stresses, the refractory oxides fail by Intergranular Creep Fracture; like the metals, these ceramics show wedge-cracking at higher stress levels and failure by void growth at lower stresses.

The boundaries of the fields shown in Fig. 11 have a finite width. Their exact position varies with strain-rate, purity, grain-size and method of fabrication, so that a map which described typical behaviour is properly drawn with boundaries of a width that encompasses this variation. In addition, the transition from one mechanism to another can be gradual and can include a regime of mixed-mode fracture. The shading shown on the field boundaries indicates both these effects.

The oxides show all the mechanisms which we identified in the b.c.c. and h.c.p. metals. But the totally brittle mechanisms which disappear above 0.1 T_M in b.c.c. metals, and about 0.2 T_M in hexagonal metals, extend to 0.5 T_M or above in the oxides; and the areas occupied by the other mechanisms (which permit at least limited ductility) are correspondingly smaller.

4.5 *Covalent and H-bonded Ceramics: Ice (Fig. 12)*

Silicon carbide and nitride are the principal candidates for high temperature load-bearing ceramics, and are at present being developed for turbine components, heat exchangers and high temperature bearings. These two ceramics have, in common with ice, the property that they retain their high strength to very high homologous temperatures. Creep becomes significant only above 0.6 to 0.7 T_M - higher than any other class of solid. But a direct consequence is that brittle modes of failure persist in these ceramics to much higher fractions of the melting point; and none of them show any regime of real ductility.

Fig. 12, the map for ice, typifies this behaviour. It shows that totally brittle mechanisms (Cleavage 1 and 2) are dominant up to half the melting point or above, and that a cleavage fracture (Cleavage 3) persists right up to the melting point.

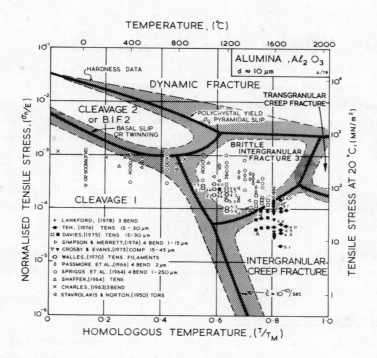

Fig. 11   A map for Alumina, Al_2O_3. (The references, in order, are: ([68-78]).)

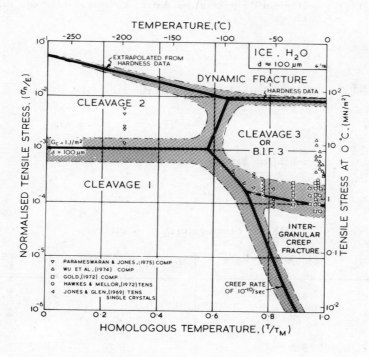

Fig. 12   A map for ice, H_2O. (The references, in order, are: ([79-84]).)

5.   Mechanisms of Fracture and Order of Magnitude of K_c and G_c

The diagrams of the last section showed that, below 0.3 T_M, materials fail by one of three alternative classes of mechanism: Cleavage, Ductile Fracture and (in very) pure metals) Rupture. At and near a crack tip in a thin sheet, the stress-state approximates plane stress, and the range of dominance of the mechanisms is almost identical with that shown in Figs. 8 to 12. But in a thick plate, the stress-state is a more extreme one, with (in Mode 1 loading) a much larger hydrostatic component. This has the effect of expanding the cleavage fields at the expense of that of ductile fracture, but - as far as is known - no new mechanisms of fracture appear. The maps, therefore, give a qualitative picture of the way in which crack extension mechanisms change with temperature.

We now examine the approximate magnitudes of the plane stress fracture toughness, K_c, or toughness, G_c, that we might expect from each mechanism, and tabulate the results as a chart of toughness versus mechanism.

5.1 Crack Extension by Cleavage

In the regimes we have called Cleavage 1 and 2, cracks extend without general plasticity. In many ceramics, there is little or no crack tip plasticity either: the yield strength is so large that the cohesive strength (eq. 2.1) is exceeded before even local slip can take place.

Roughly speaking, this sort of cleavage fracture will occur when the stress at the crack tip is sufficient to pull atoms apart, that is (using eq. 2.1) when

$$\sigma(r) = \frac{K_1}{\sqrt{2\pi r}} > \frac{E}{10}$$

at a distance $r \simeq b$ from the tip, where b is the atom size. We thus find

$$K_c \simeq \frac{E}{10} \sqrt{2\pi r} \tag{5.1}$$

Substituting for E and b, we find the values given in Table 2.

TABLE 2: Cleavage with no plasticity

MATERIAL	$E(GN/m^2)$	b(m)	$K_c \approx \frac{E}{10}\sqrt{2\pi b}$ (MPa $\sqrt{m}$)	$G_c \approx \frac{K_c^2}{E}$ (J/m^2)
Tungsten	406		1.8	7.7
Steel	200		0.9	3.8
Magnesium	42	} 3×10^{-10}	0.2	0.8
Alumina, (Al_2O_3)	390		1.7	7.4
Ice	9.1		0.1	0.2

In summary, when materials cleave, without plasticity, by the propagation of an atomically sharp crack which simply stretches the atomic bonds at the crack tip until they fail, the fracture toughness is low, from 0.1 to about 2 MPa $\sqrt{m}$. Experiments support this: the measured fracture toughness of ice is close to 0.1 MPa $\sqrt{m}$; that for alumina is about 3 MPa $\sqrt{m}$.

Metals are more ductile than this. Although there is negligible general plasticity in the regimes of Cleavage 1 and Cleavage 2, of tungsten, say, or of magnesium, there is appreciable local plasticity, and the toughness is larger than the minimum values calculated in Table 2.

When general plasticity preceeds cleavage failure (Cleavage 3) the toughness increases substantially. Experiments in this regime (which straddles room temperature for many b.c.c. and h.c.p. metals) show values of K_c between 2 and 20 MPa$\sqrt{m}$ (or of G_c between 30 and 3000 J/m^2).

5.2 *Crack Advance by Ductile Tearing*

The ductility of most solids increases with increasing temperature, until it becomes sufficiently large that crack advance by the nucleation, plastic growth and coalescence of holes (section 2.3) replaces cleavage. The local criterion for crack advance is that a sufficient plastic strain occurs in a volume element at the crack tip that the holes in it coalesce.

Consider first a crack tip, surrounded by a plastic zone of approximate size

$$r_y = \frac{K^2}{2\pi\sigma_y^2}$$

beyond which the matrix is elastic. If the solid work-hardens such that

$$\sigma = A\varepsilon^n$$

the strains within the zone are given by

$$\varepsilon = \frac{B}{r^{n/n+1}}$$

Matching the elastic strains

$$\varepsilon^{el} = \frac{K}{E(2\pi r)^{\frac{1}{2}}}$$

with those in the plastic zone at $r = r_y$, we find, within the zone,

$$\varepsilon(r) = (\frac{K^2}{2\pi\sigma_y^2 r})^{\frac{n}{n+1}} \cdot \frac{\sigma_y}{E} \quad (r < r_y) \tag{5.2}$$

If we then require that

$$\varepsilon > \varepsilon_f$$

at a distance r = r* (which we identify with the inclusion spacing), we find:

$$K_c \approx \left[2\pi\sigma_y^2 r^* \left(\frac{E\varepsilon_f}{\sigma_y}\right)^{\frac{n+1}{n}} \right]^{\frac{1}{2}} \qquad (5.3)$$

This has the lower limit

$$K_c^{min} \approx (2\pi\sigma_y r^* E \varepsilon_f)^{\frac{1}{2}} \qquad (5.4)$$

for perfect plasticity (n = ∞). If E = 200 GN/m², σ_y = 5×10⁻³ E; r* = 10 μm and ε_f = 1, we find:

$$K_c = 100 \text{ MPa } \sqrt{m} \qquad or \qquad G_c = 5\times10^4 \text{ J/m}^2$$

a very good estimate of the toughness of a tough steel.

Ductile tearing, then, leads to large values of K_{1C} (20-500 MPa $\sqrt{m}$) or of G_c (10⁴ to 10⁵ J/m²). Under certain circumstances, the toughness may be less than this. In certain high-strength alloys, for instance, plasticity at the crack tip becomes localised in bands of intense shear; the crack tip advances by "void-sheet linkage", at a lower value of K. There exists, too, a regime of mixed fibrous and cleavage fracture, the crack propagating across some grains by cleavage but passing through others by ductile fracture. Again, the toughness is lower than that of a fully ductile, fibrous, fracture.

5.3 Crack Advance by Rupture

Thin sheets of pure metals can exhibit crack advance by Rupture: local reduction of the section to zero. This requires a local strain of unity in a slice of material with a height about equal to the sheet thickness, t. The value of K_c is given by eq. 5.3 or 5.4, with the inclusion spacing replaced by t:

$$K_c^{min} \approx (2\pi t \sigma_y E)^{\frac{1}{2}}$$

Taking t = 1 mm, E = 200 GN/m² and σ_y = 5×10⁻³ E, we have:

$$K_c^{min} \approx 1000 \text{ MPa } \sqrt{m} \qquad or \qquad G_c \approx 5\times10^6 \text{ J/m}^2$$

Rupture, then, leads to the highest toughness of all, which can probably be regarded as an upper limit to the toughness of a material.

The relation between toughness and crack-advance mechanism, as deduced above, is summarised in Table 3.

6. Mechanisms of Fracture and Fatigue Crack Growth

Below 0.3 T_M, fatigue cracks - like cracks under static loads - can advance by distinct mechanisms: Cleavage, Ductile Fracture and by a plastic tearing which is

TABLE 3. Magnitudes of G_{1C} and K_{1C} and their relationship to the mechanisms of crack advance

	TOUGHNESS G_C (J/m²)	FRACTURE TOUGHNESS K_{1C} (MPa √m)	G_{1C}/Eb	$K_{1C}/E\sqrt{b}$
Plastic Rupture (Section 2.7)	10^6–10^7	500–2000	~10^5	>100
Fibrous, by void growth and coalescence ("Ductile Fracture", Section 2.3)	10^4–10^6	20–500	10^2–10^4	10–100
Unstable shear: void sheet linkage	10^3–10^5	10–100	~10^3	2–20
Mixed fibrous and cleavage	10^3–2×10^4	10–50	~10^2	2–10
Cleavage preceded by slip ("Cleavage or B.I.F. 3", Section 2.2)	30–300	2–20	1–10	.5–5
Cleavage without slip ("Cleavage or B.I.F. 1 and 2", Section 2.2)	1–100	0.2–5	0.1–1	.1–2
2 × (surface energy), metals	0.5–3	0.4–1	0.1	~.2
2 × (surface energy), ceramics	0.5–4	0.2–1	0.1	~.2
2 × (surface energy), polymers	0.1–1	0.01–.05	0.1–10	~.2

the cyclic analog of Rupture. We can deal with them only in the most approximate way; but it is useful to do so since it gives insight into the relationship between the static modes of fracture described by the maps and the rate of fatigue crack growth, $\frac{da}{dn}$.

6.1 *Crack Advance by Plastic Tearing*

If no other mechanism is available, fatigue cracks in ductile solids advance by a mechanism akin to Rupture. The tensile part of the cycle opens the crack, creating new surface at its tip; the compressive part then folds the new surface forward[85]. In a clean environment, the crack surfaces may reweld, and crack advance is slow or negligible; more usually, contamination prevents rewelding, and the crack advances by roughly half the crack opening displacement[86]. If the plastic zone at the crack tip is small compared with the specimen dimensions, we have, for the crack opening displacement,

$$\delta \approx \frac{K^2}{\sigma_y E} \tag{6.1}$$

and

$$\frac{da}{dN} \approx \frac{\Delta K^2}{2\sigma_y E} \tag{6.2}$$

This is an upper limit to crack propagation by this mechanism. Both rewelding and cyclic hardening slow the crack.

6.2 *Crack Advance by Ductile Fracture*

Let the stress-strain response of the material ahead of the crack be described by:

$$\sigma = A\varepsilon^n$$

Then, if the plastic zone at the crack tip is small, the strains in it are given by eq. 5.2. If, over a distance, r, ahead of the crack which exceeds the inclusion spacing, ℓ, (where

$$\ell = \frac{1}{\sqrt{N_A}} \tag{6.3}$$

and N_A is the number of inclusions per unit area) the failure strain, ε_f, is exceeded, then the crack will advance by r. Inverting eq. 5.2, we find

$$\frac{da}{dN} = r = \frac{\Delta K^2}{2\pi\sigma_y^2} \cdot \left(\frac{\sigma_y}{E\varepsilon_f}\right)^{\frac{n}{n+1}} \tag{6.4}$$

$$= \frac{\Delta K^2}{2\pi\sigma_y E\varepsilon_f}$$

for large n (perfect plasticity)

But, if, as is more usually the case, the distance, r, is smaller than the mean inclusion spacing, only inclusions closer than r to the crack front will link with it. The number of such particles, per unit length of crack, is $N_a \ell$, and each one which links with cracks increases the cracked area by r^2, giving a mean crack advance of

$$\frac{da}{dN} = N_a \ell r^2$$

Using eq. (6.3) and (6.4) we find

$$\frac{da}{dN} = \frac{1}{\ell} \left\{ \frac{\Delta K^4}{4\pi^2 \sigma_y^4} \left(\frac{\sigma_y}{E\varepsilon_f}\right)^{\frac{2n}{n+1}} \right\} \qquad (6.5)$$

$$\approx \frac{\Delta K^4}{4\pi^2 \sigma_y^2 E^2 \varepsilon_f^2 \ell} \quad \text{for large n.}$$

It is useful to compare the ratio ψ of these rates to that when the crack advances by Rupture (eq. 6.1). The result is

$$\psi = \frac{1}{\pi\varepsilon_f} \qquad \text{when } r > \ell$$

$$\psi = \frac{\Delta K^2}{2\pi\sigma_y E\varepsilon_f^2 \ell} \qquad \text{when } r < \ell$$

Roughly speaking, unless both ε_f and ℓ are small ($\varepsilon_f < 0.3$, $\ell < 10$ μm) this ductile fracture mechanism will be overshadowed by simple plastic tearing. This is because the increment of crack advance is, under many circumstances, very small - far smaller than the inclusion spacing - so that the probability of finding an inclusion close enough to the crack front to link with it in any given cycle is negligible.

6.3 *Crack Advance by Stable Cleavage*

One way of understanding crack advance by stable cleavage is to suppose that cleavage can occur, in favourably situated grains, for a distance r+ ahead of the present position, of the crack front, extending the crack to the point where the stress associated with the cyclically hardened material near the crack tip has fallen to a value σ_c. We take this stress field to have the general form

$$\sigma = \frac{A}{r^{\frac{1}{n+1}}}$$

Matching this to the elastic field at the distance r_y, where

$$r_y = \frac{\Delta K^2}{2\pi\sigma_y^2}$$

we find

$$\sigma = \left(\frac{\Delta K^2}{2\pi r \sigma_y^2}\right)^{\frac{1}{n+1}} \sigma_y \qquad (6.6)$$

Hence

$$\frac{da}{dN} = r^* = \left(\frac{\sigma_y}{\sigma_c}\right)^{n+1} \frac{\Delta K^2}{2\pi \sigma_y^2} \qquad (6.7)$$

and its ratio, ϕ, to the rate of crack advance by plastic tearing is

$$\phi = \frac{1}{\pi}\left(\frac{\sigma_y}{\sigma_c}\right)^{n+1}$$

A perfectly plastic solid ($n = \infty$) fails catastrophically if $\sigma_y > \sigma_c$, and shows no crack advance whatever by cleavage if $\sigma_y < \sigma_c$. But if the material hardens, so that n is finite, then the crack advances stably by cleavage, the increments increasing rapidly as the temperature falls through the value at which $\sigma_y = \sigma_c$. Roughly speaking, we expect stable crack advance by cleavage in the regime we have called "Cleavage 3", and a rising probability of catastrophic cleavage advance as we enter the "Cleavage 2" or "Cleavage 1" fields.

7.   Summary

Crystalline materials can be classified by their fracture behaviour. Materials with similar bonding and crystal structure behave in a similar way, over the entire temperature range from 0 K to their melting points. Nickel, for example, typifies the f.c.c. metals; tungsten, the refractory b.c.c. metals; magnesium, the h.c.p. metals; alumina, the high-temperature refractory oxides, and so on.

For each class, a map can be constructed showing the disposition, in stress-temperature space, of each mechanism of fracture: cleavage, ductile fracture and so forth. These mechanisms have been identified and studied in round bars tested in simple tension. Observations suggest that the mechanisms responsible for crack advance during monotonic or cyclic loading are closely related to these identified mechanisms, though they may be shifted (in a predictable manner) in stress-temperature space because the stress-state at the crack tip is other than simple tension.

Order-of-magnitude calculations of K_c or G_c, based on the micromechanisms, allow a mechanism to be associated with each of various ranges of toughness (Table 3). Similarly, approximate estimates of fatigue crack growth rate give insight into the role of the micromechanisms in crack advance.

Acknowledgements

I wish to acknowledge the financial support of the Science Research Council.

References

1. M.F. Ashby, "Fracture 77", ICF 4, Waterloo University Press, 1, 1, (1977).

2. M.F. Ashby, C. Gandhi and D.M.R. Taplin, Acta Met. 27, (1979).

3. A. Kelly, "Strong Solids", Clarendon Press, Oxford, Ch.1, (1966).

4. A. Kelly, W.R. Tyson and A.H. Cottrell, Phil. Mag. 15, 567, (1967).

5. N.H. Macmillan, J. Mat. Sci. 7, 239, (1972).

6. C.J. McMahon and M. Cohen, ACta Met. 13, 591, (1965).

7. C. Gandhi and M.F. Ashby, Overview 4, Acta Met. 27, (1979).

8. A. Argon, J. Im and R. Safoglu, Met. Trans. 6A, 825, (1975).

9. A. Argon and J. Im, Met. Trans. 6A, 839, (1975).

10. L.M. Brown and W.M. Stobbs, Phil. Mag. 23, 1201, (1971).

11. L.M. Brown and W.M. Stobbs, Phil. Mag. 34, 351, (1976).

12. S.H. Goods and L.M. Brown, Overview 1, Acta Met. 27, 1, (1979).

13. F.A. McClintock, J. Appl. Mech. 35, 363, (1968).

14. J.R. Rice and D.M. Tracey, J. Mech. Phys. Solids 17, 201, (1969).

15. P.F. Thomason, J. Inst. Met. 96, 360, (1968).

16. P.F. Thomason, Int. J. Fract. Mech. 7, 409, (1971).

17. L.M. Brown and J.D. Embury, Proc. 3rd Int. Conf. on the Strength of Metals and
    Alloys, Institute of Metals, London, (1973).

18. F.C. Monkman and N.J. Grant, Proc. ASTM 56, 593, (1956).

19. F.W. Crossman and M.F. Ashby, Acta Met. 23, 425, (1975).

20. W. Beere and M.V. Speight, Met. Sci. 4, 172, (1978).

21. G.H. Edward and M.F. Ashby, Cambridge University Engineering Department Report
    CUED/C/MATS/TR.36, (1978).

22. D. Hull and D.E. Rimmer, Phil. Mag. 4, 673, (1959).

23. M.V. Speight and J.E. Harris, Met. Sci. J. 1, 83, (1967).

24. R. Raj and M.F. Ashby, Acta Met. 23, 653, (1975).

25. T. Chuang, Ph.D. Thesis, Brown University, (1975).

26. T. Chuang and J.R. Rice, Acta Met. 21, 1625, (1973).

27. E.W. Hart, Acta Met., 15, 351, (1967).

28. M.A. Burke and W.D. Nix, Acta Met. 23, 793, (1975).

29. Metals Handbook A.S.M. vol.1 (8th edition) (1961).

30. American Inst. Phys. Handbook, McGraw-Hill Book Co. (Third Edition), New York
    (co-ordinating editor D.E. Gray) (1972).

31. G.A. Alers, J.R. Neighbours and H. Sato, J. Phys. Chem. Solids 13, 40, (1960).

32. P.E. Armstrong and H.L. Brown, Trans. AIME 230, 962, (1964).

33. T.S. Lundy, F.R. Winslow, K.L. Pawel and C.J. McHargue, Trans. AIME, 233, 1533, (1965).

34. W. Koster, Z. Metallk 39, 1, (1948).

35. W.E. Teffe, J. Res. Nat. Bur. Stand. 70A, 277, (1966).

36. R. Bass, D. Rossberg and G. Ziegler, Z. Phys. 149, 199, (1957).

37. D.A. Woodford, Metal Science 3, 234, (1969).

38. W.M. Yim and N.J. Grant, Trans. AIME 227, 868, (1963).

39. J.P. Dennison and B. Wilshire, J. Inst. Metals 91, 343, (1963).

40. P.W. Davies and J.P. Dennison, J. Inst. Metals 88, 471, (1960).

41. P. Shahinian and M.R. Achter, Trans. AIME 215, 37, (1959).

42. J. Weertman and P. Shahinian, Trans. AIME 206, 1223, (1956).

43. W.D. Jenkins, T.G. Digges and C.R. Johnson, J. Res. NBS 53, 329, (1954).

44. W.D. Jenkins, T.G. Digges, J. Res. NBS. 48, 313, (1952).

45. J.O. Stiegler, K. Farrell, B.T.M. Loh, and H.E. McCoy, Trans. ASM 60, 494 (1967).

46. P.N. Flagella, "High temperature creep rupture behaviour of unalloyed tungsten", GE-NMPO, GEMP-543, (1967).

47. P.N. Flagella, J. AIAA 5(2), 281, (1967).

48. D.L. McDonnells and R.A. Signorelli, "Stress rupture properties of tungsten wire from 1200 to 2500 F", NASA, TN, D-3467, (1966).

49. H.E. McCoy, "Creep rupture properties of tungsten and tungsten base alloys", ORNL-3992, (1966).

50. W.D. Klopp, W.R. Witzke and P.L. Raffo, Trans. AIME 233, 1860, (1965).

51. R.F. Brodrick and D.J. Fritch, Proc. ASTM 64, 505, (1964).

52. J.F. Tavernelli, GE Report No. 64-Ime-226, Cleveland, Ohio, (1964).

53. E.C. Sutherland and W.D. Klopp, NASA TN D-1310, (1963).

54. A.S. Rabenstein, Marquardt Corp. Contract Report No. AF 33 (657) -8706, Report 281-2Q-3, (1962).

55. H.G. Sell, H.H. Keith, R.C. Koo, R.H. Schnitzel and R. Corth, Westinghouse Elec. Corp., Report WADD TR 60-37, Part II, (1961).

56. A. Donlevy and J.K.Y Hum, Machine Design 11, 244, (1961).

57. E.L. Hermon, R.P. Morgan, N.F. Graves and G. Reinhardt, "Investigation of the properties of tungsten and its alloys", Union Carbide, Mat. Res. Lab. Report WADD, TR 60-144, AF(616)5600, (1960).

58. L.F. Glasier, R.D. Allen and I.L. Saldinger, "Mechanical and physical properties of the refractory metals", Aerojet-General Corp., Report No. M1826, (1959).

59. W.V. Green, Trans. AIME 215, 1057, (1959).

60. J.W. Pugh, Proc. ASTM 57, 906, (1957).

61. J.H. Bechtold and P.G. Shewmon, Trans. ASM 46, 397, (1954).

62. N.G. Needham, J.E. Wheatley and G.W. Greenwood, Acta Met. 23, 23, (1975).

63. M.W. Toaz and E.J. Ripling, Trans. AIME 206, 936, (1956).

64. F.E. Hauser, P.R. Landon and J.E. Dorn, Trans. AIME 206, 589, (1956).

65. F.E. Hauer, P.R. Landon and J.E. Dorn, Trans. ASM 48, 986, (1956).

66. J.W. Suiter and W.A. Wood, J. Inst. Metals 81, 181, (1952).

67. Nuclear Engineering Data Sheet No. 5, Magnesium, J. Nucl. Eng., Vol.3,
     Feb. (1958).

68. J. Lankford, J. Mat. Sci. 13, 351, (1978).

69. S.K. Teh, Ph.D. Thesis, Materials Department, Queen Mary College, University
     of London, p.234, (1976).

70. C.K.L. Davies, "Physical Metallurgy of Reactor Fuel Elements", (edited by
     J. Harris and T. Sykes, published by the Metals Soc.), p.99, (1975).

71. L.A. Simpson and G.J. Merrett, J. Mat. Sci. 9, 685, (1974).

72. A. Crosby and P.E. Evans, J. Mat. Sci. 8, 1573, (1973).

73. K.F.A. Walles, Proc. Brit. Cer. Soc. 15, 157, (1970).

74. E. Passmore, A. Moschetti and T. Vasilos, Phil. Mag. 13, 1157, (1966).

75. R.M. Spriggs, J.B. Mitchell and T. Vasilos, J. Amer. Cer. Soc. 47, 323, (1964).

76. P.T.B. Shaffer, "High Temperature Materials: No. 1 Materials Index", Plenum
     Press, New York, (1964).

77. R.J. Charles, "Studies of the brittle behaviour of ceramic materials",
     ASD-TR-61-628, 467, (1963).

78. J.A. Stavrolakis and F.H. Norton, J. Amer. Cer. Soc. 33, 263, (1950).

79. V.R. Parameswaran and S.J. Jones, Journal of Glaciology 14, 305, (1975).

80. H.C. Wu, K.J. Chang and R. Schwarz, Eng. Fract. Mech. 20, 845, (1974).

81. L.W. Gold, National Research Council of Canada, Division of Building Research
     Technical Paper No. 369, (1972).

82. L.W. Gold, Phil. Mag. 26, 311, (1972).

83. I. Hawkes and M. Mellor, J. Glaciology 11, 103, (1972).

84. S.J. Jones and J.W. Glen, J. Glaciology 8, 463, (1969).

85. J.F. Knott, "Fundamentals of Fracture Mechanics", Butterworths, ch.9, (1983).

86. P. Newmann, H. Vehoff and F. Fuhlrott, "Fracture 77", ICF4, Waterloo, Canada,
     2, 1313, (1977).

THEORETICAL BACKGROUND TO ELASTIC FRACTURE MECHANICS

L. P. Pook and R. A. Smith*

*National Engineering Laboratory, East Kilbride,
Glasgow G75 0QU, U.K.*
**Cambridge University Engineering Department, Trumpington Street,
Cambridge CB2 1PZ, U.K.*

Summary

Over the last decade or so great advances have been made in the engineer's ability to assess quantitatively the fracture and fatigue properties of materials containing cracks. Similitude of small scale laboratory tests and real components has been achieved through the stress intensity factor parameter.

This paper reviews the characterisation of crack tip stress fields by the stress intensity factor and the limitations which define the applicability of linear elastic fracture mechanics (L.E.F.M.). The plane strain fracture toughness, a measure of a material's resistance to catastrophic crack advance, is discussed. The use of the stress intensity factor range to quantify fatigue crack growth is described, together with threshold and statistical aspects of stable growth. The limitations of short cracks in L.E.F.M. and, finally, some aspects of combined mode loading are introduced.

1. Introduction

The applied mechanics framework required for the discussion of the behaviour of cracked bodies under load, has become known as "fracture mechanics".

As in all branches of applied mechanics very considerable simplification results if linearity is assumed. In particular the concept of stress intensity factor is central to the theory of linear elastic fracture mechanics (L.E.F.M.). This paper concentrates on the practical application of the stress intensity factor as a fracture criterion and to constant amplitude fatigue crack growth; in particular the limitations and modifications which arise from the actual behaviour of metallic materials are discussed.

Present day fracture mechanics deal largely with macroscopic aspects of crack behaviour. Thus fracture surfaces are assumed to be smooth although on a microscopic scale they are generally very irregular. The basic assumptions are the same as in

ordinary strength of materials theory; the material is a homogeneous isotropic continuum
(that is microscopic irregularities in structure are neglected); stress is proportional
to strain; strains are small and distortions are neglected. The material is also
usually assumed to be free from large scale self-equilibrating internal stress, and
body forces such as those due to gravity.

It should be made clear at the outset that we are dealing with cracks characterised only by their length, and not notches which have a well defined root-radius.

Well established topics are not referenced, for further information see References
1 - 11. More recent developments and some specific points are referenced in detail.

2.   Modes of Crack Surface Displacement

There are three modes of crack surface displacement which can occur when a cracked
body is loaded, and in which crack growth can take place. These, Fig. 1, are:

I   The opening mode. The crack surfaces move directly apart; it is analogous to an
      edge dislocation.

II   The edge-sliding mode. The crack surfaces move normal to the crack front and
      remain in the crack plane; it is again analogous to an edge dislocation.

III   The shear mode. The crack surfaces move parallel to the crack front and remain
      in the crack plane; it is analogous to a screw dislocation.

The superimposition of these three modes is sufficient to describe the most
general case; it is conventional to add the Roman numerals, I, II and III to describe
each Mode, but other notations are also in current use.

In isotropic materials under essentially elastic conditions, cracks loaded both
statically and cyclically, tend to grow in Mode I irrespective of initial orientation.
Attention in this paper is therefore largely confined to this Mode. The main exceptions are when a crack follows a plane of weakness or when a crack grows on planes at
45 degrees through the thickness. This latter mode usually occurs in thin sheets and
is sometimes erroneously called a shear mode, because it is on planes of maximum shear
stress in an uncracked sheet. However, this is incorrect; it is actually a combination
of Modes I and III. The direction and plane of growth of a Mode I crack is approximately (exactly for symmetrical loadings) perpendicular to the maximum principal
applied stress. A crack which has grown entirely in Mode I is not necessarily straight
and crack trajectories are not readily determined. As a general rule, a crack tends
to be attracted by the nearest free surface and may follow a curved path even under
initially symmetrical loading conditions. Cracks in structures are frequently found
to follow complex paths. Ensuring that a crack maintains its initial plane and direction
is an important factor in the design of fracture mechanics based test specimens.

The complete solution of a crack growth problem obviously includes the determination of the crack trajectory. However a crack loaded in Mode I will usually grow in
Mode I in its initial direction. Under combined loading the crack direction will
change abruptly as growth starts. In basic discussions of the conditions under which

a crack will grow, it is usual to consider the two-dimensional case and to assume that the initial crack is straight and that crack growth is an extension of the original crack. This can often be done without significant loss of generality.

3. Stress Intensity Factors

Crack surfaces are shear and normal stress-free boundaries adjacent to the crack tip and therefore dominate the distribution of stresses in that area. Remote boundaries and loading forces affect only the intensity of the stress field at the crack tip. There is a particular type of elastic stress field corresponding to each mode of crack surface displacement; these may be described in terms of the stress intensity factor, K, which provides a convenient single parameter description have the dimensions (stress) $\times$ (length)$^{\frac{1}{2}}$ and usual units MPa $\sqrt{m}$. The stress intensity factor actually represents the first term in the series expansion for the elastic stress field at a crack tip, and is, for many purposes, a sufficiently accurate representation of the elastic stress field. Individual stress components and displacements are proportional to $K/r^{\frac{1}{2}}$, where r is distance from the crack tip (see Appendix).

Material properties in the presence of a crack can be measured in terms of the opening mode stress intensity factor, K_I, in just the same way as the tensile or fatigue properties of a plain specimen are measured in terms of stress. For example, the higher the value of K_I the more severe the crack, and when a critical value K_c is reached, a crack will extend under a static load; K_c is therefore a measure of a material's fracture toughness, or resistance to brittle fracture. The symbol K_{Ic} would be more logical as the subscript I refers to a Mode I critical condition. Conventionally the symbol K_c implies Mode I and K_{Ic} has a special restricted meaning. K_c is sometimes used (not here) to imply 45° crack growth in thin sheets. Fatigue crack growth data can conveniently be correlated in terms of ΔK_I, the range of K_I during a fatigue cycle. The notation K_{Iscc} is used to denote the minimum value of K_I necessary for crack growth under corrosive conditions.

For sheets of infinite extent, the stress intensity factors are defined by

$$K_I = \sigma(\pi a)^{\frac{1}{2}} \qquad K_{II} = \sigma(\pi a)^{\frac{1}{2}} \qquad K_{III} = \tau(\pi a)^{\frac{1}{2}}. \qquad (1)$$

The conventional $\pi^{\frac{1}{2}}$ included in equation (1) is sometimes omitted, particularly in early work.

For Modes I and II the sheet can be two-dimensional, for Mode III it is assumed to be infinitely thick. Values of K_I for some simple finite geometries are given in Fig. 2. Numerous solutions for various configurations have been published; Reference 8 is a convenient compilation. Stress intensity factors can be obtained analytically for only a limited number of cases, more generally numerical solutions must be obtained using a computer; published expressions are often for curves fitted to series of discrete results and care must be exercised not to use the expression outside the ranges specified.

For some purposes expressions can conveniently be written in the general form

$$K_I = \alpha\, \sigma(\pi a)^{\frac{1}{2}} \qquad (2)$$

where α is a geometry correction factor of the order of one.

L. P. Pook and R. A. Smith

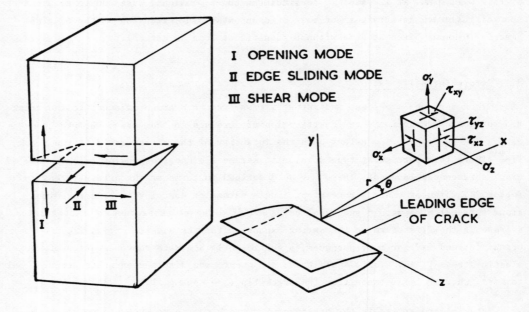

Fig. 1 Mode direction notation and crack tip coordinates.

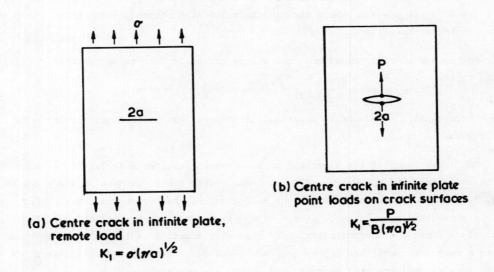

(a) Centre crack in infinite plate, remote load

$$K_1 = \sigma(\pi a)^{1/2}$$

(b) Centre crack in infinite plate point loads on crack surfaces

$$K_1 = \frac{P}{B(\pi a)^{1/2}}$$

Fig. 2 Stress intensity factors for various geometries.

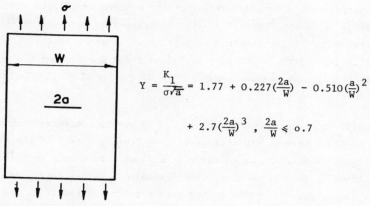

$$Y = \frac{K_1}{\sigma\sqrt{a}} = 1.77 + 0.227\left(\frac{2a}{W}\right) - 0.510\left(\frac{a}{W}\right)^2$$

$$+ 2.7\left(\frac{2a}{W}\right)^3 , \quad \frac{2a}{W} \leqslant 0.7$$

(c) Centre crack in plate of finite width remote load

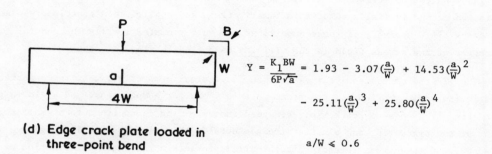

$$Y = \frac{K_1 BW}{6P\sqrt{a}} = 1.93 - 3.07\left(\frac{a}{W}\right) + 14.53\left(\frac{a}{W}\right)^2$$

$$- 25.11\left(\frac{a}{W}\right)^3 + 25.80\left(\frac{a}{W}\right)^4$$

$$a/W \leqslant 0.6$$

(d) Edge crack plate loaded in three-point bend

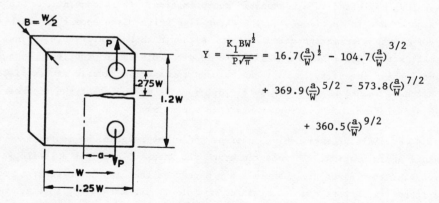

$$Y = \frac{K_1 BW^{\frac{1}{2}}}{P\sqrt{\pi}} = 16.7\left(\frac{a}{W}\right)^{\frac{1}{2}} - 104.7\left(\frac{a}{W}\right)^{3/2}$$

$$+ 369.9\left(\frac{a}{W}\right)^{5/2} - 573.8\left(\frac{a}{W}\right)^{7/2}$$

$$+ 360.5\left(\frac{a}{W}\right)^{9/2}$$

(e) ASTM compact tensile specimen (CTS)

Fig. 2 (cont.) Stress intensity factors for various geometries

Unfortunately only a limited number of solutions are available for geometries of practical interest such as cracks emanating from notches or fillets and useful generalisations are not easy. Empirical fits of engineering accuracy using a gross stress basis have been made[12] for the case of a crack of length ℓ emanating from the root of a semi-elliptical notch, depth D, root radius ρ and $D > \rho$. For $\ell > 0.13\,(D\rho)^{\frac{1}{2}}$, the effective crack length (a in equations) is $\ell + D$, and for $\ell < 0.13\,(D\rho)^{\frac{1}{2}}$ it is $\ell + 7.69\,\ell\,(D/\rho)^{\frac{1}{2}}$.

Hydrostatic pressure has no effect on K_I. However, pressures within a crack, not balanced by external forces, are equivalent to a tensile stress of the same magnitude across the crack. The effect of introducing a crack into a body containing large scale residual stresses is to relieve the residual stresses on the crack plane. Provided the crack is not too large, the corresponding stress intensity factor is the same as if stresses, equal in magnitude to the original residual stress, but opposite in sign, were applied to the crack surfaces. This must be added to the stresses due to external loads. The presence of residual stresses of unknown magnitude can be a serious obstacle to the application of fracture mechanics.

An apparent objection to the use of the stress intensity factor approach is the violation of the initial assumption of small strain and negligible distortion even at the crack tip. However, if these conditions are only violated locally the general character of the stress field in the <u>vicinity</u> of the crack tip, is unchanged.

The elastic stress analysis assumes an ideal elastic material, that is, a perfectly elastic isotropic continuum. Practical materials are not homogeneous, and yield in the high stress region at a crack tip. Provided that yielding is confined to a small region right at the crack tip, the elastic stresses outside this region are only slightly affected, and the stress intensity factor still provides a reasonable description of the crack tip stress field. Small scale non-linear effects due to microstructural irregularities, internal stresses, local irregularities in the crack surface and the actual fracture process, can similarly be regarded as within the crack tip stress fields and therefore neglected in a reasonable approximation. It is conventional to treat 45° crack growth in thin specimens and the shear lips which often appear on thick specimens, as Mode I growth when making calculations. Although this is difficult to justify by the 'small scale' argument, it does not cause difficulties in practice. By a similar argument, stress intensity factors can be used to describe elastic stress fields at sharp notches, indeed elastic stress fields, mutatis mutandis, at the tips of sharp notches are similar to those for cracks (see Appendix).

Some materials of engineering interest cannot be regarded as isotropic even to a reasonable approximation. The elastic crack tip stress fields for anisotropic materials are different from isotropic materials and depend on the elastic constants. Although stress intensity factors can be obtained for anisotropic materials, they are used only for certain specialised applications such as the fracture toughness testing of wood[13].

4. Effect of Yielding

An uncracked plate loaded in uniaxial tension is in a state of plane stress, that is, there is no stress in the thickness direction; this is still so in the bulk of the plate when a crack is introduced, but highly stressed materials adjacent to the crack tip is constrained by the less highly stressed surrounding material, and stresses are induced in the thickness direction in the interior of the plate at the crack tip.

This situation is referred to as plane strain in fracture mechanics. Limited plastic flow due to yielding of the material adjacent to the crack tip does not affect the situation in a thick plate of a ductile metal (Fig. 3): a plate is said to be thick if the thickness is at least $2.5\,(K_I/\sigma_Y)^2$, (σ_Y = yield stress, usually taken as the 0.2 per cent proof stress). When the thickness is very much less than $2.5\,(K_I/\sigma_Y)^2$, the crack tip plastic zone size becomes comparable with the thickness; yielding can take place on 45° planes, relaxing the stresses through the thickness, so that the whole plate is in a state of plane stress. In fatigue the stress state is conventionally described by the situation at the maximum load in the fatigue cycle. A stress intensity factor provides a reasonable description of the stress field at a crack tip if the plastic zone is small compared with the crack length; this is so if the net section stress does not exceed $0.8\,\sigma_Y$.

The approximate radius, r_p of the plastic zone at a crack tip in a ductile metal is given by

$$r_p = \frac{1}{2\pi}\,(K_I/\sigma_Y)^2 \qquad\qquad (3)$$

for plane stress and one third of this amount for plane strain. Provided again that r_p is small compared with the crack length and that the maximum net section stress does not exceed $0.8\,\sigma_Y$, the plastic zone has little effect on the value of K_I; if required a correction can be made by using $(r_p + a)$ instead of a, in an iterative manner, in the calculations. Failure to check whether large scale yielding might be occurring is the commonest error in the application of L.E.F.M., and quoted results for which no check appears to have been made should be regarded as suspect.

In fatigue the reversed yielding which takes place on unloading is only of limited extent, so a similar correction to ΔK_I is not usually necessary. If required, it can be made using equation (3) but with K_I replaced by ΔK_I and σ_Y by $2\,\sigma_Y$. The limited extent of the reversed plastic zone means that a plate that appears to be in a state of plane stress may not be so after unloading, a question which does not appear to have been discussed in the literature. Occasionally the terms plane strain and plane stress are associated with square and slant fracture respectively. This practice has no scientific basis and is to be deprecated. The fractures are better differentiated by the physical micromechanism which has caused them.

Since the stress intensity factor actually represents only the first term of the series expansion for the crack tip stress field (see Appendix), and while for many purposes it provides a reasonable approximation, higher order terms must sometimes be taken into account. In particular the second term represents a stress parallel to the crack and hence is strongly influenced by biaxiality. It can have a significant influence on

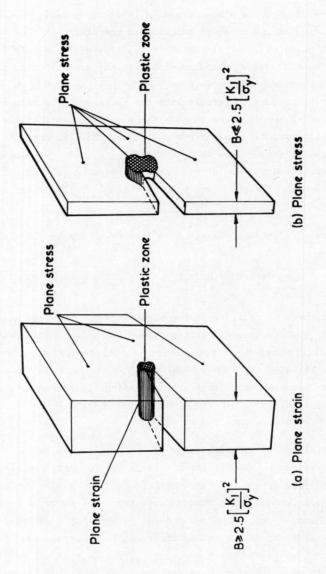

Fig. 3 Stress state, thickness and plastic zone sizes.

plastic zone size and crack directional stability (see Appendix). Detailed effects of these higher terms have been extensively discussed by Eftis et al.[14].

5. Measuring Fracture Toughness

A full discussion of this topic is outside the scope of this paper. Although techniques based on elastic plastic theory form an important part of fracture toughness testing, discussion will be limited here to elastic theory only.

A good way to understand the concept of fracture toughness is to consider how it is measured, since it is a material property which at the present time can be determined accurately only by experiment. By far the most important measure of fracture toughness is K_{Ic}, the opening mode, plane-strain fracture toughness because this is how many catastrophic failures occur in practice and it is a minimum material toughness value. Because of its importance, much effort has been devoted to devising a universally accepted test procedure for determining K_{Ic}.

In principle, measurement of K_{Ic} is simple: a fatigue crack is grown in a specimen, and K_{Ic} is calculated from the specimen dimensions and the load required to make the crack extend catastrophically. In practice, there are a number of experimental and interpretational difficulties, for example, the crack must be sufficiently long to cause failure below general yield. There is usually some slow stable crack growth as the load increases, making it necessary to define K_{Ic} as the value of K_I corresponding to an arbitrary amount of crack growth, in a manner analogous to the determination of a proof stress in a tensile test. Detailed procedures are given in standard test methods[15,16]. Typical values of K_{Ic} for various engineering materials are given in Table 1.

Under plane stress conditions, that is in thin sections, slow stable cracking is often extensive, so that a single parameter may not be adequate to characterise the fracture toughness, and the R-curve method[17] becomes appropriate. The method involves the continuous measurement of load and the resulting slow stable crack growth. The load values are converted to K_I values called crack growth resistance, R. The resulting plot of K (or R) values versus the crack growth at the K_I values is the R-curve. An R-curve typical of those obtained from structural alloys is shown in Fig. 4; the increasing K required to continue the crack growth is quite typical. Note that the R-curve is a function of crack growth, Δa, rather than the absolute crack length and that it extends to well above K_{Ic}. A K_c value can be taken directly from the curve, but it applies only to the specific amount of crack growth selected as critical, and only to the specimen thickness used in this R-curve. This restricted value is often adequate. A K_{Ic} value is actually a carefully specified point on an abrupt R-curve. The definition of K_c as the value of K_I necessary for crack growth is only adequate for an ideal material in which the resistance to crack growth is independent of the amount of crack growth.

L. P. Pook and R. A. Smith

Table 1. Typical values of plane strain fracture toughness, K_{Ic}

Material	Modulus E , MPa	Yield Stress σ_y , MPa	Toughness K_{Ic} , MPa $\sqrt{m}$	Thickness requirement $2.5\left[\dfrac{K_{Ic}}{\sigma_y}\right]^2$ mm
Steels				
Medium carbon	2.1×10^5	2.6×10^2	54	110
Pressure vessel				
(ASTM A533B Q+T)		4.7×10^2	208	487
High strength alloy		14.6×10^2	98	11
Maraging steel		$18 \ \times 10^2$	76	4.4
AFC 77 Stainless		15.3×10^2	83	7.9
Aluminium alloys				
2024 T8	72×10^4	4.2×10^2	27	10.4
7075 T6		5.4×10^2	30	7.9
7178 T6		5.6×10^2	23	4.2
Titanium alloys				
Ti-6Aℓ-4V	1.08×10^5	10.6×10^2	73	12.6
(High Yield)		$11 \ \times 10^2$	38	3.1
For comparison				
Concrete	$\sim 4 \times 10^4$	80	$0.2 - 1.4$	
WC-Co composites	$\sim 1 \times 10^5$	3×10^2	13	4.7
PMMA	3×10^3	30	1	2.8

Note: Representative values only - not to be employed as design data.

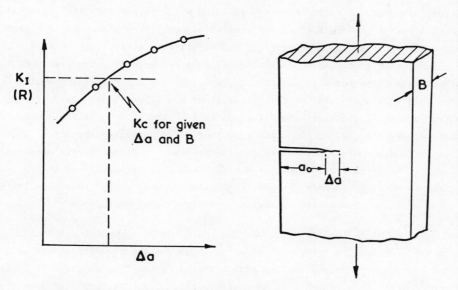

Fig. 4 R-Curve fracture toughness test procedure.

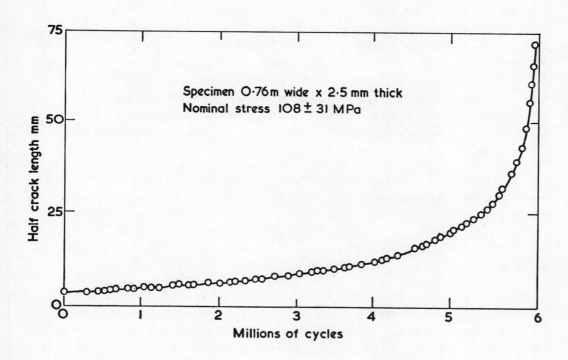

Fig. 5 Growth curve for a central crack in a mild steel specimen.

6. Fatigue Crack Growth

Now consider the problem of a crack growing under a stress cycle of constant amplitude, that is, a loading sequence in which all stress cycles are identical. It is assumed that loads are applied and removed smoothly at a reasonable frequency, say around 30 Hz, so that impact conditions and strain rate effects are avoided. It is also assumed that no time dependent effects, such as corrosion, contribute to the growth process. The loading conditions, crack geometry and material geometry are assumed such that at no time do the stresses and crack lengths involved give rise to a maximum value of K_I greater than or equal to K_c. The type of growth considered is commonly referred to as fatigue crack growth or fatigue crack propagation; these terms are, in fact, misnomers since no fracture mechanisms other than static ones need be involved; it would be more correct to use the term that has developed in fracture mechanics terminology, namely, sub-critical crack growth, except that this includes all types of crack growth such as stress corrosion crack growth which take place below K_c.

In this section the term crack growth when used without qualification as in 'fatigue crack growth data', implies Mode I crack growth, that is stage II in Forsyth's notation[18]. This is somewhat of an oversimplification. The expected direction of crack growth in a uniaxially loaded sheet is normal to the loading direction with the fracture face on a plane through the thickness at 90° to the plane of the specimen (Mode I). In some materials, for example, zinc and titanium, this is what occurs. However, in other materials such as steels, copper alloys and aluminium alloys, a transition to growth on a plane through the thickness inclined at approximately 45° to the plane of the sheet (a combination of Modes I and III) usually takes place after an initial period of Mode I growth. The transition usually occurs when a critical value of ΔK_I for a given material and thickness is exceeded, and when the plastic zone size at the crack tip becomes comparable to the sheet thickness. Growth rates and crack openings are relatively large and the usual striations in the fracture face tend to be replaced by ductile dimples indicating that considerable ductile strain is occurring. In this paper, this transition is ignored, it can however lead to a thickness dependence in fatigue crack growth behaviour.

The first accurate fatigue crack growth data were obtained from wide, long, thin sheets containing a small transverse central slit to initiate cracks; the sheet is usually subjected to a wholly tensile loading cycle applied normal to the crack, namely $\sigma_m \pm \sigma_a$ where $\sigma_m > \sigma_a$. This centre cracked tension specimen is still used extensively. The compact tension specimen[15] is particularly convenient as it is economical in both material and machine load requirements.

Rates of growth are obtained by measuring crack length at convenient intervals, either manually or by automatic methods, fitting a cruve of crack length against number of cycles to the experimental points (see Fig. 5) and taking the slope of this curve at stipulated crack lengths or at stipulated numbers of cycles. A full account of experimental techniques and data reduction methods can be found in a tentative standard test method[19].

6.1 Presentation of Data

Several different ways of presenting crack growth data, and 'laws' of fatigue crack growth have been suggested; some are empirical, others have been derived theoretically by making various plausible assumptions. All these laws, some of which have been discussed elsewhere[3,20], can be regarded as valid in the sense that they describe a particular set of data and can be used to predict crack growth rates in situations similar to those used to collect the data. It is sometimes possible to fit the same set of data to apparently contradictory laws and hence no decision on which law is the more correct can be made. Invariably, the data are presented either directly by plotting crack length against N, number of cycles, or indirectly by plotting crack growth rate against some function of σ_a and/or a. No method is noticeably a better representation of the data than any other and hence the choice of a particular method of analysis becomes a matter of the convenience with which the data can be subsequently applied to practical problems. On these grounds, the use of the stress intensity factor has no serious rivals; nor is it surprising, in view of the success of linear elastic fracture mechanics in dealing with static crack growth, that a similar approach should apply to the analysis of crack growth under a cyclic stress, particularly as this generally occurs at a lower stress level. The availability of a master curve for a particular material, relating the cyclic crack growth rate and the range of stress intensity factor, enables a designer to predict growth rates for any cracked body configuration; he is not limited to situations similar to those pertaining to the cracked specimen geometry used to generate the original data. In using data, it must be remembered that for some materials, fatigue crack growth rates are thickness dependent, when in doubt tests should be carried out using material similar in thickness to that in the structure.

In the analysis of cyclic crack growth data, the applied loading cycle ($\sigma_m \pm \sigma_a$) is usually described by ΔK_I, which equals $K_{Imax} - K_{Imin}$, i.e. the values of the opening mode stress intensity factor K_I, calculated from the maximum and minimum stress during the fatigue cycle, using the appropriate equation for the configuration concerned. If the minimum stress is compressive, it is conventionally taken as zero. This is a simplification based on the assumption that a crack closes when the load falls to zero, which is only correct for the purely elastic case. In practice, due to crack tip plasticity effects, a crack may close above or below zero load. Because of the wake of plastically deformed material left by a propagating crack, a crack may close at above the minimum load in the cycle even when this is above zero. This phenomenon is usually referred to as crack closure and reduces the effective values of ΔK_I to below the conventionally calculated values used in this paper. If K_{Imax} is well below K_c, ΔK_I plays the major role in determining crack growth behaviour; if ΔK_I is maintained constant, the growth rate will be constant. In much of this paper, it is assumed that σ_m has no effect.

For many materials in which crack growth under a cyclic load is possible, the growth rate under the loading cycle $\sigma_m \pm \sigma_a$ where $\sigma_m > \sigma_a$ (and most available data so conforms because the use of thin sheets requires $\sigma_m > \sigma_a$ to prevent buckling unless special jigs are used) can be represented by the equation [21]

L. P. Pook and R. A. Smith

$$\frac{da}{dN} = D(\Delta K_I)^m \qquad\qquad (4)$$

where N is the number of cycles and D and m are material constants; m is around 3 for many metals.

When a centre crack specimen is used, both K_{max} and ΔK_I increase with crack length but the stress ratio R = $\sigma_{min}/\sigma_{max}$ remains constant. Data are usually presented as plots of da/dN against ΔK_I for constant R.

If the maximum cyclic load is such that general yielding occurs, it may still be possible to apply linear fracture mechanics provided that the alternating stress is small. In this case, it can be argued that the unloading displacements during the first cycle, and all subsequent cycles, will be essentially elastic so that it is possible to calculate ΔK_I although K_{IMax} cannot be calculated. This argument has been found to be justified for some materials where ΔK_I correlates data satisfactorily at stresses beyond general yielding, but such data do not necessarily agree with those obtained under essentially elastic conditions. Data should therefore always be checked to see whether extensive yielding at the maximum load could have affected results. Some typical data[3] are shown in Fig. 6. They were obtained on mild steel sheet specimens having cracks of overall lengths up to 100 mm; curves were fitted to the basic crack length versus number of cycles data for each specimen and growth rates obtained from the appropriate slope. The results are plotted as a scatter band of da/dN against ΔK_I. The transition from growth on a 90° to growth on a 45° plane through the sheet thickness has been ignored. Data have been regarded as valid for which the gross maximum stress in the loading cycle did not exceed one half the 0.1 per cent proof stress of the material and this combined with the limitation on overall crack length ensured that behaviour was essentially elastic. Data which were invalid by this criterion are indicated by dashed lines. Another possibility is to regard data as invalid if the maximum net section stress exceeds 80 per cent of the yield stress. This removes the need to limit crack length, but is still not applicable to some specimens such as the compact tension specimen where a criterion similar to that used for fracture toughness testing would be needed[19].

It is seen in general that the data is indeed well represented by equation (4) where m is around 3. It is, however, more appropriate to characterise the data by a value of m and a value of ΔK_I at da/dN = 10^{-6} mm/cycle. Such values for various materials[22] are given in Table 2. The bands would be expected to flatten at either end. At the upper end, the growth rate will tend to increase as either K_{Imax} approaches K_c or ($\sigma_m + \sigma_a$) approaches the yield stress of the material. At the lower end, there is a cut-off at a growth rate of about one lattice spacing per cycle. This is the threshold value ΔK_{th} which is discussed later. Lower average rates are sometimes observed but crack growth cannot then be taking place along the whole of the crack front on each cycle.

Because Mode I crack growth is dependent on crack opening which, for a given crack length, is proportional to I/E, i.e. nominal strain, this might be considered a more appropriate parameter to correlate data from different metals than nominal stress. Data[3] for mild steel, copper, aluminium and titanium are compared on this basis in

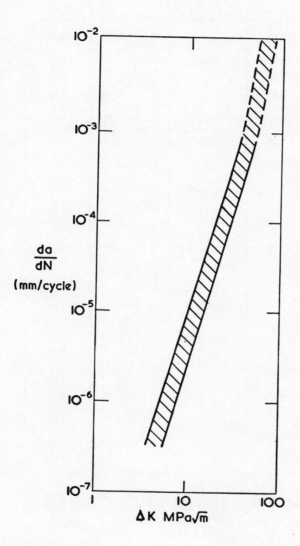

Fig. 6 Crack growth rate data for mild steel

L. P. Pook and R. A. Smith

Table 2. Fatigue crack growth data for various materials

Material	Tensile strength (MPa)	0.1 or 0.2 per cent proof stress (MPa)	R	m	ΔK for da/dN = 10^{-6} mm/c (MPa $\sqrt{m}$)
Mild steel	325	230	0.06 – 0.74	3.3	6.2
Mild steel in brine*	435	–	0.64	3.3	6.2
Cold rolled mild steel	695	655	0.07 – 0.43	4.2	7.2
			0.54 – 0.76	5.5	6.4
			0.75 – 0.92	6.4	5.2
Low alloy steel*	680		0 – 0.75	3.3	5.1
Maraging steel*	2010		0.67	3.0	3.5
18/8 Austenitic steel	665	195 – 255	0.33 – 0.43	3.1	6.3
Aluminium	125 – 155	95 – 125	0.14 – 0.87	2.9	2.9
5% Mg- Aluminium Alloy	310	180	0.20 – 0.69	2.7	1.6
HS30W Aluminium Alloy (1% Mg, 1% Si, 0.7% Mn)	265	180	0.20 – 0.71	2.6	1.9
HS30WP Aluminium Alloy (1% Mg, 1% Si, 0.7% Mn)	310	245 – 280	0.25 – 0.43	3.9	2.6
			0.50 – 0.78	4.1	2.15
L71 Aluminium Alloy (4.5% Cu)	480	415⎞	0.14 – 0.46	3.7	2.4
L73 Aluminium Alloy (4.5% Cu)	435	370⎠	0.50 – 0.88	4.4	2.1
DTD 687A Aluminium Alloy (5.5% Zn)	540	495	0.20 – 0.45	3.7	1.75
			0.50 – 0.78	4.2	1.8
			0.82 – 0.94	4.8	1.45
ZW1 Magnesium Alloy (0.5% Zr)	250	165⎞	0	3.35	0.94
AM503 Magnesium Alloy (1.5% Mn)	200	107⎠	0.5	3.35	0.69
			0.67	3.35	0.65
			0.78	3.35	0.57
Copper	215 – 310	26 – 513	0.07 – 0.82	3.9	4.3
Phosphor bronze*	370		0.33 – 0.74	3.9	4.3
60/40 brass*	325		0 – 0.33	4.0	6.3
			0.51 – 0.72	3.9	4.3
Titanium	555	440	0.08 – 0.94	4.4	3.1
5% Al Titanium alloy	835	735	0.17 – 0.86	3.8	3.4
15% Mo Titanium alloy	1160	995	0.28 – 0.71	3.5	3.0
			0.81 – 0.94	4.4	2.75
Nickel*	430		0 – 0.71	4.0	8.8
Monel*	525		0 – 0.67	4.0	6.2
Iconel*	650		0 – 0.71	4.0	8.2

* Data of limited accuracy obtained by an indirect method.

Fig. 7 where da/dN is plotted against $\Delta K_I/E$. It is seen that the data fall within a band. It follows therefore that the growth rate characteristics of any alloy might be similar to that of the base metal if alloying results in no change in modulus. The data in Table 2 show that this is the case for steels and it is in general true; however, there will be deviations if, for example, elements of fast fracture are promoted by 2nd phase particles.

If the crack growth data can be represented by equation (4) and

$$\Delta K_I = \alpha \Delta \sigma (\pi a)^{\frac{1}{2}} \qquad (5)$$

then the number of cycles required for a crack to grow from an initial length a_o to a final length a_f can be obtained by integration. Thus for constant α

$$N = \frac{a_o^{m/2}}{D(m/2 - 1)\Delta K_o^m} \left[\frac{1}{a_o^{m/2-1}} - \frac{1}{a_f^{m/2-1}} \right] \qquad (6)$$

or
$$N = \frac{a_o}{d(m/2 - 1)\Delta K_o^m} \left[1 - \left(\frac{a_o}{a_f} \right)^{m/2-1} \right]. \qquad (7)$$

Other crack growth equations and expressions for ΔK_I can be similarly combined, but numerical integration is usually necessary. Care must be taken to ensure that the integration does not extend beyond the ranges of validity of the equations concerned. Provided that this is done, and the crack growth equation used is a reasonable fit to the data, the precise form of the crack growth equation has little influence on the final result[20].

6.2 Mechanisms

Under microscopic examination the most striking feature of many of the fracture faces created by a fatigue crack is the presence of distinct line markings, parallel to each other and normal to the direction of crack growth. These lines are generally called striations (Fig. 8). Each striation corresponds to one stress cycle and thus the distance between striations is the amount that the crack has moved forward during that cycle. This one-to-one correspondence between striation and applied stress cycle has now been demonstrated experimentally many times. At high rates of crack growth, striations tend to give way to ductile dimples or cleavage facets, depending on the ductility of the material, and fatigue fracture surfaces are sometimes indistinguishable from those produced by monotonic loading.

The presence of brittle particles, especially brittle intermetallics, in the microstructure of a material, such as in the high strength aluminium alloys, can result in sudden spurts of crack growth. As the crack tip reaches the intermetallic inclusion and this fractures suddenly, an increment of crack growth depending on the inclusion size is added. Thus, although comparison of striation markings in different aluminium alloys reveals similar growth rates through the matrix for a given ΔK_I, the overall growth rate is anomalously fast, the more so for those alloys containing the

L. P. Pook and R. A. Smith

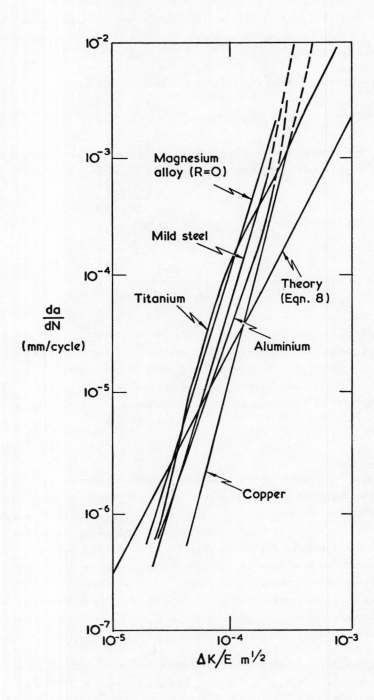

Fig. 7 Crack growth rate data for various materials
        compared on the basis of strain.

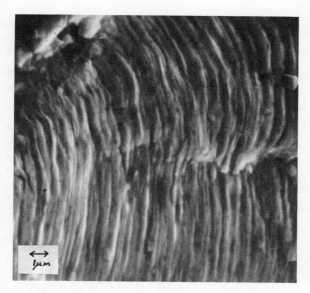

(a) Mild steel at room temperature, well developed striations

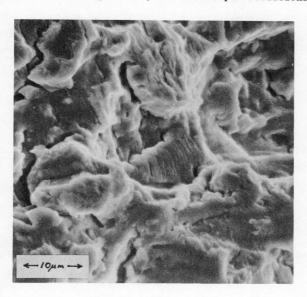

(b) Mild steel at -100°C. Few striations mixed with static
    mechanisms of failure, leading to an increased growth rate
    (cf. Fig. 9).

Fig.8. S.E.M. fractographs of typical fatigue crack surfaces for constant
        amplitude loading. In both cases the direction of crack
        propagation is from left to right. (M J Cowdery - unpublished
        data)

most severe inclusions. The effect is illustrated in Fig. 9; it also leads to a
marked dependency on tensile mean stress, and the presence of such static modes of
crack growth can result in thickness dependence in fatigue crack growth behaviour.

Under cyclic loading a crack can grow even though the value of $K_{I max}$ corresponding
to the range ΔK_I may be much less than K_c. Hence energy considerations cannot enter
into the argument[3]. Several theories have been put forward to explain how this
might occur, all including some type of progressive accumulation of damage in the
material ahead of the crack tip. A progressive reduction in ductility due to cyclic
work-hardening is a common assumption, but often the details of the fracture process
are conveniently lumped together and simply called damage.

In fact crack growth occurs under cyclic loading not as a consequence of any
progressive structural damage but merely because unloading resharpens the crack tip
at each cycle[3]. No damage mechanism peculiar to 'fatigue' is necessary to explain
crack growth other than that which occurs under a static load. It should be possible,
therefore, to deduce the increment of crack growth in each cycle from an analysis of
the changing crack tip geometry during its opening and closing.

In the case of, for example, a thin sheet of infinite width containing a central
slit of overall length 2a subjected to a zero to maximum tensile loading cycle, the
sequence of crack opening and closing is as in Fig. 10. Pook and Frost[23] assumed
that the part of the crack tip profile subjected to tensile stresses greater than the
yield stress ($\sigma_x > \sigma_Y$) retains its length on unloading and for ductile metals having
E/σ_Y of the order of 10^3 this leads to

$$\frac{da}{dN} = \frac{9}{\pi} \left(\frac{\Delta K_I}{E}\right)^2 . \tag{8}$$

It is interesting to note that existing experimental data have been said[24] to conform
to

$$\frac{da}{dN} = \frac{8}{\pi} \left(\frac{\Delta K_I}{E}\right)^2 . \tag{9}$$

Equation (8) is for plane stress; for plane strain conditions the equivalent equation
is

$$\frac{da}{dN} = \frac{9}{\pi} \left(\frac{\Delta K_I}{E}\right)^2 (1 - \nu^2)^2 \tag{10}$$

which for $\nu = \frac{1}{3}$ gives an equation only slightly different from the plane stress case,
i.e.

$$\frac{da}{dN} = \frac{7}{\pi} \left(\frac{\Delta K_I}{E}\right)^2 . \tag{11}$$

Although the equations were derived for the loading cycle 0 to σ, they can be applied
to other loading cycles provided that ΔK_I is calculated from the range of stress $\Delta\sigma$.

It would be possible to refine these arguments by incorporating crack tip profiles
and details of yielding obtained, for example, from computer programs. However,

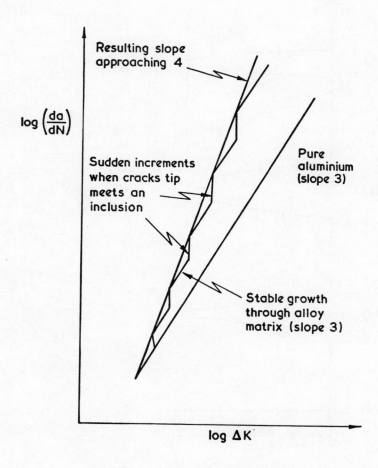

Fig. 9   Non-metallic inclusions giving rise
         to faster growth rates.

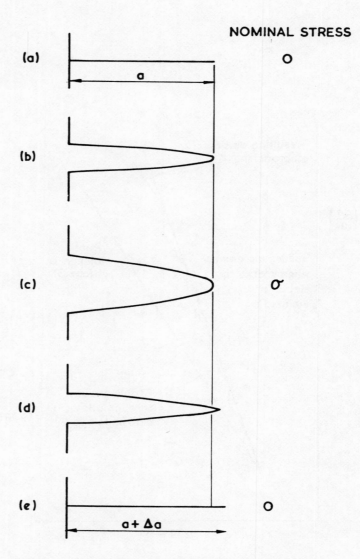

NOMINAL STRESS

(a)   O

a

(b)

(c)   σ

(d)

(e)   O

a + Δa

The sequence (a) to (e) is repeated for each
successive cycle

Fig. 10 Repeated sequence of crack opening and
closing under cyclic loading, 0 to σ.

Rice[25] has pointed out that any continuum mechanics theory of crack growth will result in a $(\Delta K_I/E)^2$ dependence unless a characteristic dimension is introduced. Thus, in general, a more refined theory will simply alter the numerical factor in the above equations. A comparison of the growth rate line predicted by the above plane stress equation (8) has been added to Fig. 7, the experimental data plotted in terms of $\Delta K_I/E$ against da/dN. The theoretical line, which it must be emphasised was obtained with the use of no arbitrary coefficients or constants, agrees well with experimental rates around 3×10^{-5} mm/cycle, where the increment of growth per cycle is of the order of the grain or sub-grain size. However, experimental rates are underestimated at high growth rates and overestimated at low growth rates.

Thus it is seen that ΔK_I is a satisfactory parameter to describe crack growth data; there will always be a need to determine material coefficients experimentally to allow for such factors as mean stress, environment, frequency, inhomogeneity of material etc. However, except in the case of corrosion, such factors do not affect the basic mechanism by which a Mode I crack grows, that is, the continual resharpening of its tip as the load is reduced. It is perhaps convenient to define a neutral environment as one which does not affect the basic mechanism of crack growth, an inert environment as one which permits a degree of rebonding on unloading and therefore retards growth, and a corrosive environment as one which assists crack growth.

6.3 Threshold

Equation (4) implies that any value of ΔK_I, no matter how small, will result in a positive value of da/dN. However, most experimental growth rate data show that the growth rate tends to zero at some positive value of ΔK_I. Indeed, experimental tests on specimens containing cracks have indicated that a definite value of ΔK_I exists below which a crack remains dormant. This critical value of ΔK_I is called the threshold value and is denoted by ΔK_{th}.

Thresholds can be obtained by a variety of techniques, which all usually give essentially the same result. The most obvious is simply to follow the da/dN against ΔK_I curve downwards. However, unless this is done very carefully, the threshold can be seriously overestimated[26]. A straightforward, if somewhat tedious technique, is to determine an S/N curve for precracked, stress-relieved specimens, with endurance plotted against the initial value of ΔK_I, ΔK_o, rather than stress. Fig. 11 shows some results for NiCrMoV steel tested at 300°C. ΔK_{th} values for various materials[22] are shown in Table 3. Unlike the rate of crack growth, which is largely independent R, ΔK_{Ic} normally decreases as R increases. For many materials ΔK_{th} is approximately proportional to $\{(1 - R)/(1 + R)\}^{\frac{1}{3}}$.

It could be argued that if a value of ΔK_I is insufficient to create an element of new surface anywhere along the crack front equal to a lattice spacing, then the crack must of physical necessity remain dormant. In fact, experimental values of ΔK_{th} correspond reasonably well with values of ΔK_I calculated from the growth law da/dN = $D(\Delta K)^m$ for a value of da/dN equal to one lattice spacing (say 3×10^{-3} mm).

Carefully controlled experiments suggest that continuous crack growth at average rates of much less than one lattice spacing per cycle can sometimes be observed[27]

Table 3. Values of ΔK_{th} for various materials

Material (Ferrous)	Tensile strength (MPa)	R	ΔK_{th} (MPa $\sqrt{m}$)
Mild steel	430	-1	6.4
		0.13	6.6
		0.35	5.2
		0.49	4.3
		0.64	3.2
		0.75	3.8
Mild steel at 300°C	480	-1	7.1
		0.23	6.0
		0.33	5.8
Mild steel in brine	430	-1	~2.0
		0.64	1.15
Mild steel in brine with cathodic protection	430	0.64	3.9
Mild steel in tap water or SAE30 oil	430	-1	7.3
		-1	6.3
Low alloy steel	835	0	6.6
	680	0.33	5.1
		0.50	4.4
		0.64	3.3
		0.75	2.5
NiCrMoV steel at 300°C	560	-1	7.1
		0.23	5.0
		0.33	5.4
		0.64	4.9
		0.67	2.7
Maraging steel	2010	-1	6.0
18/8 Austenitic steel	685	0	6.0
	665	0.33	5.9
		0.62	4.6
		0.74	4.1
Grey cast iron	255	0	7.0
		0.50	4.5

Material (Non-ferrous)	Tensile strength (MPa)	R	ΔK_{th} (MPa $\sqrt{m}$)
Aluminium	77	-1	1.0
		0	1.7
		0.33	1.4
		0.53	1.2
L65 Aluminium alloy (4.5% Cu)	450	-1	2.1
	495	0	2.1
		0.33	1.7
		0.50	1.5
		0.67	1.2
L65 Aluminium alloy (4.5% Cu) in brine		0.50	1.15
ZW1 Magnesium alloy (0.6% Zr)	250	0	0.83
		0.67	0.66
AM503 Magnesium alloy (1.6% Mn)	165	0	0.99
		0.67	0.77
Copper	225	-1	2.7
	215	-1	2.5
		0.33	1.8
Titanium	540	0.60	2.2
Nickel	455	-1	5.9
	430	0	7.9
Monel	525	0.33	6.5
		0.57	5.2
		0.71	3.6
Iconel		-1	5.6
	655	0	7.0
	650	0.33	6.5
		0.50	5.2
		0.67	3.6
		-1	6.4
		0.57	7.1
		0.71	4.7
			4.0

(Fig. 12). It is probable that crack growth does not necessarily cease abruptly as ΔK_{th} is reached but that within a narrow band of ΔK_I values, crack growth only takes place on a part of the crack front during each cycle thus producing very low average growth rates.

6.4 Accuracy and Scatter

The analysis of scatter in fatigue crack growth data presents special problems[28], in particular standard statistical techniques[29] cannot be used.

Crack growth at ΔK_I values significantly higher than ΔK_{th} is sensibly reproducible; Fig. 13 shows crack growth curves obtained from stainless steel sheets tested under nominally the same conditions[3]. Discussion so far has been largely restricted to situations which can be viewed two-dimensionally, but in practice, crack growth on a microscopic scale is three-dimensional and is an irregular process. Thus, both ΔK_I at any point along a crack front and the corresponding value of da/dN will be random variables. An estimate of the mean ΔK_I can be calculated from the usual two-dimensional expression for stress intensity factor and it is reasonable to assume that the corresponding mean da/dN can be calculated for the mean value of ΔK_I by using equation (4).

Without a detailed knowledge of the distribution of da/dN for a given mean ΔK_I it is impossible to carry out quantitative statistical calculations to determine the width of the scatter band. However, a standard statistical result states that if a large number $\bar{N}$ of random samples (e.g. individual cycles at a given ΔK_I) of each $\bar{n}$ items (e.g. individual points along a crack front) is drawn from a population which has mean μ and standard deviation $\bar{\sigma}$, the means of the $\bar{N}$ samples will form a distribution with mean μ and standard deviation $\bar{\sigma}/\bar{n}^{\frac{1}{2}}$. Thus the width of the scatter band would be expected to be proportional to $1/B^{\frac{1}{2}}$ where B is specimen thickness and also to $1/\ell^{\frac{1}{2}}$ where ℓ is the effective distance over which an average crack growth rate is obtained. The value of ℓ depends[28] on the method of measurement and data reduction; it will be increased by data smoothing techniques. A consequence is that scatter in the total crack life, given for example by equation (7) cannot be estimated from the scatter in fatigue crack growth rate data.

At values of ΔK_I close to ΔK_{th}, crack growth may only be taking place along part of the crack front and average crack growth rates of less than one lattice spacing/cycle can be measured. It is obvious that at such critical conditions extremely close control of load amplitude is essential if the data is to be meaningful. A fatigue crack growth threshold determined by the method described in Section 6.3 is a mean value.

The dependence of scatter in da/dN versus ΔK_I data on precise data reduction techniques can lead to problems in the estimation of values of m and D in equation (4), or in fitting more elaborate techniques to various parts of the da/dN versus ΔK_I relationship. How this can arise is shown schematically in Fig. 14. Theoretically (Section 6.2) a slope corresponding to m = 2 would be expected with cut-offs at the upper and lower ends corresponding to static failure and the threshold respectively. In practice these will normally be approached gradually, as indicated by the dashed lines, giving an overall sigmoidal curve but scatter will usually prevent determination of the precise shape of the curve, and fitting straight lines to different parts of the

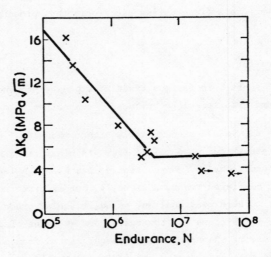

Fig. 11 Tests on cracked NiCrMoV steel plates at 300°C.

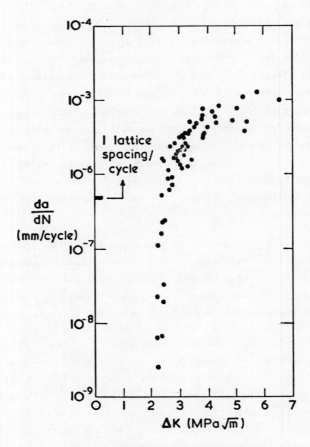

Fig. 12 Slow fatigue crack growth data
for 7075-T6 Aluminium Alloy

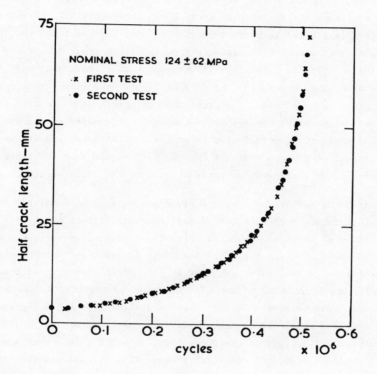

Fig. 13 Crack growth curve for two similar 18/8
          Austenitic steel sheets.

data will often give different values for m and D as indicated in Fig. 14. For this reason, it is perhaps preferable to quote data on the value of m together with the value of ΔK_I for a convenient rate of crack growth. Fitting a straight line to a wide range of data usually gives a value of m of around 3 as in Figs 6 and 7. More elaborate equations which take into account curvature at either end of the data are sometimes used. The utility of such equations, all of which are empirically based, must be judged by the intended application, the most important point being to ensure that they are not extrapolated beyond the range of the experimental data.

7. Short Crack Limitations

The utility of the concept of stress intensity factors centres on its ability to describe the stress in the vicinity of a crack tip accurately[30]. Because the stress intensity factor is a first term approximation to a series solution, the accuracy of this approximation decreases with distance from the crack tip. Recent numerical studies[31] for an infinite plate ($\alpha = 1$), suggest that if the 'near crack tip' field is limited to a/10, then errors in the order of 10 per cent appear in the local stress components. Other calculations[32] suggest that in practical geometries ($\alpha \neq 1$) the errors are somewhat greater. Nevertheless the stress intensity factor has proved to be a successful engineering correlation parameter for toughness and stable crack growth, and in this respect we may conclude that in the a/10 region near the crack tip stress intensity factors give a reasonable representation of the local stress field.

Stress intensity factors have been derived making all the usual simplifying assumptions of continuum mechanics, including isotropic, linear material. So for a global application of fracture mechanics, Fig. 15, where σ represents the stress applied to a structure, the near crack tip field should be at least the size of the largest structural feature of a real material, that is, the grain size. Since this size is typically $\sim 10^{-2}$ mm, a crack of at least 0.1 mm would be required before a stress intensity factor could be used. On the other hand, if σ represents the boundary stresses applied to a single grain, the crack length a would be half a grain size, while the near crack tip field at the grain boundary would extend over a distance of some 5×10^{-4} mm, many orders of magnitude greater than the lattice spacing and comfortably satisfying the continuum requirements. However, within a grain it may no longer be possible to regard the material as isotropic. This local application, Fig. 15, is familiar, for example, in the derivation of a Petch type relationship between yield strength and grain size.

However, in a real material, plastic deformation occurs at the crack tip. We argue (Section 4) that the elastic relation is still able to describe the crack tip conditions, if the plastic zone is limited in size compared with the near crack tip field, which is then still assumed to dominate the crack tip plastic response. A tentative limitation of the plastic zone is 1/5 of the size of the near crack tip elastic field. We now conclude that the plastic zone must be limited to 1/50 of the crack length. Much discussion[33] has led to this criterion being generally accepted as a limitation of the maximum size of the plastic zone allowed in a valid fracture toughness test. For the case of fatigue crack propagation tests, the applied stress levels are usually low enough to avoid large plastic zone size difficulties: indeed

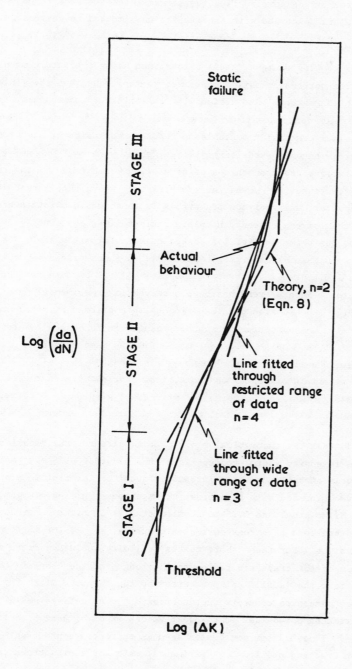

Fig. 14 Relationship between theoretical
and experimental values of m.

the range of stress intensity factor ΔK_I has proved to be a spectacularly successful parameter for correlating fatigue crack growth data. However, for the practical case of a <u>crack</u> initiated at the root of a <u>notch</u>, the notch generated plasticity may totally surround the small crack, thus invalidating the stress intensity factor concept[34]. This section, however, is concerned with the limitations imposed by decreasing the absolute size of the crack to which the concept of stress intensity factor is applied.

First consider a growing fatigue crack: rather than using a fracture mechanics equation to calculate a notional plastic zone size, we can argue that the minimum structural feature in the material associated with the crack tip zone would be a sub-grain slip band, $\sim 5 \times 10^{-4}$ mm. Now if the crack size is to be 50 times larger than this feature, the minimum crack size amenable to fracture mechanics treatment using stress intensity factors becomes surprisingly large, about 0.25 mm. Secondly, consider the case of a fatigue crack on the point of growing – subjected to the threshold stress intensity factor range, ΔK_{th}. As the crack size to which this threshold level is applied becomes smaller, a larger applied stress is required to maintain a constant ΔK_{th}. If, however, this stress exceeds the plain fatigue limit σ_e, crack growth is bound to occur. Thus, as shown in Fig. 16a, based on data for mild steel (R = - 1, σ_e = 210 MN/m², ΔK_{th} = 6 MN/m$^{-\frac{3}{2}}$), the growth threshold of short cracks is controlled by the plain fatigue limit, causing an apparent decrease, Fig. 16b, in the threshold stress intensity factor. Such a trend has been observed in experimental data[22], whilst the form of Fig. 16b has also been experimentally confirmed by Kitagawa and Takahashi[35]. Not all the short crack threshold results in Reference 22 are accounted for by this argument, and an R-curve type mechanism has been suggested[36] as a possible explanation. The minimum crack length a_o for constant ΔK_{th} will, of course, vary with different materials and specimen geometries. For example, for centre notched plates (α = 1), $a_o = (1/\pi)(\Delta K_{th}/\sigma_e)^2$, which for mild steel gives $a_o \sim 0.26$ mm, whilst for heat treated Cr-Mo steel (σ_e = 480 MPa, $\Delta K_{th} \sim 6$ MPa $\sqrt{m}$), a_o becomes 0.05 mm.

Thus we conclude that the theoretical minimum crack size for the global application of the stress intensity factor concept is of the order of 0.25 mm. Calculations using the lowest levels of applied stress intensity factor of interest in practical fatigue problems have coincided with this order of magnitude – giving minimum crack sizes of 0.05 mm in Ni/Mo steel and 0.26 mm in mild steel. It might be argued that for the case of the threshold in stress corrosion cracking, K_{Iscc}, the minimum crack size might become smaller. For these short cracks, validity would appear to rest on by how much the ratio of the crack tip radius to the length of the crack is changed, by chemical attack, from the 'small' value required by the theory. Clark[37] has claimed that fracture mechanics concepts can describe K_{Iscc} defects as small as 0.25 mm, whilst at the same time he noted that 'the lowest values of K_{Iscc} were associated with the smallest cracks'! Thus 0.25 mm would also seem an appropriate practical limitation for stress corrosion cracking problems. Experimental data for short cracks to supplement the limited amount now available would be a welcome practical contribution to fracture mechanics knowledge.

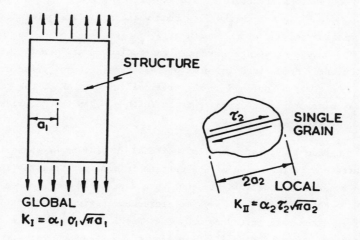

Fig. 15 Schematic of global and local levels of application
of the stress intensity factor concept.

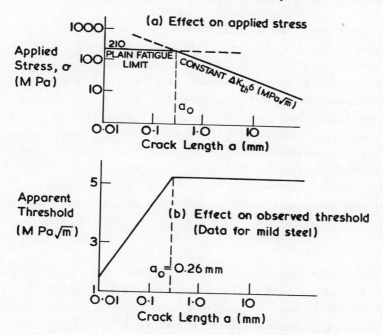

Fig. 16 Short cracks and the threshold stress intensity
factor.

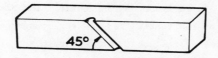

Fig. 17 Notch angle modification of Charpy test piece.

8.   Combined Mode Behaviour

Conventional fracture mechanics specimens are designed such that the initial crack is in Mode I. A crack-like flaw from which a failure originates will not necessarily be so oriented, and crack growth will, in general, not be in the plane of the initial crack. However fracture toughness and fatigue crack growth threshold behaviour can conveniently be defined in terms of the stress intensity factors for the initial crack. Thus ΔK_{IIth} may be defined as the critical value of ΔK_{II}, the range of K_{II}, necessary to cause crack growth which leads to failure, even though crack growth is not in the plane of the initial crack.

In Mode I, variations from the ideal initial crack shape lead merely to some uncertainty in the value of K_I, whereas in combined Mode testing (that is when any Mode other than Mode I is present) such variations can produce unwanted deformation modes. For example, in a specimen intended to give pure Mode II, deviations from the derived crack path introduce unwanted Mode I displacements, and crack front curvature introduces unwanted Mode III displacements. Because of the complicated three-dimensional situation, it is usually not practical to obtain accurate numerical values for the stress intensity factors involved.

In general the direction of crack growth is not in line with the original crack, and stress intensity factors change radically as soon as growth starts. A number of essentially two-dimensional criteria have been suggested for the determination of initial crack direction under combined Mode I and Mode II; a recent survey[38] points out that the preferred direction is in general not well defined. Existing criteria are nearly all based on elastic theory and may not necessarily hold in the presence of a plastic zone. With combined Mode I and Mode II loading under essentially elastic conditions, fatigue cracks grow in a direction such that K_I is a maximum and K_{II} tends to zero[39]. A natural criterion for fatigue crack growth, but for which a full solution is not yet available, would therefore be to take the direction in which K_{II} for an infinitesimal crack is zero: this initial direction is about that given by the equation[40]

$$K_I \sin \theta = K_{II} (3 \cos \theta - 1) \tag{12}$$

where θ is measured from the original crack direction. Negative values of K_I are not permitted and the root required is that which lies in the range $\pm 70.5^{\circ} \ldots$. If Mode III displacements are present, the problem becomes three-dimensional and is further complicated because a preferred plane of crack growth will in general only intersect the initial crack plane at one point[3].

Various features of elastic crack tip stress fields have been examined with a view to predicting behaviour in combined mode situations. Thus Sih[9,41] suggested that strain energy density is an important parameter. The basic idea has recently been re-examined[42] and the implication for fracture toughness behaviour discussed. It was pointed out some time ago[43] that for a sharp notch at a 45° angle (Fig. 17) the through thickness stress was essentially zero even in thick plates, the same was later shown to be true for cracks[44]. In solids which show a ductile/cleavage transition the operative stress system is an important parameter which controls failure.

For impact tests using a Charpy testpiece with notch inclined at 45° as in Fig. 17 the change in stress state from plane strain to plane stress reduced the energy transition temperature by about 80°C compared with conventional tests[45].

9.   Conclusions

In this paper it has only been possible to give a brief outline of some of the more important aspects of the theoretical background to elastic fracture mechanics. Attention has been concentrated on the concept of the stress intensity factor which can be regarded as a convenient one parameter description of near crack tip elastic stress fields.

A good theoretical framework is therefore now available for the description of crack fracture processes and the quantification of both fatigue crack growth and fracture toughness properties. The stress intensity factor provides a powerful similitude parameter linking situations of different geometry and loading.

The limitations of the linear elastic fracture mechanics approach have been described. It is worth emphasising that failure to check the extent of plastic yielding is common in applications of L.E:F.M. to practical problems, therefore quoted results for which no check appears to have been made should be regarded as suspect.

Acknowledgements

This paper contains Crown copyright material which is published by permission of the Director, National Engineering Laboratory, Department of Industry.

Part of the work reported was supported by the Engineering Materials Requirements Board of the Department of Industry.

Notation

a	Crack length, half length for internal crack
a_o	Minimum crack size
Δa	Amount of crack growth
B	Specimen thickness
D	Crack depth, constant in crack growth equation
E	Young's modulus
f	A subscript, final value
G	Shear modulus
K	Stress intensity factor, subscripts I, II, III denote mode
K_c	Fracture toughness
K_{Ic}	Plane strain fracture toughness
K_{Imax}	Maximum value of K_I in fatigue cycle
K_{Imin}	Minimum value of K_I in fatigue cycle
K_{Iscc}	Threshold for stress corrosion crack growth
ΔK_I	Range of K_I in fatigue cycle
ΔK_{II}	Range of K_{II} in fatigue cycle

ΔK_{th}	Threshold value of ΔK_I
ΔK_{IIth}	Threshold value of ΔK_{II}
ℓ	Effective length, crack length at notch
m	Exponent in crack growth equation
N	Number of cycles
$\bar{N}$	Number of samples
$\bar{n}$	Number in sample
P	Load
R	Stress ratio ($\sigma_{min}/\sigma_{max}$), resistance to crack growth
r	Distance from crack tip
r_P	Plastic zone radius
W	Specimen width
α	Geometry correction factor
μ	Mean value
ν	Poisson's ratio
ρ	Notch root radius
σ	Stress
σ_a	Alternating stress
σ_e	Plain fatigue limit
σ_m	Mean stress
σ_{max}	Maximum stress in fatigue cycle, stress at root of notch
σ_{min}	Minimum stress in fatigue cycle
σ_Y	Yield stress (taken as 0.2 per cent proof stress)
$\Delta\sigma$	Range of stress in fatigue cycle
τ	Shear stress
o	As subscript, initial value

APPENDIX

Elastic Stress Fields

The elastic stress fields and displacements corresponding to the three modes of crack surface displacement are[7,10], referring to Fig. 1 for notation (where u, v and w are displacements in the x, y, z directions).

Mode I:

$$\sigma_x = \frac{K_I}{(2\pi r)^{\frac{1}{2}}} \cos\frac{\theta}{2}\left(1 - \sin\frac{\theta}{2}\sin\frac{3\theta}{2}\right)$$

$$\sigma_y = \frac{K_I}{(2\pi r)^{\frac{1}{2}}} \cos\frac{\theta}{2}\left(1 + \sin\frac{\theta}{2}\sin\frac{3\theta}{2}\right)$$

$$\tau_{xy} = \frac{K_I}{(2\pi r)^{\frac{1}{2}}} \sin\frac{\theta}{2}\cos\frac{\theta}{2}\cos\frac{3\theta}{2}$$

$$\sigma_z = \nu(\sigma_x + \sigma_y)$$

$$\tau_{xz} = \tau_{yz} = 0 \qquad\qquad (A.1)$$

$$u = \frac{K_I}{G}\left[\frac{r}{2\pi}\right]^{\frac{1}{2}} \cos\frac{\theta}{2}\left(1 - 2\nu + \sin^2\frac{\theta}{2}\right)$$

$$v = \frac{K_I}{G}\left[\frac{r}{2\pi}\right]^{\frac{1}{2}} \sin\frac{\theta}{2}\left(2 - 2\nu - \cos^2\frac{\theta}{2}\right)$$

$$w = 0.$$

Note that the crack opens into a parabola, and that because a crack is regarded as a mathematical 'cut', θ must lie within the range $\pm\pi$.

Mode II:

$$\sigma_x = -\frac{K_{II}}{(2\pi r)^{\frac{1}{2}}} \sin\frac{\theta}{2}\left(2 + \cos\frac{\theta}{2}\cos\frac{3\theta}{2}\right)$$

$$\sigma_y = \frac{K_{II}}{(2\pi r)^{\frac{1}{2}}} \sin\frac{\theta}{2}\cos\frac{\theta}{2}\cos\frac{3\theta}{2}$$

$$\tau_{xy} = \frac{K_{II}}{(2\pi r)^{\frac{1}{2}}} \cos\frac{\theta}{2}\left(1 - \sin\frac{\theta}{2}\sin\frac{3\theta}{2}\right)$$

$$\sigma_z = \nu(\sigma_x + \sigma_y) \qquad\qquad (A.2)$$

$$\tau_{xz} = \tau_{yz} = 0$$

$$u = \frac{K_{II}}{G}\left[\frac{r}{2\pi}\right]^{\frac{1}{2}} \sin\frac{\theta}{2}\left(2 - 2\nu + \cos^2\frac{\theta}{2}\right)$$

$$v = \frac{K_{II}}{G}\left[\frac{r}{2\pi}\right]^{\frac{1}{2}} \cos\frac{\theta}{2}\left(1 + 2\nu + \sin^2\frac{\theta}{2}\right)$$

$$w = 0.$$

Equations (A.1) and (A.2) are written for plane strain; they can be changed to plane stress by writing $\sigma_z = 0$ and substituting

$$\frac{1 - \nu}{1 + \nu} \quad \text{for} \quad 1 - 2\nu \quad \text{and} \quad \frac{2}{1 + \nu} \quad \text{for} \quad 2 - 2\nu.$$

Mode III:

$$\tau_{xz} = - \frac{K_{III}}{(2\pi r)^{\frac{1}{2}}} \sin \frac{\theta}{2}$$

$$\tau_{yz} = \frac{K_{III}}{(2\pi r)^{\frac{1}{2}}} \cos \frac{\theta}{2}$$

$$\sigma_x = \sigma_y = \sigma_z = \tau_{xy} = 0 \tag{A.3}$$

$$w = \frac{K_{III}}{G} \left(\frac{2r}{\pi}\right)^{\frac{1}{2}} \sin \frac{\theta}{2}$$

$$u = v = 0.$$

Equations (A.1)-(A.3) are for static or slowly moving cracks and were obtained from the series expansion of the stress fields by neglecting higher terms in r. They can be regarded as a good approximation when r is small compared with the other dimensions of the body in the x-y plane and are exact as r tends to zero.

K_I is taken as positive when the crack surfaces move apart. A negative K_I only has meaning if the crack is regarded as a narrow slit because if the crack surfaces are pressed together the crack has no effect on the stress distribution. The signs of K_{II} and K_{III} are conventionally positive when displacements are as shown in Fig. 1.

Provided that the notch root radius is small compared with the notch depth, the stresses near the tip of a notch of conic outline are similar in form to those of a crack, but with the origin of r taken at a distance $\frac{\rho}{2}$ outwards from the centre of the notch root, radius ρ

$$\sigma_x = \frac{K_I}{(2\pi r)^{\frac{1}{2}}} \cos \frac{\theta}{2} \left(1 - \sin \frac{\theta}{2} \sin \frac{3\theta}{2}\right) - \frac{K_I}{(2\pi r)^{\frac{1}{2}}} \frac{\rho}{2r} \cos \frac{3\theta}{2}$$

$$\sigma_y = \frac{K_I}{(2\pi r)^{\frac{1}{2}}} \cos \frac{\theta}{2} \left(1 + \sin \frac{\theta}{2} \sin \frac{3\theta}{2}\right) + \frac{K_I}{(2\pi r)^{\frac{1}{2}}} \frac{\rho}{2r} \cos \frac{3\theta}{2} \tag{A.4}$$

$$\tau_{xy} = \frac{K_I}{(2\pi r)^{\frac{1}{2}}} \sin \frac{\theta}{2} \cos \frac{\theta}{2} \cos \frac{3\theta}{2} - \frac{K_I}{(2\pi r)^{\frac{1}{2}}} \frac{\rho}{2r} \sin \frac{3\theta}{2}.$$

For a notch which does not close under a given compressive load, a negative value of K_I has meaning. Note also the relationship between stress concentration factors and stress intensity factors

$$K_I = \lim_{\rho \to 0} \frac{\sigma_{max}}{2} (\pi \rho)^{\frac{1}{2}} \tag{A.5}$$

which provides an alternative definition of the stress intensity factor, where σ_{max} is the stress at the root of the notch.

The elastic stress field can be more accurately represented by including further terms. The first four terms for the opening mode, expressed in polar coordinates for compactness, are

$$\sigma_r = \frac{a_1}{4}\left(\frac{2a}{r}\right)^{\frac{1}{2}}\left(5\cos\frac{\theta}{2} - \cos\frac{3\theta}{2}\right) + a_2\cos^2\theta +$$

$$+ \frac{a_3}{4}\left(\frac{r}{2a}\right)^{\frac{1}{2}}\left(3\cos\frac{\theta}{2} + 5\cos\frac{5\theta}{2}\right) + \frac{a_4}{2}\left(\frac{r}{2a}\right)(\cos\theta + \cos 3\theta) + 0\left(\frac{r}{2a}\right)^{\frac{3}{2}}$$

$$\sigma_\theta = \frac{a_1}{4}\left(\frac{2a}{r}\right)^{\frac{1}{2}}\left(3\cos\frac{\theta}{2} + \cos\frac{3\theta}{2}\right) + a_2\sin^2\theta +$$

$$+ \frac{a_3}{3}\left(\frac{r}{2a}\right)^{\frac{1}{2}}\left(5\cos\frac{\theta}{2} - \cos\frac{5\theta}{2}\right) + 3a_4\left(\frac{r}{2a}\right)(\cos\theta - \cos 3\theta) + 0\left(\frac{r}{2a}\right)^{\frac{3}{2}} \qquad (A.6)$$

$$\tau_{r\theta} = \frac{a_1}{4}\left(\frac{2a}{r}\right)^{\frac{1}{2}}\left(\sin\frac{\theta}{2} + \sin\frac{3\theta}{2}\right) - \frac{a_2}{2}\sin 2\theta +$$

$$+ \frac{a_3}{4}\left(\frac{r}{2a}\right)^{\frac{1}{2}}\left(\sin\frac{\theta}{2} - \sin\frac{5\theta}{2}\right) + a_4\left(\frac{r}{2a}\right)(\sin\theta - 3\sin 3\theta) + 0\left(\frac{r}{2a}\right)^{\frac{3}{2}}.$$

The coefficients a_1, a_2, a_3 and a_4 have the dimensions of stress. Because

$$a_1 = \frac{K_I}{2(\pi a)^{\frac{1}{2}}} \qquad (A.7)$$

it is equivalent to the opening mode stress intensity factor K_I, this term dominates the stress field near the crack tip and controls crack initiation; the other terms become increasingly important further away from the crack tip. If the coefficient a_2 is positive, the crack will tend to deviate increasingly from its original path. If a_2 is negative the cracks will grow in their original paths. The sign of a_2 can be determined from the isochromatic fringes on a photoelastic model; if they lean forward in the direction of crack growth a_2 is negative and if they lean back it is positive. The terms in a_2 represent stresses parallel to the crack, and crack deviation can be prevented by applying a compressive load parallel to the crack.

REFERENCES

1   BILBY, B.A. Fracture. In Taplin, D.M.R. (ed.). Fracture 1977, 4, 1, Pergamon
    Press, (1978).

2   STANLEY, P. (ed.). Fracture mechanics in engineering practice. Applied Science
    Publishers, London, (1977).

3   FROST, N.E., MARSH, K.J. and POOK, L.P. Metal fatigue. Oxford: Clarendon Press,
    (1974).

4   BROEK, D. Elementary engineering fracture mechanics. Noordhoff Leyden, (1974).

5   KNOTT, J.F. Fundamentals of fracture mechanics. Butterworths, London, (1973).

6   POOK, L.P. NEL Report No. 465. East Kilbride, Glasgow: National Engineering
    Laboratory, (1970).

7   PARIS, P.C. and SIH, G.C. ASTM STP 381, 30, American Society for Testing and
    Materials, Philadelphia, Pa., (1965).

8   ROOKE, D.P. and CARTWRIGHT, D.J. A compendium of stress intensity factors. HMSO,
    (1976).

9   SIH, G.C. Handbook of stress intensity factors. Lehigh University, Bethlehem,
    Pa., (1973).

10 TADA, H., PARIS, P.C. and IRWIN, G.R. The stress analysis of cracks handbook.
    Del Research Corporation, Hellertown, Pa., (1973).

11 MICHAEL, C., and SEWARD, S.K. Int. J. Fract., 14, R151, (1978).

12 SMITH, R.A. and MILLER, K.J. Int. J. Mech. Sci., 19, 11, (1977).

13 BARRETT, J.D. Engng. Fract. Mech., 8, 711, (1976).

14 EFTIS, J., SUBRAMONIAN, N. and LIEBOWITZ, H. Engng. Fract. Mech., 9, 189, (1977).

15 Standard method of test for plane-strain fracture toughness of metallic materials.
    E399, 1978 Annual Book of ASTM Standards, Part 10. Philadelphia, Pa., (1978).

16 Methods for plane-strain fracture toughness (K_{Ic}) testing. BS 5447: British
    Standards Institution, (1977).

17 ASTM STP 527, (1973).

18 FORSYTH, P.J.E. Proc. Crack Propagation Symp., p. 76. Cranfield: College of
    Aeronautics, (1962).

19 Tentative method of test for constant-load-amplitude fatigue crack growth rates
    above 10^{-8} m/cycle. ASTM E 647-78T, Philadelphia, Pa., (1978).

20 HOEPNER, D.W. and KRUPP, W.E. Engng. Fract. Mech., 6, 47, (1974).

21 PARIS, P.C. and ERDOGAN, F. J. Bas. Engng., 85, 528, (1963).

22 POOK, L.P. J. Strain Anal., 10, 243, (1975).

23 POOK, L.P. and FROST, N.E. Int. J. Fract. Mech., 9, 53, (1973).

24 POULOSE, P.K., MORRAL, J.E. and McEVILY, A.J. In: Sih, G.C., Van Elst, H.C. and
    Broek, D. (eds). Prospects of fracture mechanics, p. 161. Noordhoff, Leyden,
    (1974).

25 RICE, J.R. ASTM STP 415, p. 247, (1967).

26 HUDAK, S.J., BUCCI, R.J., SAXENA, A. and MALCOLM, R.C. AFML-TR-78-40. Air Force Materials Lab., Wright-Patterson Air Force Base, (1978).

27 JOHNSON, H.H. and PARIS, P.C. Engng. Fract. Mech., 1, 3, (1968).

28 POOK, L.P. J. Soc. Env. Engng., 15-4, 3, (1976).

29 LITTLE, R.E. and JEBE, E.H. Statistical design of fatigue experiments. Applied Science Publishers Ltd, London, (1975).

30 SMITH, R.A. Int. J. Fract. Mech., 13, 717, (1977).

31 EVANS, W.T. and LUXMOORE, A.R. J. Strain Anal., 11, 177, (1976).

32 WILSON, W.K. ASTM STP 410, 75, (1966).

33 BROWN, W.F. and SRAWLEY, J.E. ASTM STP 410, 1, (1966).

34 SMITH, R.A. and MILLER, K.J. Int. J. Mech. Sci., 20, 201, (1978).

35 KITAGAWA, H. and TAKAHASHI, S. Proc. 2nd International Conference of Mechanical Behaviour of Material. p. 627, American Society for Metals, (1976).

36 POOK, L.P. and GREENAN, A.F. Proc. Fatigue Testing and Design Conf., City University, London, 1976, 2, 30.1. Buntingford, Herts: Society of Environmental Engineers, (1976).

37 CLARK, W.G. ASTM STP 601, 138, (1976)

38 SWEDLOW, J.L. ASTM STP 601, 506, (1976).

39 IIDA, S. and KOBAYASHI, A.S. J. Bas. Engng., 91, 764, (1969).

40 ERGODAN, F. and SIH, G.C. J. Bas. Engng., 85, 519, (1963).

41 SIH, G.C. and CHA, B.C.K. Engng. Fract. Mech., 6, 699, (1974).

42 RADAJ, D. and HEIB, M. Materialprüf, 20, 256, (1978).

43 DIXON, J.R. Proc. Conf. Physical Basis of Yield and Fracture. Oxford: Institute of Physics and Physical Society, 6, (1966).

44 POOK, L.P. Engng. Fract. Mech., 3, 205, (1971).

45 POOK, L.P. Engng. Fract. Mech., 4, 483, (1972).

APPLICATION OF FRACTURE MECHANICS TO INDUSTRIAL PROBLEMS

G. J. Neate, G. M. Sparkes, A. T. Stewart*
and H. D. Williams

*Central Electricity Generating Board, Midlands Region Scientific
Services Department, Ratcliffe-on-Soar, Nottingham NG11 0EE, U.K.*
**South Western Region Scientific Services Department,
Bridgwater Road, Bristol BS13 8AN, U.K.

Summary

The development of the science of fracture mechanics in the early sixties has
made it possible to characterise brittle-fracture, fatigue, creep and stress-corrosion
behaviour of materials and hence to assess the integrity of components which contain
cracks and similar defects. In the Central Electricity Generating Board the application of fracture mechanics to service problems has been vigorously pursued for a
number of years and has provided considerable economic benefits. This paper presents
three typical case histories.

The first describes the analysis of fatigue cracking in a large (500 MW) generator
rotor which was returned to service in its cracked state. It then operated satisfactorily until its withdrawal from service some two years later, having saved some
£16 million which would have been the additional generating cost using smaller, less
efficient, units. Creep cracking in CrMoV pipework welds provides the second example,
where criteria for acceptance of tolerable defects had to be developed. Finally, an
investigation after the failure of a steam turbine disc, due to stress-corrosion
cracking, led to a programme of examination and rehabilitation of many similar machines.

In each of these cases particular consideration is given to the fracture mechanics
aspects of the problems and areas of further development are discussed.

1)   **INTRODUCTION**

Components and structures operating within the boilers, turbines and ancillary equipment of conventional fossil-fired power stations are designed on a safe-life basis. Lives in excess of 150,000 hours are required from stations and together with the high capital cost of plant this precludes prototype testing.

Over such long times small deviations from the design condition can produce deformation and cracking. Such deviations can arise from inadequacies of design or during manufacture and erection, commissioning, operation or maintenance and repair. This paper is concerned with the assessment of cracks discovered in components during service. Three case histories are presented describing cracking in different components, namely an alternator rotor, welded joints in steam pipes and low-pressure turbine discs. The causes of cracking vary and separately involve fatigue, creep and stress corrosion. Particular consideration is given to the fracture mechanics aspects of the problems and areas of further development are discussed.

2)   **FATIGUE CRACKING IN A LARGE GENERATOR ROTOR**

  2.1   Introduction

Many components in power plant are subjected to high-frequency, low-amplitude fatigue stresses and can accumulate in excess of 10^{10} cycles in their lifetime. The recognition that, for most materials, there exists a threshold stress-intensity range below which fatigue cracks do not grow is of particular importance for such components since assessments can then be made as to their long-term tolerance to high-frequency loading.

A good example of a fracture-mechanics safety assessment is provided by a incident in 1975 in the CEGB's Midlands Region plant where extensive fatigue cracking was discovered in the alternator rotor of a 500 MW turbo-generator.[1] The rotor (Fig 1) has a centre section 6.5m long and 1.1m diameter and is machined from a single forging. Two longitudinal banks of 14 slots are machined along its length to accept the copper windings leaving two solid pole pieces between them. A series of transverse slots (inertia slots) is cut into each pole face to counter the effect of the winding slots and make the stiffness of the rotor approximately uniform about any transverse axis, thereby reducing vibration. The rotor spins at 3,000 rev/min in normal operation in an atmosphere of hydrogen to assist cooling.

  2.2   The Cracking Incident

The rotor was examined at a routine outage after being in service for about six years and it was found that extensive overheating of the rotor had occurred, particularly at the ends of the inertia slots (Fig 2) where it was

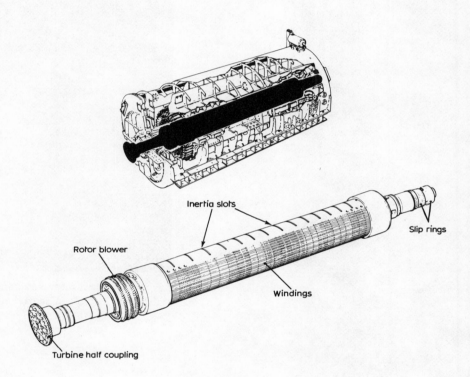

Fig.   1   The Alternator of a 500MW Generating Unit.

Fig. 2   Overall view of damaged rotor
          showing overheating marks at
          ends of inertia slots.

Photograph by courtesy of G.E.C.
Turbine Generators Ltd

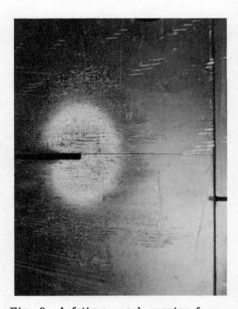

Fig. 3   A fatigue crack running from
          the end of an inertia slot across
          to the winding slot.

estimated that temperatures of around 800°C had been reached.   More
seriously, cracks could be seen emanating from the inertia slots travelling
along the surface to the adjacent winding slots (Fig 3) a distance of about
110 mm.   Ultrasonic examination of the rotor showed that there were cracks
at all inertia slots except those at each end of the rotor; in these four slots
only one small crack was found.   The other cracks were surprisingly similar
in profile all along the rotor, the maximum depth being about 180 mm below
the surface.

The overheating damage was consistent with the rotor having been
subjected to a large "negative-phase-sequence" electrical overload.   Examination of station records showed that such an event had occurred during
recommissioning tests in 1969 when the rotor had completed less than six-
months service.   The heating during this incident introduced high residual
tensile stresses approaching the ultimate tensile strength of the rotor steel
at the ends of the inertia slots.   The presence of such high residual stresses
was confirmed by strain-gauge measurements at one of the uncracked slot
ends.[1]

2.3   Fractographic Examination

Examination of samples machined from inertia slots at the centre and at
the ends of the rotor body confirmed that crack initiation had occurred by a
ductile "over-load" mechanism giving defects about 8 mm long (Fig 4).
Subsequent crack propagation in the rotor had occurred by fatigue under the
influence of the cyclic bending stress imposed by its own weight (66t).

Well-defined "beach-marks" could be seen on the fatigue fracture of the
small crack in the end inertia slot (Fig 4) and had been produced on
occasions when the rotor had been stopped.   As the rotor slows down,
excitation of resonant frequencies produces small increases in stress which
give rise to the beach-marks.

The spacing of these beach-marks initially increases away from the slot
end but, approaching the crack tip, they progressively become closer together
until they are separated by a distance of less than 30 μm (Fig 5).   By
comparing the position of the beach-marks with the operating history of the
rotor subsequent to the overheating it is possible to estimate crack growth
rates; such an analysis is shown in Fig 6.   Crack growth accelerated steadily
during the first 35 mm of growth to a maximum rate of about 3 x 10^{-7} mm
cycle^{-1}, beyond which it steadily decelerated to a very low level or even

G. J. Neate *et al.*

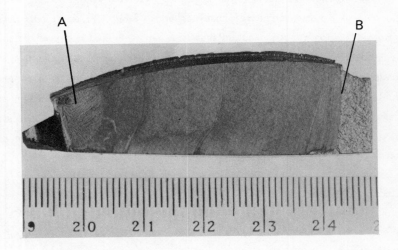

Fig. 4   The fracture surface of an end inertia
slot crack.   The ductile crack initiation
can be clearly seen at A.   Several beach-
marks are evident on the fracture which
become very close together near the crack
tip   (at B).

Fig. 5.   A scanning electron micrograph showing
the close beach-mark spacing in the region
of the crack tip. The picture shows an
area of 1.35 mm^2

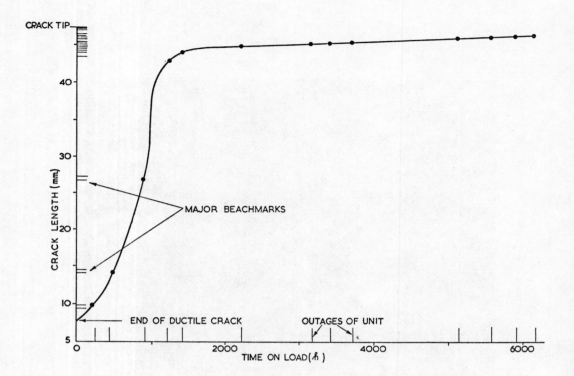

Fig. 6 Beachmark analysis for crack at end inertia slot

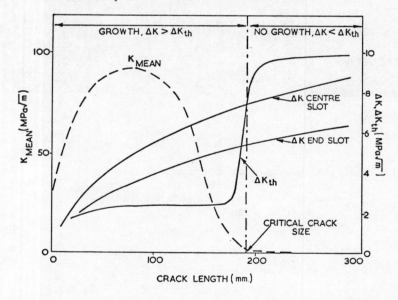

Fig. 7 Variation of ΔK, ΔK_{th} and K_{mean} with crack depth for end and
centre inertia slot cracks.

arrested altogether.

No beach-marks were apparent in the sample from a central inertia slot; this implies that the crack growth rate must have been much faster here since the crack front must have travelled the whole width of the sample (70 mm) before the first plant shut-down. This is consistent with the much higher bending stress at this position which would cause a ten-fold increase in fatigue crack growth rate.

2.4 Fracture Mechanics Analysis

At the time of the discovery of cracking all the cracks were of very similar dimensions. This can only be explained if the cracks at the centre of the rotor arrested much earlier than those at the ends. This behaviour can be readily explained in terms of fracture-mechanics concepts.

The threshold stress intensity range (ΔK_{th}) is dependent on the mean stress intensity, particularly at mean stress intensities of less than 10 MPa$\sqrt{m}$. At the ends of the inertia slots the initial mean stress was high due to the large residual tensile stresses induced by the heating effects. As the crack propagated it entered material of progressively lower mean stress and ΔK_{th} steadily increased. Eventually, the stress intensity range (ΔK) became equal to ΔK_{th} and crack arrest occurred under normal operating conditions (Fig 7). Some crack growth may still have occurred during start-up and shut-down of the rotor due to the higher bending stresses experienced at critical rotor speeds. However, in view of the small number of cycles experienced in such regimes, the extent of crack growth would be very small. The similarity of crack sizes at most inertia slots arose because this situation occurs at a similar depth at all points along the rotor, the position of crack arrest being controlled predominantly by the mean stress intensity rather than the cyclic stress-intensity range (Fig 7).

2.5 Return to Service

At the time the cracking was discovered, there was no spare rotor available and a replacement would have taken at least two years to manu-facture. As it was known that the rotor had operated successfully for more than six years after crack initiation had occurred and since a detailed metallurgical examination had concluded that, in all probability, the cracks were no longer growing under the normal operating stresses, it was decided to return the rotor to service until such time as a new rotor was available.

The possibility that the cracks were still propagating at the centre of the rotor, where the bending stress is highest, could not be ruled out. Further cracking would change the stiffness of the rotor and, it was calculated that, provided vibration levels were monitored at intervals of about 400 hours, any deterioration in integrity would be detected well before a catastrophic failure could occur.

The rotor operated satisfactorily for more than two years, during which time no significant changes in vibration behaviour were observed. Following its withdrawal from service, re-examination using ultrasonic techniques showed that little change in overall crack dimensions had occurred, demonstrating the soundness of the decision to return it to service.

If the rotor had not been used in this interim period, the additional cost of replacing the electricity using smaller less efficient units would have been about £16 million.

3) CREEP CRACKING IN CrMoV PIPEWORK WELDS

3.1 Introduction

In 1968 a weld joining a large diameter forged adaptor piece to a steam chest failed catastophically, after approximately 9,000 hours service, releasing a large quantity of steam into the turbine hall. The steam chest and forging were of $1Cr1Mo0.3V$ and $\frac{1}{2}Cr\frac{1}{2}Mo\frac{1}{4}V$ respectively and had been joined with $2\frac{1}{4}Cr1Mo$ weld metal. Since this original incident, a number of other events involving the leakage of steam have occurred, although in these cases failure was not accompanied by complete severance of the joints.

Subsequent investigation of the original failure showed it to have been due to the growth of a large defect in the heat-affected zone (HAZ) on the steam-chest side of the weld which had formed during stress-relief heat treatment and which had therefore been present when the joint entered service (Fig 8). The discovery of cracks of comparable severity in similar joints on the same and sister units, all of which had escaped detection when the welds were radiographed prior to commissioning, prompted the systematic inspection of $CrMoV/2\frac{1}{4}Cr1Mo$ pipework welds using ultrasonic techniques. This programme was instituted in 1970 and it soon became clear that a high proportion of welds was defective. For both economic and practical reasons, the response to the situation could not be to repair all joints found to be cracked and it was therefore necessary to define some criteria for the acceptance of defects

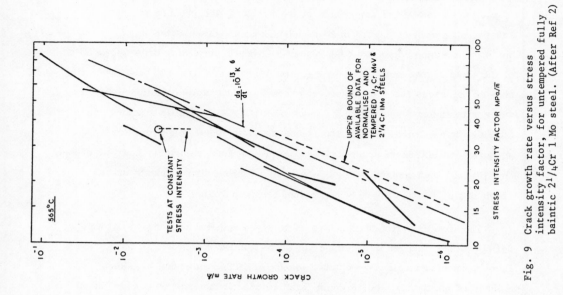

Fig. 9 Crack growth rate versus stress
intensity factor, for untempered fully
baintic $2^1/_4$Cr 1 Mo steel. (After Ref 2)

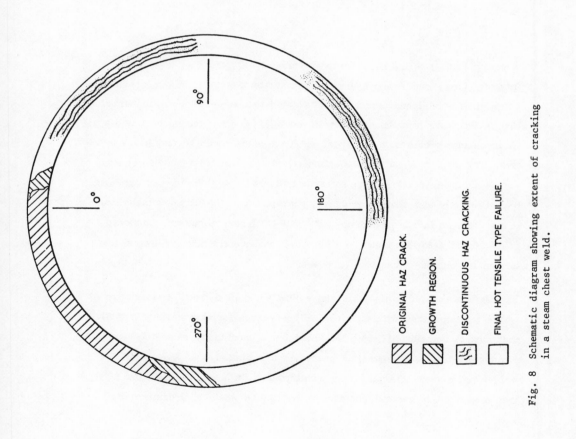

Fig. 8 Schematic diagram showing extent of cracking
in a steam chest weld.

for specified periods of further service.

3.2   The Approach Adopted

At the time of the emergence of the problem, the phenomenon of subcritical growth of cracks in material undergoing creep deformation had not been investigated to any great extent and hence there was little appreciation of the factors governing crack-propagation behaviour.   The approach eventually adopted to assess the significance of cracks was therefore conditioned by the success of linear elastic fracture mechanics (LEFM) to brittle fracture and fatigue.   It was reasoned that the stress intensity factor might provide adequate correlation of creep crack propagation rates in materials of low creep ductility and high matrix strength where only limited displacements due to creep might be expected to occur in the crack tip region.

The first material of this type to be investigated within the CEGB was $2\frac{1}{4}$Cr1Mo pipe steel in the untempered, fully–bainitic condition.   Siverns and Price[2]   tested single-edge-notched-tension (SENT) specimens containing notches of about 0.1 relative depth (a/w) at 565°C (the maximum main steam temperature in coal-fired plant) and obtained a correlation of the form

$$\frac{da}{dt} = AK^n \tag{1}$$

where $\frac{da}{dt}$ (mh^{-1}) is the crack propagation rate, K (MPa$\sqrt{m}$) the stress intensity factor and A and n material constants (Fig 9).   However, since the correlation established for this steel related to a material condition simulating that in the HAZ of a non stress-relieved weld, it was considered that its use in assessing defects in fully stress-relieved welds would be unduly conservative.   Values for A and n in equation (1) of 10^{-13} and 6 respectively gave somewhat lower crack growth rates than Siverns and Price[2] had obtained experimentally and also provided an upper bound to the data available from a few tests on SENT specimens   (a/w = 0.1) of normalized and tempered $\frac{1}{2}$CrMoV and $2\frac{1}{4}$Cr1Mo material (Fig 9).   Consequently this expression was chosen for defect assessment purposes.

It was decided to use this single "law" for all defects, irrespective of where they occurred within a weld.   The reasons for this were principally that lack of data for $2\frac{1}{4}$Cr1Mo weld metal and uncertainty as to the controlling parameters in ductile materials precluded formulation of a growth law for weld-metal defects.   Another important reason for using a single law was that it was not in general possible to distinguish whether circumferential defects lying close to the fusion line actually lay in the weld metal or in the HAZ so that it was always necessary in practice to assume these to be in the latter location and hence to use a growth law appropriate to brittle materials.

It was possible, however, to treat circumferential defects differently from transverse weld metal defects with respect to the active stress tending to cause growth. Thus any pipework system stresses were only of concern in relation to circumferential cracks, whereas the highest pressure stresses were experienced by transverse defects. The same value for the welding residual stress was assumed in respect of both types of defect and, as a means of introducing a conservative feature into the analysis, no allowance was made for the relaxation of this stress in service. The values of the various components of stress assumed for each defect type are summarised in Table I and the calculated allowable crack sizes are given in Table II.

3.3   The Benefits Derived

The post-commissioning inspection programme in the Midlands Region showed that a high percentage of welds was defective, many of which would have required immediate repair had British Standard 2633 (1966), which does not allow any crack-like defects in high temperature/high pressure pipework weldments, been strictly adhered to. This would have placed an intolerable strain on man-power resources and also could only have been achieved at considerable cost, the replacement generation cost for a 500 MW unit being approximately £20,000 per day.

As a result of applying the defect-assessment procedure described above, some 2,500 welds which had developed crack-like defects have been allowed to remain in service in Midlands Region plant. These have been left in service either for a few thousand hours to be repaired at a scheduled plant outage or indefinitely subject, where necessary, to further periodic ultrasonic inspections. In cost terms, therefore, the benefit has been considerable, with the estimated net saving to the Midlands Region being £3.75 million excluding any allowance for costs associated with replacement generation costs or failures that might have occurred had no repairs been carried out.

Application of the acceptance standard has, nevertheless, resulted in approximately 10% of defective welds being repaired. This repair rate is not insignificant and experience suggests that it is much greater than that which would have actually been sufficient to assure system integrity. Thus no weld that has been assessed has subsequently failed or leaked steam and, as far as can be determined from successive inspections of welds, defects have generally grown at less rapid rates than predicted. The majority of welds have now been inspected at least once so that the largest benefit potentially achievable from a reduction in repair rate is in respect of stations under construction rather than existing plant. However, the re-inspection of welds in commissioned plant containing cracks of only relatively small size has accounted for the expenditure of substantial sums (about £150,000 annually in Midlands Region) and hence this is also an area where large cost savings are possible if the conservatism inherent in the assessment procedure could be reduced. In the absence of alternative models for creep crack growth, statistical methods of analysing data on defect sizes and weld failures are presently being developed towards this end.

A benefit resulting from the research programmes has been the appreciation of the factors which affect the propensity for cracks to form during stress-relief and also the general tolerance of welds to defects. Thus a high residual element content in the parent material has been shown to lead to HAZs that are prone to cracking and which have a generally low defect tolerance, whereas the converse characteristics are shown by well-tempered fine-grained HAZs. Recognition of the importance of obtaining refined structures in the HAZ has led to the development of improved weld procedures which ensure this and it is hoped that adherence to these will result in the problem largely being overcome. Although it is somewhat early to judge whether this expectation is being fully realised, present indications are encouraging.

3.4   Retrospective Appraisal

It has become clear in recent years that an LEFM approach to the assessment of cracks in bodies operating in the creep range is not valid in that the stress intensity factor does not provide correlation of crack growth rate data independent of crack-component geometry. Thus it is now apparent that component failure times and crack growth rates are a function of crack-component geometry and applied load and can only be determined from a knowledge of the multi-axial stress rupture criteria obeyed by the material of interest and of the stress distribution developed ahead of a notch or crack.[3-5] Relationships of the form of equation (1) determined from tests on laboratory samples are, therefore, only of use in comparing the effects of changes in material properties and microstructure on crack propagation and rupture behaviour (and then strictly only if samples of identical dimensions are tested in each case).

In the present case, the success of the approach adopted to the assessment of defect significance is the result of a deliberately conservative value having been chosen for the welding residual stress and of treating this as a primary load. Had these over-pessimistic assumptions not been made, non-conservative estimates of the sizes of allowable defects might have been arrived at with potentially serious consequences. This example is thus illustrative of a more general point in that, when undertaking an assessment of the significance of defects on the integrity of any component, it is only possible to work within the limits of knowledge existing at the time. Where there is any doubt as to the validity of the scientific and/or engineering principles being applied, inherently conservative features should be incorporated into the assessment procedure to guard against a non-conservative result being obtained.

4) STRESS-CORROSION CRACKING IN STEAM TURBINE DISCS
   4.1 Introduction
        In 1969, after approximately 30,000h service, one of the 60 MW low-pressure turbines at Hinkley Point "A" Power Station suffered a catastrophic failure whilst undergoing a routine overspeed test at 3200 rev/min.[6]   After a lengthy investigation and reconstruction of the turbine the cause of the failure was identified as stress-corrosion cracking at the keyway of one of the shrunk-on discs. The investigation into the consequences [7] of the failure led to the formulation of a national examination and rehabilitation programme of low-pressure turbines from 60 MW non-reheat machines.[8]

        This section describes the role of fracture mechanics in this important industrial problem. In 4.2 its part in the Hinkley Point "A" failure investigation is described and in 4.3 its contribution to the formulation of the national 60 MW turbine examination programme is discussed.

   4.2 Role of Fracture Mechanics in the Hinkley Point "A" Failure Investigation
        The evaluation of critical defect sizes for radial cracks at the keyways of heavy-section discs can be made using linear-elastic fracture mechanics. The calculation of stress intensities for the semi-circular keyways of the Hinkley Point "A" machines is described by Kalderon[6].   For a crack of semi-elliptical aspect ratio at the crown of a disc keyway the stress intensity, K_I, is given approximately by:

$$K_I = \sigma \sqrt{\frac{\pi}{1.12} a} \left[1 + \frac{K_t - 1}{(1 + a/\rho)^3} \right] \qquad (2)$$

where σ = disc-bore tangential stress (362 MPa at the failure speed of 3200 rev/min);

      a = keyway crack depth;

      K_t = stress concentration factor for semi-circular keyway (3);

and ρ = radius of the keyway crown (20.6 mm).

The stress intensities calculated using equation (2) are shown in Figure 10. The full line represents stress intensities calculated on the assumption that in the absence of the crack conditions would have remained elastic. However for short cracks this is not the case as the local stress given by

$$\sigma \left[1 + \frac{K_t - 1}{(1 + a/\rho)^3} \right]$$

would exceed the yield point of the steel (690 MPa).[6] The dotted line makes allowance for yielding by assuming that the local stress can never exceed the yield point. This is an oversimplification but, at the time, it was not considered worthwhile introducing elastic-plastic refinements into the determination of stress intensity factors when considerable variability was observed in the values of fracture toughness with which the stress intensities were to be compared.

The material of the failed disc at Hinkley Point "A" was 3CrMo steel made by the acid-open-hearth method. The discs were chemically segregated, temper embrittled and had a wide scatter of fracture toughness with a minimum value about 40 MPa$\sqrt{}$m. Therefore, from Fig 10, the fracture-mechanics assessment predicts that a defect at the keyway of only 1-2 mm deep would be likely to cause brittle fracture on overspeed. This prediction was vindicated by the fact that the stress corrosion defect which initiated the Hinkley Point disc failure was 1.5 mm deep.[6]

Consequently the application of fracture mechanics theory to the Hinkley Point "A" failure was successful in that it enabled a quantitative explanation to be given to the initiation of catastrophic brittle fracture from a small crack.

4.3 Role of Fracture Mechanics in Formulating the Turbine Examination Programme

Following the Hinkley Point "A" failure a fracture-mechanics survey [7] was made of all rotors of broadly similar design and dimensions. The

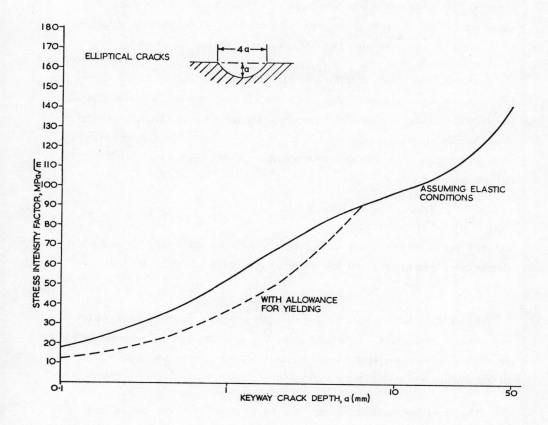

Fig. 10 Stress intensity at Hinkley Point disc keyway at rotor speed of
3200 rev/min (based on Kalderon[6]).

approach used was to compare the expected disc fracture toughness with the calculated stress intensity for two arbitrary keyway crack depths of 1.5 and 3 mm. This comparison was then used to classify the degree of risk, assuming the existence of stress-corrosion cracking but without any judgement as to whether conditions for crack initiation and propagation existed.

Integrity appraisals of this type required fracture toughness data and a knowledge of any variation of this toughness with temperature and with position and direction within the forging. However, for most of the discs in question, there was an absence of explicit data of this sort. Fortunately it was possible to infer fracture toughness data from Charpy V-notch impact test results. The correlation used was:

$$K_{Ic} = \frac{6600}{60 - B} \quad MPa\sqrt{m} \tag{3}$$

where B is the excess temperature (^{O}C) - namely the difference between the disc service temperature and the fracture appearance transition temperature (FATT).

FATT data had not been recorded on all the discs involved so a multiple-regression analysis was carried out using the available data on composition, mechanical properties, heat treatment, steelmaking process and disc size in an attempt to predict values of FATT.[7]

The above approach led to the examination in 1970 of two rotors from reheat machines which were deemed to be in the highest risk category. However in both cases the disc bores and keyways were found entirely crack free. This led to the conclusion that environmental factors were important and the problem could not be treated solely in terms of disc properties. The most outstanding difference between the Hinkley Point "A" machines and those that showed no cracking is in the steam cycle: the reheat turbines operate in dry steam, the non-reheat turbines in wet steam. Consequently it was concluded that stress corrosion was associated with wet steam and would be confined to the early stage discs of non-reheat machines.[7]

The fracture mechanics assessments showed that the non-reheat sets with the greatest risk of failure were in the 60 MW rating range. Consequently in 1972 a national examination/rehabilitation programme of all the machines in this category was instigated.[8]

At the time there was little surplus generating capacity and there was an urgent need to eliminate the risk whilst maintaining a high plant availability. However it was envisaged that information obtained from the continuing examination programme would enable engineering judgements to be made which could influence the timing and the extent of the rest of the rehabilitation programme. It was also anticipated that fracture mechanics safe-life assessments, based on the results from the extensive parallel research programme on stress corrosion crack growth rates and fracture toughness, would provide a quantitative basis for many of the engineering judgements necessary.

For example the discs on one of the CEGB's generic type of 60 MW turbine were manufactured from 3NiCrMoV steel made by the basic-electric-arc method and were found to have a consistently high fracture toughness with a typical value of 120 MPa$\sqrt{\text{m}}$.[8] The disc-bore tangential stress at 3200 rev/min for this type of rotor is 340 MPa and the radius of the disc keyway crown is 9.53 mm. Hence, from equation (2), the critical keyway crack depth for brittle fracture at overspeed is about 40 mm. The maximum rate of stress-corrosion crack propagation for this steel, measured in pre-cracked specimens exposed in steam rigs utilizing power station or laboratory steam, is 10^{-7} mm/s [8] (i.e. 3 mm/year). Consequently safe-life assessments for this type of rotor enabled a priority for examination to be established which enabled delays in the rehabilitation programme to be accommodated.

5) ## CONCLUDING REMARKS

The histories described above demonstrate the variety of problems encountered in operating plant to which fracture mechanics can be applied. The problems represent deviations from design which threatened the safety of plant or system efficiency and in which financial loss was prevented or minimised by the actions taken.

Problems such as these have a high degree of complexity and a range of unknowns which render it difficult to model the situation without making further assumptions. While there are occasions when making the most pessimistic of assumptions yields a practically useful result, more often a careful choice has to be made of the values for parameters and the sensitivity of the result to those choices analysed.

Within the industrial environment the solutions devised by the specialist in
fracture mechanics are executed by other departments responsible for the operation
or maintenance of the plant.   Consequently an early indication of the likely solution
is important.   Rapid approximate methods of analysis are particularly valuable
followed by confirmation later by more rigorous computation.   It is also important
to establish at an early stage any constraints of time, money and manpower which
other departments recognise in the situation.

There are three general areas in which fracture mechanics are involved in
industrial problems: these are failure diagnosis, defect assessment and reliability
analysis.   Each area has its own difficulties and contains scope for further
development.

Failure investigations suffer where evidence is destroyed in the incident.
Information on the precise geometry, or the distribution of residual stresses and
erection loads may be lost leaving recourse only to measurements of these parameters on similar surviving components.   However, a fracture surface is usually
recovered from a failure and it is believed that there is more information locked
away on it than can currently be interpreted.   The case history of the alternator
rotor illustrated the use of a beach-mark analysis and a better understanding of the
minimum changes in stress, environment and temperature necessary to cause a
beach-mark would improve interpretive ability.   Valuable guides to the mechanism
and rate of crack growth and the crack tip stress intensity factor can be obtained
from examination of the morphology of the fracture surface in the scanning electron
microscope, using parameters such as the ratio of intercrystalline to
transcrystalline fracture and the routine examination of laboratory samples could
extend this diagnostic approach.   There is also opportunity to develop new techniques
and one   recent success is the use of oxide dating which can provide information on
temperature, environment and crack growth rate from fracture surface oxides. [10]

In assessing cracked components for their residual lives and likely mode of
final failure, steady improvements have been made as the data base of materials
properties has widened and as computer technology has speeded the process of stress
analysis.   It has often been found that information on operating stresses at elevated
temperatures is inadequate and recent developments with high-temperature strain
gauges are now providing some of the answers.   Similarly the measurement of
residual stress and the provision of samples of the defects adds much confidence to
the recognition of non-propagating cracks.   There is scope for further improvement
in non-destructive testing (NDT) particularly in the assessment of the accuracy of

defect sizing; this requires the provision of samples from service for NDT evaluation and subsequent confirmation by sectioning. Defective components can be returned to service with more confidence if an early warning of their growth can be obtained. This stimulates a continuing interest in the development of monitoring techniques with such methods as vibration analysis, on-load NDT, leak detection, acoustic emission, crack-opening-displacements meters etc.

In an industry with thousands of like components, the failure of one may have widespread implications on the reliability of the rest of the population. The fracture mechanics practitioner may therefore be called upon to assess the likelihood of failure elsewhere and to formulate the strategic options available. These can include setting priorities for NDT inspection as in the case of turbine discs, limiting operational parameters such as temperature or pressure, proof testing, continuous monitoring or removal from service pending inspection or repair. A pilot investigation can provide statistical information on the incidence of cracking for assessing priorities and records of fabrication history compiled at the constructional phase can be invaluable in service problems even 10-15 years after commissioning.

Increased attention is being given to the validation of defect assessment approaches from the observations of defect behaviour on plant by NDT inspection. Within the CEGB this is being co-ordinated between the five Regions at the Component Integrity Centre which is based in the Midlands Region. This operates within selected problem areas by compiling data on the incidence or growth of defects on plant and investigating these in terms of current fracture under-standing so that the recommendations can be made from a broad practical base.

The application of fracture mechanics to service problems has been pursued vigorously in the CEGB for a number of years. It has proved most successful when combined with other approaches to the problems and has provided significant economic benefits.

6) ACKNOWLEDGEMENT

This paper is published by permission of the Central Electricity Generating Board (Midlands Region).

7) REFERENCES

1) A T STEWART, K A HAINES and H D WILLIAMS, Conf on "Fracture Mechanics in Engineering Practice". University of Sheffield, 14-16th Sept, 1976 Paper 21. Applied Science Publishers, Barking pp 323-338, (1977)

2)   M J SIVERNS and A T PRICE, Nature, 228 (5273), 760 (1970)

3)   G J NEATE, J Mat Sci and Eng 33, 165 (1978)

4)   D R HAYHURST, F A LECKIE and C J MORRISON, Proc Roy Soc, Series A, 460, 243 (1978)

5)   B L FREEMAN and G J NEATE, J Mat Sci and Eng, 36, 241 (1978)

6)   D KALDERON, Proc Instn Mech Engrs, 186, 341-377, (1972)

7)   J L GRAY, Proc Instn Mech Engrs, 186, 379-390, (1972)

8)   J M HODGE and I L MOGFORD, Proc Instn Mech Engrs, 193, 93-109, (1979)

9)   G T JONES, Proc Instn Mech Engrs, 186, 31-32/72, D122, (1972)

10)   L W PINDER, CEGB Midlands Region, Private Communication, (1979)

TABLE I

Values of Stress Components Used in Equation (1)

Defect Type	Pressure Stress (MPa)	Weld Residual Stress (MPa)	System Stress (MPa)	Total (MPa)
Circumferential	15	60	30	105
Transverse	30	60	-	90

TABLE II

Allowable Defect Sizes for 100,000 hours Operation in Pipe-Pipe Joints of 60 mm Wall Thickness

Defect Orientation	Defect Type	Defect Size, mm
Circumferential	Surface, semi-circular	3
	Embedded, circular	6
Transverse	Surface, semi-circular	4
	Embedded, circular	7

GREEN'S FUNCTIONS IN FRACTURE MECHANICS

D. J. Cartwright and D. P. Rooke*

Department of Mechanical Engineering, University of Southampton, Southampton S09 5NH, U.K.
*Materials Department, Royal Aircraft Establishment, Farnborough, Hampshire GU14 6TD, U.K.

Summary

The use of Green's functions in the determination of stress intensity factors is described and applied to the solution of problems in fracture mechanics. Methods of obtaining further Green's functions from existing ones are presented. It is shown that several commonly used simple methods of determining stress intensity factors can be expressed in terms of approximate Green's functions. Many important Green's functions are presented and some of these are used to solve several problems of practical importance to the aerospace industry e.g. cracks in stiffened sheets and cracks in pin-loaded lug-joints.

1. Introduction

Many structures will contain crack-like flaws before they enter service or will develop them during their service life. Fracture mechanics provides a means of quantifying the growth of cracks thereby enabling the safety of the structure, during its service life, to be assured and the most economic inspection intervals to be adopted.

The basic assumption of fracture mechanics is that the growth of cracks is controlled by the stress field near its tip; with certain limitations this field is characterised by the 'stress intensity factor'. The application of fracture mechanics to a crack problem requires that the stress intensity factor for the crack be known. The determination of this factor is often easier than a general stress analysis as only the stresses near the crack-tip need be determined. Because of the wide application of the stress intensity factor approach many methods of evaluating them for various types of cracked configurations have been developed. These methods, both theoretical and experimental, have been reviewed [1, 2, 3].

The choice of a method of solution for any given practical configuration will depend on the following: time available; the required accuracy; the cost and the frequency with which the solution is to be used. If the configuration is complex it may be necessary to use an experimental method as well or instead of a theoretical one. Some methods [3] are especially suited to a wide variety of crack configurations. The techniques based on Green's functions are of this type and offer scope for further development and application. The Green's function technique is presented in this paper and two areas where they are of particular use are described. The first is a systematic use of known Green's functions to develop those for more complex configurations. The second is the development of engineering methods of evaluating stress intensity factors by approximating Green's functions.

Some applications of the technique are described, in particular cracks at loaded holes and cracks in stiffened structures. The Green's functions developed give an insight into the importance of different types of loading and structure and demonstrate the versatility of the technique. A collection of some of the more useful Green's functions are presented in section 5.

2. Basic principles of Green's functions

The Green's function, first postulated by George Green in 1828, is defined as the response of a system to a standard input. The standard input is usually in the form of an impulse. Stedman [4] has reviewed the use of Green's functions in many fields of mathematical physics. Some examples of classical Green's functions are: the voltage output, as a function of time, of an electronic circuit in response to an input voltage pulse; the dynamic response of a mechanical system set in motion by an impulsive blow; the stress field produced in an elastic body in response to a force acting at a point in the body. If the body in the last example contains a crack, the stress intensity factor at the crack tip which arises in response to the point force may be considered as a special case of a Green's function. The important property of these functions is that, when suitably defined, they contain all the essential information about the system. They can thus be used to obtain the response of the system to any input by considering it as being composed of large numbers of small impulses. The total response is the sum of all the individual responses due to each input impulse acting separately. For the Green's function representation to be valid the system must have the following properties:

i)   Causality - if there is no input there is no response

ii) Invariance - the response to a given input is always the same

iii) Linearity - if the response to input I_1 is R_1 and the response to
        I_2 is R_2 then the response to $I_1 + I_2$ is $R_1 + R_2$.

These three conditions lead to the following result for the response $R(\eta)$ to a general input $I(\eta)$:

$$R(\eta) = \int I(\eta) G(\eta - \eta') d\eta' \qquad (1)$$

where $G(\eta - \eta')$ is defined as the Green's function and is a function of the differences $\eta - \eta'$. The variables η and η' may represent positions and/or time.

3. Stress intensity factors as Green's functions

The stress intensity factor is known [5] for the two-dimensional problem of a cracked sheet containing a crack of length $2a$ which has localized forces acting at points on its surfaces (see figure 1). If the forces act normal to the crack faces, i.e. a force per unit thickness of P acting on one face and an equal and opposite force acting on the other face, then the opening mode stress intensity factor K_I at tip A is given by

$$K_I = \frac{P}{\sqrt{\pi a}} \left[\frac{a + x_0}{a - x_0} \right]^{\frac{1}{2}} \equiv \frac{P}{\sqrt{\pi a}} G(x_0) \qquad (2)$$

where x_0 is the distance of the point of application of the force from the centre of the crack. If forces Q act tangentially to the crack faces then the sliding-mode stress intensity factor K_{II} at tip A is given by

$$K_{II} = \frac{Q}{\sqrt{\pi a}} \left[\frac{a + x_0}{a - x_0} \right]^{\frac{1}{2}} \equiv \frac{Q}{\sqrt{\pi a}} G(x_0) \qquad (3)$$

For tip B at the other end of the crack the stress intensity factors are obtained from equations (2) and (3) by replacing 'x_0' with '$-x_0$'. The function $G(x_0)$ in equations (2) and (3) can be used as a Green's function to obtain stress intensity factors for cracks subjected to boundary pressures acting on the crack faces. If a pressure $p(x)$, $-a \leqslant x \leqslant a$, acts normal to the crack faces the stress intensity factor is given by

$$K_I = \frac{1}{\sqrt{\pi a}} \int_{-a}^{a} p(x) \, G(x) \, dx \qquad (4)$$

For the case of $p(x) = p$ (a constant), equation (3) gives the well known result $K_I = p\sqrt{\pi a}$. A similar result can be obtained for a distribution of shearing forces on the crack. For symmetrical point forces on the crack faces the pressure distribution can be represented by $p(x) = P\delta(x - x_0)$ where $\delta(x - x_0)$ is the Dirac delta function. Substitution of this expression for $p(x)$ reduces equation (4) to equation (2).

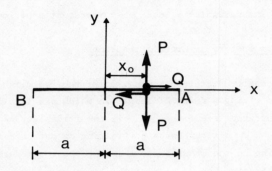

Fig. 1 Crack loaded with point forces

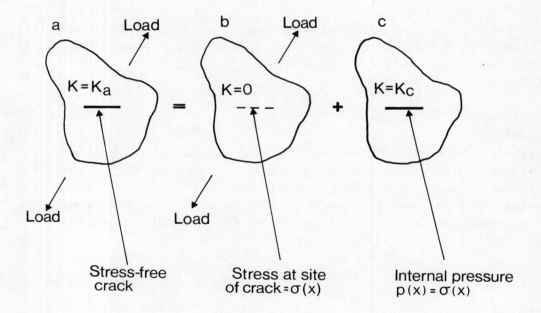

Fig. 2 The equivalence of stress intensity factors for external
boundary loads and internal pressures; $K_a = K_c$

Equation (3) can be used together with an important result derived by
Bueckner [6], to obtain opening mode stress intensity factors for cracked bodies
subjected to arbitrary forces on their boundaries. Bueckner's result is that the
stress intensity factor for a crack in a body subjected to external forces is
identical to that for a similar crack, subjected to internal pressure in a
similar body which has no external forces acting on it. The internal pressure
$p(x)$ acting in the crack is equal to the stress that would exist normal to the
crack-line along the crack-site in the uncracked body subjected to the external
forces. An analogous procedure exists for shear stresses and the calculation of
sliding-mode stress intensity factors. This principle is illustrated schematically
in figure 2. For many bodies and external force distributions the stresses along
the crack-site may be difficult to evaluate. Often Green's function techniques can
be used in these evaluations. Recently Nisitani [7] has derived stress-field
Green's functions for different bodies, so that the internal stress distribution
can be derived for any externally applied forces on these bodies.

4. Systematic use of Green's functions

Known Green's functions for both stress fields and stress intensity factors
can often be used systematically to build up stress intensity factors for unsolved
crack problems. Some examples are shown in figure 3 where G^K and G^σ refer to
Green's functions which are associated with stress intensity factors and stress
fields respectively. The Green's function defined in equation (3) is a special case
of that derived by Erdogan [8] for a crack in a sheet with an arbitrary force
anywhere in the sheet. The stress-field Green's functions are also available [8]
for this cracked configuration. The ones required are defined in figure 3B.
Hartranft and Sih [9] have obtained the stress intensity factor for a crack of
length a in a half-plane, the crack being subjected to two equal and opposite forces
(per unit thickness)P, normal to the crack face and a distance x_0 from the edge of
the sheet (see figure 3C). An iterative method was used which required a knowledge
of the Green's functions given in figures 3A and 3B. The initial solution required
was that of a crack of length 2a with point forces ±P at $x = \pm x_0$; the Green's
functions for this configuration are obtained from figure 3B, i.e.

$$K_I = \frac{P}{\sqrt{\pi a}} \left[G_B^K(x_0;a) + G_B^K(-x_0;a) \right], \tag{5}$$

$$\sigma_x(y,o) = P \left[G_B^\sigma(x_0,y;a) + G_B^\sigma(-x_0,y;a) \right] = 2PG_B^K(x_0,y;a), \tag{6}$$

$$\tau_{xy}(y,o) = P \left[G_B^\tau(x_0,y;a) + G_B^\tau(-x_0,y;a) \right] = 0. \tag{7}$$

The simplifications introduced into equations (6) and (7) follow from
symmetry considerations.

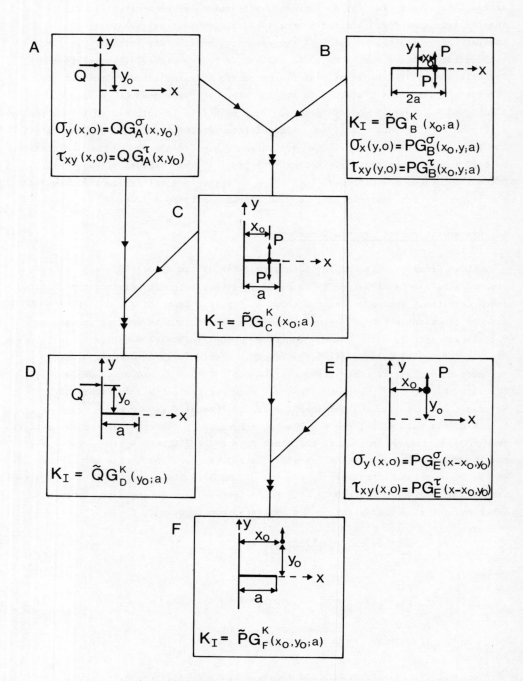

Fig. 3 Systematic use of Green's functions

$$\left[\; \tilde{P} = P/(\sqrt{\pi a}) \;,\; \tilde{Q} = Q/(\sqrt{\pi a}) \;\right]$$

The configuration described in figure 3D can be solved directly from equation (4) by using the above solution. Because of Bueckner's principle [6] p(x) can be replaced by $\sigma_y(x,o)$, defined in figure 3A, and G(x) can be replaced by $G_C^K(x_o;a)$ defined in figure 3C. This procedure has been used by Rooke and Jones [10] to obtain the desired solution. Figure 3F shows a crack of length a in a half-plane which is subjected to a force per unit thickness of P acting at the point (x_o,y_o). The stress intensity factor for this configuration can be obtained in a similar manner to that above from the Green's functions defined in figure 3C and 3E. The result $G_F^K(x_o,y_o;a)$ can then be used to derive the stress intensity factor for any arbitrary distribution of forces in the half-plane. All the configurations in figure 3 show opening mode stress intensity factors resulting from forces normal to the crack or normal to the sheet edge. The procedures outlined are also valid for arbitrary forces which lead to both opening and sliding-mode stress intensity factors.

Stress intensity factors for cracks subjected to a constant pressure on part of the crack surface are closely related to Green's functions. A particular case of this is illustrated in figure 4a where a crack of length 2a is subjected to a constant pressure. $p(x) = p_o$ between $x_o \leqslant x \leqslant x_1$. Symbolically p(x) is defined as

$$p(x) = p_o \left[H(x-x_o) - H(x-x_1) \right] \tag{8}$$

where $H(x-x_o)$ is the Heaviside step-function defined by

$$H(x-x_o) = 0, \; x<x_o \atop = 1, \; x \geqslant x_o \Bigg\} \tag{9}$$

The Heaviside step-function and the Dirac delta-function are simply related thus:

$$\frac{d}{dx} H(x-x_o) = \delta(x-x_o) \tag{10}$$

From equation (4) it follows that the stress intensity factor for this configuration is given by

$$K_I = \frac{p_o}{\sqrt{\pi a}} \int_{-a}^{a} \left[H(x-x_o) - H(x-x_1) \right] G(x) dx = \frac{p_o}{\sqrt{\pi a}} \int_{x_o}^{x_1} G(x) dx \tag{11}$$

where G(x) is defined by equation (2); the second integral in equation (11) follows from the properties of H(x) given in equation (9). This result can be used to obtain an approximate stress intensity factor for a crack subjected to an arbitrary pressure distribution. The pressure distribution is approximated by a series of strips of constant pressure as illustrated in figure 4b. The principle of superposition allows the contributions from each pressure strip to be added together.

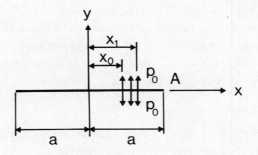

Fig. 4a   A step-pressure acting on the crack surface

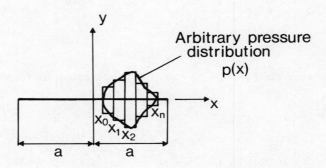

Fig. 4b   Step representation of a continuous pressure
distribution

Thus

$$K_I = \frac{p_1}{\sqrt{\pi a}} \int_{x_0}^{x_1} G(x)dx + \frac{p_2}{\sqrt{\pi a}} \int_{x_1}^{x_2} G(x)dx + \ldots\ldots + \frac{p_n}{\sqrt{\pi a}} \int_{x_{n-1}}^{x_n} G(x)dx \qquad (12)$$

where p_j is the value of $p(x)$ at the mid-point of the strip between x_{j-1} and x_j.

If each strip is of such a width that $p(x)$ does not vary much across it, then equation (12) may be written

$$K_I \simeq \frac{1}{\sqrt{\pi a}} \left\{ \int_{x_0}^{x_1} p(x)G(x)dx + \int_{x_1}^{x_2} p(x)G(x)dx \ldots\ldots + \int_{x_{n-1}}^{x_n} p(x)G(x)dx \right\}$$

$$(13)$$

By adding the integrals together, equation (13) becomes

$$K_I \simeq \frac{1}{\sqrt{\pi a}} \int_{x_0}^{x_n} p(x)G(x)dx \qquad (14)$$

the right-hand side of which is of the same form as equation (4); for a distribution of pressure over the whole crack-face x_0 is $-a$ and x_n is $+a$. Thus equation (12) will give results which approximate to those of an exact calculation using Green's functions, providing that $p(x)$ does not vary much in any strip. The number of strips can be increased indefinitely until the stress intensity factor reaches the required accuracy.

5. Available Green's functions

There are many Green's functions now available. The more important of these are shown in figure 5. Most are for two-dimensional configurations and these enable a wide variety of problems to be analysed. The Green's functions shown are mainly for Modes I and II as these are in practice more important. Complete details of the functions together with references to the original work are given in the references cited for each configuration. Many other special cases of the Green's functions in figure 5 have been determined [11, 12, 13] and it is possible to construct others by taking limits and by superposition. Solutions have also been determined [11, 12 13] for bands of pressure on the crack faces and, as shown by equation (14), these step function solutions can be superimposed to obtain arbitrary distributions on the crack surfaces.

6. Simple methods expressed as Green's functions

Several simple methods [14, 15, 16, 17, 18] have been proposed for determining stress intensity factors, particularly for the important case of cracks from holes or notches. These methods have been developed by comparing results with known

D. J. Cartwright and D. P. Rooke

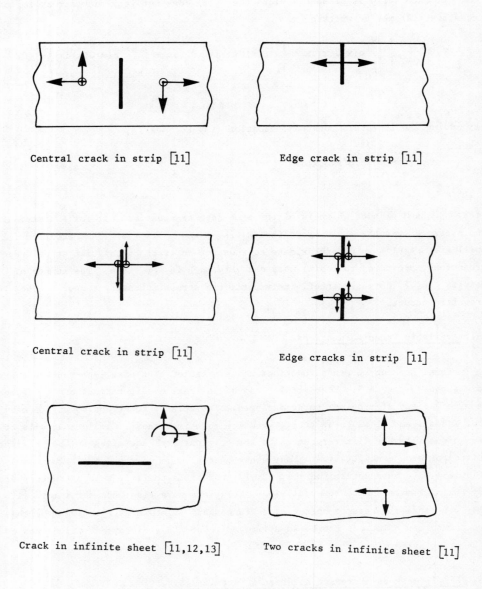

Central crack in strip [11]   Edge crack in strip [11]

Central crack in strip [11]   Edge cracks in strip [11]

Crack in infinite sheet [11,12,13]   Two cracks in infinite sheet [11]

Fig. 5(a)   Configurations with known Green's functions

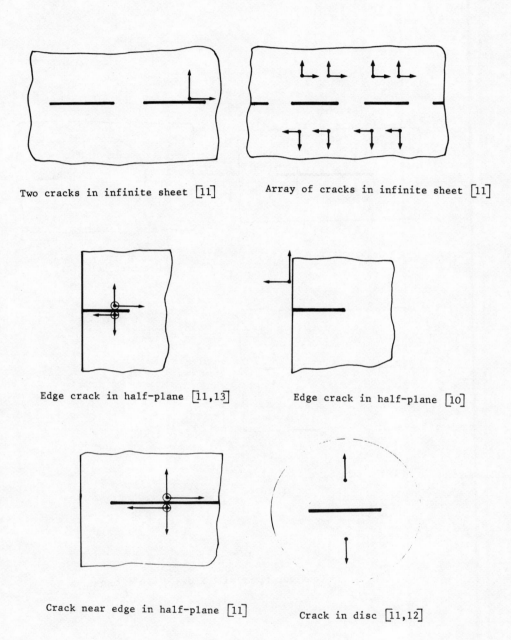

Two cracks in infinite sheet [11]   Array of cracks in infinite sheet [11]

Edge crack in half-plane [11,13]   Edge crack in half-plane [10]

Crack near edge in half-plane [11]   Crack in disc [11,12]

Fig. 5(b) Configurations with known Green's functions

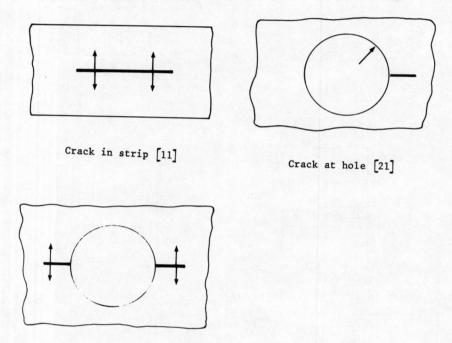

Crack in strip [11]

Crack at hole [21]

Two cracks at hole [19]

Fig. 5(c) Configurations with known Green's functions

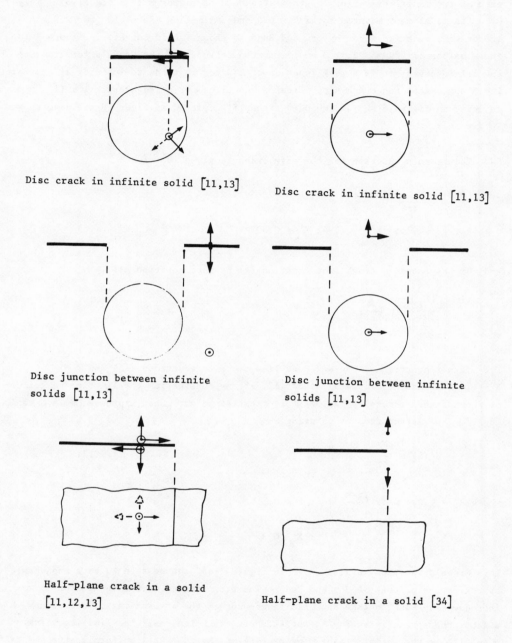

Disc crack in infinite solid [11,13]

Disc crack in infinite solid [11,13]

Disc junction between infinite
solids [11,13]

Disc junction between infinite
solids [11,13]

Half-plane crack in a solid
[11,12,13]

Half-plane crack in a solid [34]

Fig. 5(d)   Configurations with known Green's functions

stress intensity factors in particular cases. It will now be shown that these
simple methods are not arbitrary, but arise from approximations to the Green's
function. Results obtained from using them will be compared with those derived by
Hsu and Rudd [19] who used a more accurate Green's function. Hsu and Rudd determined
stress intensity factors for a symmetrical pair of opposing point forces acting on
each of two radial cracks of length ℓ at a hole of radius R (see figure 6). They
used finite element methods for $x/\ell < 0.9$ and a limiting expression for $x/\ell > 0.9$.
The Green's function given by Hsu and Rudd is shown (solid curves) in figure 7 for
three values of ℓ/R = 0.2, 1.0 and 3.0. Two features of the Green's function are of
special interest; it is a weak function of ℓ/R and it tends to infinity as the point
force approaches the crack tip. Green's functions for an edge crack [9, 11]
depicted in figure 8 and an embedded crack [8] depicted in figure 9 are also shown
in figure 7.

The Green's function for the edge crack is given [9] as

$$G_e(X) = \frac{2}{\sqrt{1-X^2}}\left\{1 + (1-X^2)\left[0.2945 - 0.3912\ X^2 \right.\right.$$
$$\left.\left. + 0.7685\ X^4 - 0.9942\ X^6 + 0.5094\ X^8\right]\right\} \qquad (15)$$

and for the embedded crack from equation (2) by superposition as

$$G_c(X) = \frac{2}{\sqrt{1-X^2}} \qquad (16)$$

where $X = x/\ell$

The Green's function of Hsu and Rudd lies close to equations (15) and (16) for
$X \to 1$. Shah has developed a method [17, 18] by considering the limiting behaviour
of known stress intensity factors for cracks at holes. When expressed as a Green's
function the method reduces to using

$$G_s(X) = \frac{2M_f}{\sqrt{1-X^2}} \qquad (17)$$

where $M_f = 1.0 + 0.12\left\{\frac{X-0.3}{0.3}\right\}^2$; $X < 0.3$

$ = 0$ $\phantom{1.0 + 0.12\left\{\frac{X-0.3}{0.3}\right\}^2xx}$; $X > 0.3$

This Green's function is also shown in figure 7 and can be seen to be a reasonable
approximation to that of Hsu and Rudd. The free surface correction factor M_f was
introduced by Shah to take approximate account of the stress-free hole-boundary which
affects the stress intensity factor at short crack lengths. The limiting value of
$M_f (=1.12)$ is the value obtained for a crack at the edge of a uniformly stressed half-
plane. The approximate Green's function proposed by Shah is sufficiently close to
the solution of Hsu and Rudd to make it useful for many applications; its use does

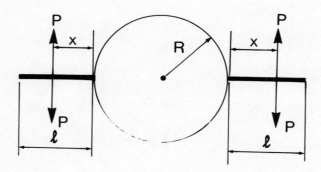

Fig. 6 Diametrically opposed radial cracks subjected to
        symmetrical point forces

D. J. Cartwright and D. P. Rooke

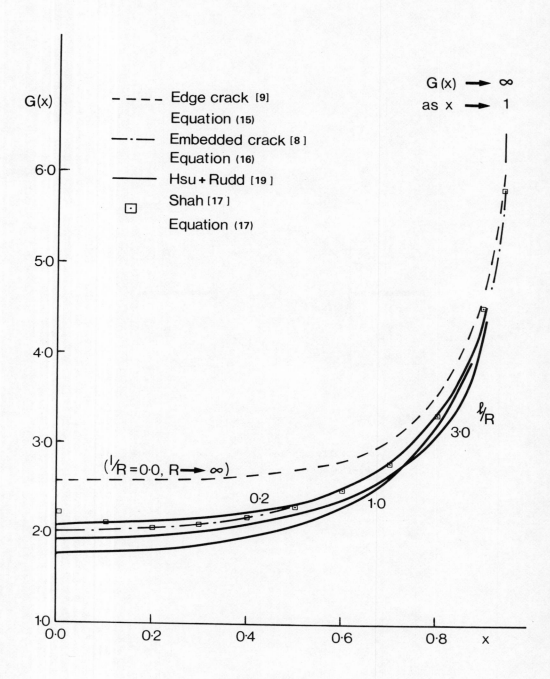

Fig. 7 Comparison of Green's Functions

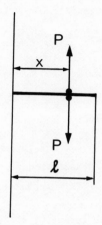

Fig. 8   Point loaded crack emanating from a stress free edge

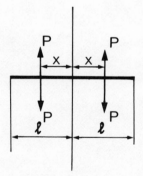

Fig. 9   Point loaded crack embedded in an infinite sheet

not depend on the notch shape and a closed form expression is convenient in numerical calculations.

The approximate methods [14, 15, 16] can also be expressed as Green's functions thereby establishing their general application to cracks at holes and notches. The Green's function $G_o(x)$ for a point loaded crack at a notch tip as shown in figure 10a is shown schematically in figure 10b. Three approximations to $G_o(x)$ will be examined, these are also shown in figure 10b and are defined as

$$G_1(x) = 1.12\pi\ell\delta(x) \tag{18}$$

$$G_2(x) = 1.12\pi\ell\delta(x-\ell) \tag{19}$$

and $\qquad G_3(x) = 1.12\pi\left[H(x) - H(x-\ell)\right] \tag{20}$

where $\delta(x)$ is the Dirac delta function, $H(x)$ is the Heaviside step-function. It will now be shown that the above Green's functions are equivalent to well known results.

From equation (4) the stress intensity factors resulting from the Green's functions in equations (18) to (20), with $\sigma(x)$, the stress over the crack site, set equal to $p(x)$ are given by:

for equation (18)

$$K_I^{(1)} = \frac{1}{\sqrt{\pi\ell}} \int_o^\ell \sigma(x)\ 1.12\pi\ell\delta(x)dx \tag{21}$$

$$= 1.12\sigma(o)\sqrt{\pi\ell}\ ; \tag{22}$$

for equation (19)

$$K_I^{(2)} = \frac{1}{\sqrt{\pi\ell}} \int_o^\ell \sigma(x)\ 1.12\pi\ell\delta(x-\ell)dx \tag{23}$$

$$= 1.12\sigma(\ell)\sqrt{\pi\ell}\ ; \tag{24}$$

and for equation (20)

$$K_I^{(3)} = \frac{1}{\sqrt{\pi\ell}} \int_o^\ell \sigma(x)\ 1.12\pi\left[H(x) - H(x-\ell)\right]dx \tag{25}$$

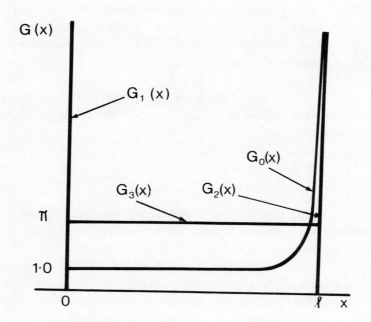

Fig. 10b Schematic Green's Functions for a crack at a notch root

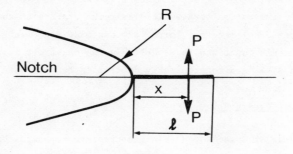

Fig. 10a Point loaded crack at a notch root

$$= 1.12\sqrt{\pi \ell} \left\{ \frac{1}{\ell} \int_0^{\ell} \sigma(x)dx \right\} \qquad (26)$$

$$= 1.12 \; \sigma_{\text{mean}} \sqrt{\pi \ell} \; . \qquad (27)$$

Equation (22) and (24) are the familiar maximum stress [16] and crack tip stress [14] approximations respectively and equation (27) is the mean stress method suggested by Williams and Isherwood [15]; several applications of these methods have been considered elsewhere [3].

Results for the case of two equal length, diametrically opposed, radial cracks at a hole in a sheet subjected to a biaxial tensile stress σ are shown in a table in figure 11. For this case

$$\sigma(x) = \sigma(1 + \frac{R^2}{(R+x)^2}) \qquad (28)$$

The results of Hsu and Rudd [19] as determined by Whitehead [20] are seen to be in close agreement with the accurate solution of Rooke and Tweed [21]; errors for each approximation are shown in parenthesis. The tip stress equation (24), results in errors of about 3% showing that the Green's function $G_1(x)$ is a satisfactory approximation to $G_o(x)$. This is because the major contribution to the stress intensity factor comes from the near tip stresses; this contribution is largely accounted for by the delta function representation of the Green's function. The maximum stress approximation is only accurate in the limit of zero crack length as only under these conditions is the delta function $\delta(x)$ a reasonable approximation to $G_o(x)$. However despite this limitation the maximum stress method is useful in that it gives an upper limit on the stress intensity factor. Furthermore it is only necessary to know the stress concentration factor for the notch rather than the entire stress field over the crack-site in the uncracked body. The mean stress method also over-estimates the stress intensity factor but in this case it is necessary to know the entire stress field over the crack-site and to determine its mean value at each crack length. Smith [22] has made use of the mean stress and the properties of Green's functions to establish bounds on stress intensity factors of edge cracks when $\sigma(x)$ is a monotonically decreasing function and $\sigma(\ell) > 0$.

7. Applications of Green's functions

The usefulness of Green's functions in fracture mechanics will now be illustrated by three examples. These are chosen to illustrate the wide variety of practical problems which may be easily and accurately solved.

$\frac{\ell}{R}$	Hsu & Rudd ref [19]	Tip stress Equation (24)	Max stress Equation (22)	Mean stress Equation (27)	Rooke & Tweed ref [21]
0.0	2.17 (-3)	2.24 (0)	2.24 (0)	2.24 (0)	2.24
0.1	1.99 (-0.5)	2.05 (+2.5)	2.24 (+12)	2.14 (+7)	2.00
0.15	1.90 (-0.5)	1.97 (+3)	2.24 (+17)	2.09 (+9)	1.91
0.20	1.83 (-0.5)	1.90 (+3)	2.24 (+22)	2.05 (+11)	1.84
0.30	1.70 (-1)	1.78 (+3.5)	2.24 (+30)	1.98 (+15)	1.72
0.50	1.54 (-1)	1.62 (+4)	2.24 (+44)	1.87 (+20)	1.56
1.00	1.34 (-2)	1.40 (+2)	2.24 (+64)	1.68 (+23)	1.37

Figure 11 Comparison of stress intensity factors $K_I/(\sigma\sqrt{\pi\ell})$

7.1 Effect of pin pressure distribution on a crack at a hole

In this example it is necessary to give a different interpretation to $p(x)$ and $G(x)$ in equation (4) since in order to solve these problems we need the Green's function which gives the response to a force acting at an arbitrary position in the body (in this case on the hole boundary) rather than that due to a force acting on the crack surfaces. For problems of this type the stress intensity factor for an arbitrary stress acting on the body is obtained from the following expression which is similar to equation (4)

$$K_I = \frac{1}{\sqrt{\pi \ell}} \int_{x_1}^{x^2} \sigma(x) \; G(x) \; dx \qquad\qquad (29)$$

where x_1 and x_2 are positions in the body between which $\sigma(x)$ is the applied stress prescribed and $G(x)$ is the stress intensity factor for a unit force acting at the position denoted by x. As an example of the use of such Green's functions we will consider a radial crack at the edge of a circular hole which is subjected to a point force on its perimeter. This type of problem is frequently encountered in considering cracked-holes in pin-loaded lugs. Often the load transfer between the pin and the hole periphery is not precisely known and it is necessary to investigate various possible load distributions. Green's function techniques are ideal for such investigations since each new distribution just involves a change in $\sigma(x)$ in equation (29).

The Green's function required is the stress intensity factor for a radial crack of length ℓ at the edge of a hole of radius R; a radial force per unit thickness of P acts at the edge of the hole in a direction which makes an angle θ with the crack (see figure 12). This stress intensity factor has been obtained by Tweed and Rooke [23]; it is plotted in figure 12 in non-dimensional form as a function of θ for various values of ℓ/R. The usefulness of Green's functions in describing the response of systems is clearly shown by these results since two important observations can be made from figure 12. The first is that the variation of K_I with θ increases as the crack length decreases, and the second is that the maximum rate of variation occurs for short cracks at small values of θ. These facts lead to important considerations in fracture mechanics applications.

The first consideration, which is of **general** importance, is that since most of the lifetime of a fatigue crack is spent while the crack is short, it is necessary to know what influences the stress intensity factor of short cracks. This information is required in order to decide on inspection intervals and maintenance schedules for structures in services. The second consideration is specific to the loaded hole configuration since assumptions have usually to be made about how the load is transferred from the pin to the edge of the hole. It is often assumed that the load is distributed, in some way, between θ_1 and θ_2 where $\theta_1 \sim 0^\circ$ and $\theta_2 \sim 180^\circ$.

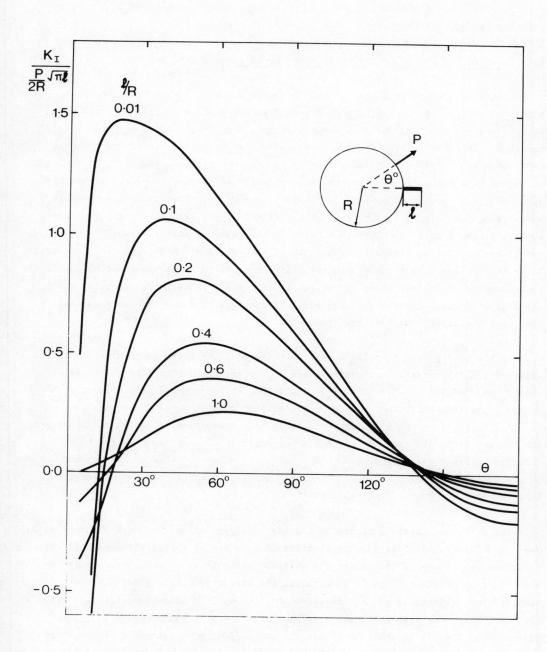

Fig. 12 Green's function for a crack at the edge of a
loaded circular hole

The rapid variation in Green's function at small values of θ means that an incorrect assumption of the load distribution and the cut-off value θ_1 can lead to significant errors in the stress intensity factor. The errors will be largest for the important region of short cracks, so great care must be exercised in simulating the load transfer between the pin and the edge of the hole.

7.2 Crack with a strip-yield zone in a stiffened sheet

Green's functions have been used extensively to analyse the effect of cracks in stiffened structures. The stiffener may be discretely attached [24] e.g. riveted or spot welded, or it may be continuously attached [25] e.g. bonded or integrally machined. Multiple stiffeners have been studied [26] and the effect of attachment deflection e.g. distortion of adhesives or rivets has been analysed [27, 28]. By using the same method it is also possible to determine the effect of repair patches [29] and the effect of debonding of the adhesive [30]. In this example a recently reported method [31] is used to examine the effect of yielding at the tip of a crack in a stiffened panel. Such problems arise in the residual static strength assessment of stiffened structures because of the relatively high loads involved. It is therefore necessary to consider the effect of yielding in the sheet on the load concentration in the stiffener and on the rivet loads. We must also consider the deflection of the attachment points, possible fracture of the attachments and the crack opening displacement of the crack.

In the configuration analysed, shown in figure 13, a sheet of modulus of elasticity E, thickness t and yield stress σ_{ys} is stiffened by a line-stiffener of area A_s and modulus of elasticity E_s. The stiffener is attached to the sheet by N rivets (symmetrically either side of the crack) of elastic compliance q spaced a distance p apart. A crack of length 2a is located symmetrically across the stiffener and has a strip-yield zone of length c at each tip; the sheet is subjected to a uniaxial stress σ perpendicular to the crack. It is assumed that the attachment points are either rigid (Etq = 0) or undergo an elastic deflection typical of thin sheet riveted structures (Etq = 3).

The stiffened panel in figure 13 has been analysed using the Green's function [8] (see also figure 5a). In solving problems of this type a series of compatibility equations are set up; these relate the extension of each attachment interval in the sheet to that of the contiguous interval in the stiffener. This gives a set of simultaneous equations which may be solved for the unknown attachment forces. Once these are known the effect of each attachment force may be summed using a displacement Green's function to obtain the crack opening displacement of the crack. Convergence of the solution is established by increasing the number of rivets in the stiffener until there is no effect on the attachment force distribution. On this basis the number of attachments N was fixed at 30 either side of the crack line.

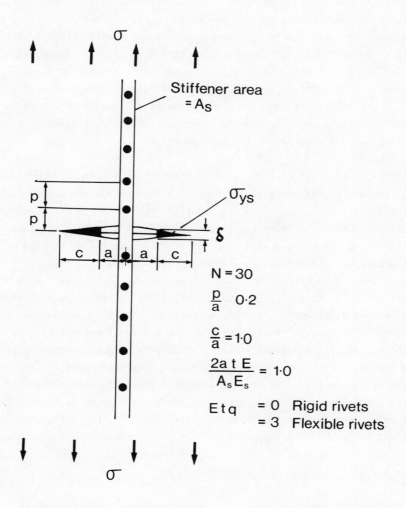

Fig. 13 Strip yield crack at a riveted stiffener

We consider a problem in which the extent of yielding in the sheet is limited to a length c equal to the crack length a. In practice this could correspond to a half-bay crack in a multi-stiffened panel where yielding is not permitted to extend past the next stiffener either side of the crack. The following aspects of the problem have been studied in detail, the effect of attachment failure on the maximum attachment load, the load concentration in the stiffener and the crack opening displacement. The influence of increasing the number, n, of failed attachment points is shown in figure 14. The crack opening displacement δ and the strip-yield zone length c are both reduced below that for an unstiffened sheet (δ_o, c_o) and increase monotonically with increasing n. The ratio of the maximum permissible applied stress σ to the strip-yield stress σ_{ys} appears to be only weakly affected by the number of failed attachment points. The reduction in σ/σ_{ys} show that the panel can carry less load for the same yield zone length. The ratio of the maximum stress σ_m in the stiffener to the remote stiffener stress σ_s decreases by approximately 22%. The ratio of the load P_1 in the unbroken attachment nearest to the crack to the remote load in the stiffener $\sigma_s A_s$ shows an increase initially followed by a decrease of approximately 37% compared to the initial value.

It is instructive to compare the maximum rivet load and the maximum stress in the stiffener for the strip-yield crack with that of a crack having the same length a but without a strip-yield zone at its tip. This is shown in figure 15, where it is seen that the effect of yielding is to increase the maximum rivet load by between 9% and 26% whilst the maximum stress in the stiffener increases by only 6%. The implications of this are that the effect of yielding in the sheet is more likely to cause further shear deflection, yield or failure of the rivets rather than yield or failure of the stiffener. In figure 16 the effect of attachment deflection on the crack opening displacement δ, maximum stiffener stress σ_m and maximum rivet load P_1 are shown as a function of the number of the failed attachment points. The attachment deflection has the effect of increasing the crack opening displacement. It is increased by approximately 32% when all attachments are intact and by 10% when eight are broken. The maximum stiffener stress is reduced by only about 6% whereas the maximum rivet load is significantly reduced by approximately 60%, both being relatively insensitive to n. Further details of the application of Green's functions to cracks with strip-yield zones in stiffened sheets are available [31].

7.3 A symmetrical crack in a stiffened sheet

The Green's function used in the previous example can be used to examine the effect of detailed stiffener design [32]. The panel to be analysed is shown in figure 17. This configuration represents a typical aircraft wing panel in which a crack is initiated at a rivet hole B and the tip A grows across the panel. The stiffeners of area A_s are attached to a sheet of thickness t at a spacing b with double rows of rivets, diameter d, having a pitch p perpendicular to the crack and a pitch h parallel to the crack; the modulus of elasticity of the sheet and the

Number of attachments failed	Strip-yield zone-ratio	Applied to yield stress ratio	COD ratio	maximum stiffener stress ratio	maximum rivet load ratio
n	$\dfrac{c}{c_0}$	$\dfrac{\sigma}{\sigma_s}$	$\dfrac{\delta}{\delta_0}$	$\dfrac{\sigma_m}{\sigma_s}$	$\dfrac{P_1}{\sigma_s A_s}$
0	0.367	0.827	0.356	1.596	0.269
2	0.451	0.799	0.438	1.499	0.287
4	0.547	0.770	0.545	1.400	0.252
6	0.638	0.745	0.651	1.317	0.208
8	0.716	0.726	0.738	1.252	0.169

Figure 14   Influence of attachment failure in a stiffened panel

n	$\dfrac{(\sigma_m)c=a}{(\sigma_m)c=o}$	$\dfrac{(P_1)c=a}{(P_1)c=o}$
0	1.06	1.09
1	1.06	1.11
2	1.07	1.14
3	1.07	1.18
4	1.07	1.22
5	1.07	1.26

Figure 15 Comparison of the maximum rivet load and the maximum
stiffener stress for c=a and c=o

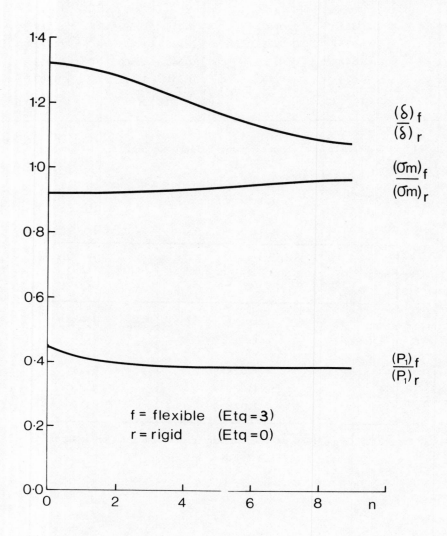

Fig. 16 Effect of attachment shear deflection on
maximum stiffener stress σ_m, maximum rivet load P_1
and crack opening displacement δ

stiffener are identical. Typical values of p, h and b together with relative area ratio $A_s/(A_s + bt)$ are given on figure 17. Since h is a significant fraction of the bay width b, it may be somewhat unrealistic to assume, in the analysis, that the stiffener can be concentrated along its centre-line. This assumption will be compared with the more realistic one of concentrating half the total stiffener area along each rivet line. The computational problem is also made more complex because of the lack of symmetry; the crack is eccentrically placed and as only one tip moves the eccentricity changes. The stress intensity factors for crack tips A and B are shown in figure 18 as a function of the crack length a. In the singly riveted model the stiffener area A_s is assumed concentrated along the stiffener centre-line and in the doubly riveted model the area A_s is distributed equally along each rivet line. As can be seen the type of model assumed affects the stress intensity factor and hence the residual static strength [33]. The stress intensity factor is greater for the single row of rivets than for the double row for all values of $a/(b - h/2)$ for tip B. For tip A the double row of rivets results in a smaller K_I than the single row for $a/(b - h/2)$ between 1.03 and 1.33. The implications are that the residual strength and fatigue crack growth rate of the cracked panel will depend strongly on the type of attachment, in this case single or double riveting. There-fore this must be taken into account in the analytic models used to solve these problems. It is interesting to note that for the doubly riveted stiffener model the critical crack tip alternates between tip A and tip B as the crack crosses the panel.

It is also possible to carry out simulated fatigue crack growth rate experiments using the computer. Both tips are allowed to move simultaneously; the increment of crack growth is determined from the fatigue crack growth law for the sheet material. Thus realistic comparisons of fatigue life can be made. Calculations with small crack increments can be time consuming; the Green's function technique makes it possible to use closed form expressions and thus solution times are shorter than for many numerical techniques.

8. Conclusions

The application of Green's function techniques in problems in fracture mechanics has been described. It has been shown to be a versatile technique for determining stress intensity factors in a wide variety of problems. Once the Green's function is known it is only necessary to determine the stress distribution along the crack site in the uncracked body. The stress analysis of uncracked bodies is, in general, simpler than the stress analysis of cracked bodies and many experimental and analytical techniques already exist. Some methods of obtaining new Green's functions from existing ones have been presented and further extensions indicated. Several commonly used approximate methods have been given a rational basis; they have been shown to depend on the existence of certain approximate Green's functions. Many important Green's functions have been collected and some of these have been used to solve practical problems in fracture mechanics. The

120   D. J. Cartwright and D. P. Rooke

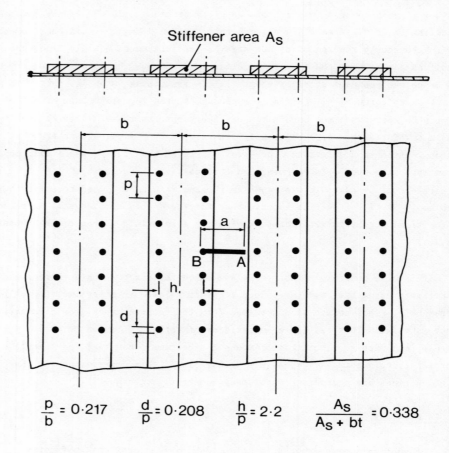

$$\frac{p}{b} = 0.217 \qquad \frac{d}{p} = 0.208 \qquad \frac{h}{p} = 2.2 \qquad \frac{A_S}{A_S + bt} = 0.338$$

Fig. 17 Cracked stiffened panel with tip B fixed at a rivet hole

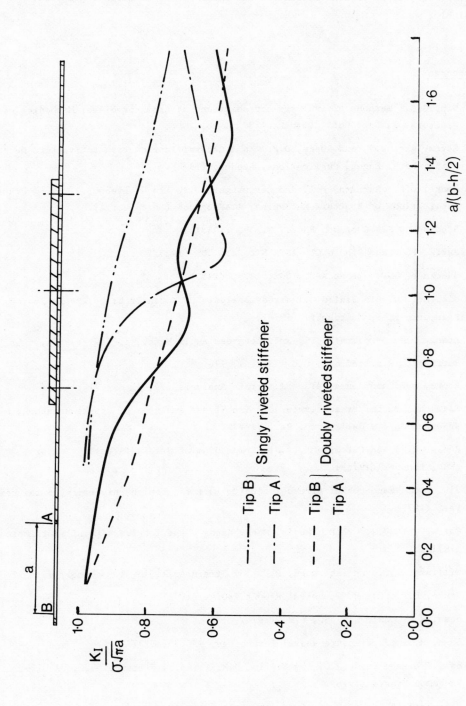

Fig. 18 Comparison of stiffener rivet patterns
         on the stress intensity factor

range of problems included cracks at loaded holes, the load transfer in stiffeners
due to attachment deflection, attachment failure and sheet yielding, and the effect
of stiffener design on asymmetrically cracked panels. The Green's function
technique is also applicable to problems in three-dimensions although applications
are more limited at present because of the small number of Green's functions
available.

References

1.   Sih, G.C. Methods of analysis and solutions of crack problems, Mechanics of
     Fracture, 1, Noordhoff, Leyden, (1973).

2.   Cartwright, D.J. and Rooke, D.P. In A General Introduction to Fracture Mechanics,
     p. 54, Mech. Engng. Publications, London, (1978).

3.   Rooke, D.P., Baratta, F.I. and Cartwright, D.J. In H. Liebowitz (Ed.), Practical
     Applications of Fracture Mechanics, AGARDograph (to appear 1979).

4.   Stedman, G.E. Contemp. Phys., 9, 49, (1968).

5.   Paris, P.C. and Sih, G.C. ASTM STP 381, 30, (1965).

6.   Bueckner, H.F. Trans ASME, 80E, 1225, (1958).

7.   Nisitani, H. In Sih, G.C., Stress Analysis of Notch Problems, Mechanics of
     Fracture, 5, 1, Noordhoff, (1978).

8.   Erdogan, F. Proc. 4th U.S. Nat. Congress Appl. Mech., 1, 547, (1962).

9.   Hartranft, R.J. and Sih, G.C. Ref. 1, 179.

10. Rooke, D.P. and Jones, D.A. J. Strain Analysis, 14, 1, (1979).

11. Tada, H., Paris, P. and Irwin, G. The Stress Analysis of Cracks Handbook, Del
     Research Corp., Hellertown, Pa., (1973).

12. Rooke, D.P. and Cartwright, D.J. Compendium of Stress Intensity Factors,
     HMSO, London, (1976).

13. Sih, G.C. Handbook of Stress Intensity Factors, Lehigh University, Bethlehem,
     Pa., (1973).

14. Cartwright, D.J. Ph.D. Thesis, Mech. Engng. Dept., University of Southampton,
     (1971).

15. Williams, J.G. and Isherwood, D.P. J. Strain Anal., 3, 17, (1968).

16. Rooke, D.P. R.A.E. Technical Report 78074, (1978).

17. Shah, R.C. ASTM STP 590, 429, (1976).

18. Shah, R.C. J. Pressure Vessel Technology, 99, 75, (1977).

19. Hsu, T.M. and Rudd, J.L. In Taplin, D.M.R. (Ed.), Fracture 1977, 3A, 139,
     Pergamon Press, (1978).

20. Whitehead, R.S. (Private Communication).

21. Tweed, J. and Rooke, D.P. Int. J. Engng. Sci., 14, 925, (1976).

22. Smith, E. Int. J. Fracture, 13, 515, (1977).

23. Tweed, J. and Rooke D.P. Int. J. Engng. Sci. (to appear).

24. Bloom, J.M. and Sanders, J.L. J. Appl. Mech., 33, 561, (1966).

25. Greif, R. and Sanders, J.L. J. Appl. Mech., 32, 59, (1965).

26. Poe, C.C. NASA TR. R-358, (1971).

27. Swift, T. Proc. Int. Conf. Prospects of Fracture Mechanics, 419, Noordhoff, (1974).

28. Cartwright, D.J. and Dowrich, G. In Fracture Mechanics in Engineering Practice, Ed. P. Stanley, 149, Applied Science, (1977).

29. Ratwani, M.M. J. Engng. Materials Technology, 100, 46, (1978).

30. Arin, K. Engng. Fracture Mech., 6, 133, (1974).

31. Cartwright, D.J. and Rich, T.P. Proc. Int. Conf. Numerical Methods in Fracture Mechanics, 550, Swansea University, (1978).

32. Wang, K. and Cartwright, D.J. In Taplin, D.M.R. (Ed.), Fracture 1977, 3B, 647, Pergamon Press, (1978).

33. Heath, W.G., Nicholls, L.F. and Kirkby, W.T. In Fracture Mechanics Design Methodology, AGARD Conf. Proc. No. 221, (1976).

34. Kassir, M.K. and Sih, G.C. Mechanics of Fracture, 2, Noordhoff, Leyden, (1975).

VARIABLE AMPLITUDE FATIGUE OF WELDED STRUCTURES

W. D. Dover

*Department of Mechanical Engineering, University College London,
Torrington Place, London, WC1E 7JE, U.K.*

INTRODUCTION

The prediction of fatigue damage in large structures is difficult because of the complexity of both the load-time history and the stress distribution. Frequently these structures experience variable amplitude loading which is difficult to analyse because of the presence of undesirable resonances, seasonal variations and corrosion.

It is not possible to provide a single approach for the analysis of variable amplitude fatigue. Instead several types of loading have been identified as suitable for analysis. Different approaches have been developed for each of these types and these will be briefly reviewed here together with a fuller account of one currently being developed for offshore structures. The nature of fatigue damage accumulation in welded structures is different to that found in other large structures. One reason for this is that the ratio of the local stress to the nominal stress is often large for the welded structure. This changes the damage process from one consisting mainly of initiation to one where crack propagation is very important. For many structures and components crack initiation and short crack growth occupy most of the life. For welded structures short crack growth and further crack extension are the two most important phases of the fatigue process.

Damage accumulation under any of these three modes is dependent on the local conditions. For crack initiation the sequence of local stress ranges and their influence on the local residual stress controls the initiation rate. The small crack situation is one where the physical presence of the crack is as important as the local stress and the plasticity produced by the stress concentration zone. As the crack grows from this initiation zone it becomes the dominant feature, and, through influencing the local compliance and providing its own stress concentrations, controls further crack extension.

These three possibilities are shown in Fig.1 together with the appropriate parameters for characterising the damage accumulation. Fig.1a illustrates initiation where the local plastic strain range $\Delta\varepsilon_p$ is likely to be important. Fig.1b is the short crack regime where the plasticity present because of the overall strain concentration makes it necessary to describe crack growth in terms

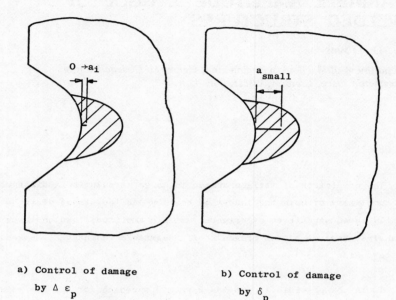

a) Control of damage   b) Control of damage
   by $\Delta \varepsilon_p$ by δ_p

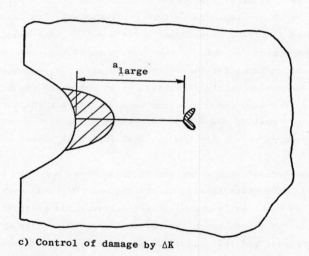

c) Control of damage by ΔK

Fig.1   Stages of fatigue damage in a structure.

of the plastic crack tip opening displacement, δ_p, (1). Fig 1c shows the third
stage where the crack is now through the initial plastic zone and damage can be
described in terms of ΔK. In determining the fatigue life for a given structure
each of these possible modes must be considered and evaluated. The eventual aim
of this type of study is to provide information of use to the designer. Thus it
is necessary to be able to describe the damage accumulation not only at the tip of
a crack in a specimen but also at the tip of a crack contained in a structure.
This requirement has led to the broadly based study of fatigue crack growth currently being undertaken by the author.

This study has evolved on three levels: the simple through crack specimen test,
the test specimen with a surface crack and the large scale model test. Detailed
studies at these three levels should provide the necessary information on how to
conduct materials tests, correlate the data, and how to present the data to the
designer.

This paper will attempt to show the progress made so far, in these studies,
especially with reference to the nature of the random loading, the presence and
shape of a crack, and the influence of a crack on the local stress.

ANALYSIS OF VARIABLE AMPLITUDE FATIGUE

There is no general approach for all types of variable amplitude loading.
Instead one has to identify the main features of each particular case and try to
analyse it using the most appropriate of the methods currently available. These
methods can be classified as follows:

a)   Cycle by cycle analysis

This is a method of analysis introduced initially for initiation studies and
now considered applicable to some cases of fatigue crack growth. As its name implies the method considers the effect of each individual cycle and also how this
cycle influences subsequent cycles. This approach would be considered suitable for
signals of Type A, Fig. 2, where the large amplitude cycle would have a considerable influence on the subsequent smaller cycles. A model is needed to
describe this load interaction and one possibility was proposed by Wheeler (2).
His model was based on the premise that the overload would cause crack retardation.
He defined a retardation factor, based on the ratio of current plastic zone size to
the distance between the current crack tip and the overload boundary, see Fig.3,
that could take this retardation into account in the estimate of current growth
rates.

This model can be used successfully with fairly simple signals but for situations where the load ratio becomes smaller and the frequency of overloads becomes
larger the method becomes too cumbersome in terms of the data required and the

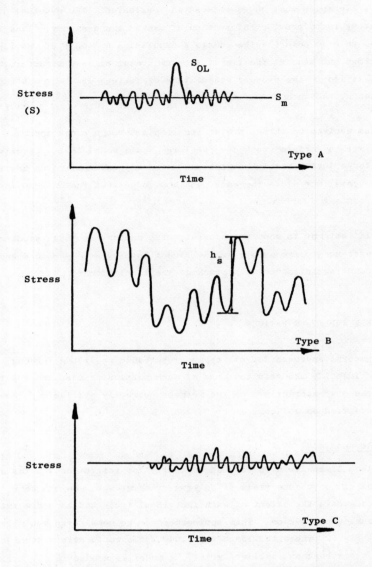

Fig.2 Three types of variable amplitude stress-time history
       showing overloads, high and low clipping ratios.

computation time needed.

One other problem which also arises is the difficulty found in defining individual stress cycle in these more complex signals, especially where the stress history has a broad band frequency content. Initiation studies (3) have shown that a
counting method known as 'rainflow', shown in Fig.4, is a conservative method of
counting cycles. In some crack growth situations this method, or a modified form,
might be suitable. For example, if the crack growth process was such that damage
accumulated in a process zone over many cycles, and the crack extension was an
intermittent process, then this sort of counting would be appropriate. Alternatively if crack extension occurs on every cycle then a simple range counting procedure, with a suitable gate to eliminate very small cycles, would be more appropriate.

b)   Standardised load sequence

If the load history was extremely irregular in nature, such as Type B in
Fig.2, it could be necessary to define a set sequence of loads. Type B is such a
sequence taken from the standardised load sequence, known as FALSTAFF, which is
used in the aircraft industry (4).

The load sequence is built up from a knowledge of the stress ranges, and number of occurrences, known to exist in certain applications, in this case combat
situations. The total load sequence is known as a flight and this is repeatedly
applied to the specimen until failure occurs. Life is estimated in terms of the
number of flights. The extremes of loading that can occur in these sequences, if
introduced correctly, can reproduce the service situation. In the case of FALSTAFF
for example the feature of crack jumping occurs frequently throughout the test. If
particular load sequences produce a characteristic form of damage in service they
must be reproduced in the laboratory test. This type of approach requires a lot of
service information, and interpretation of this data, so that the correct standardised load sequence can be formulated.

c)   S.D.F. matching with RMS control

One of the main features of Types A and B, Fig.2, is that the clipping ratio
$\left(= \dfrac{\text{peak}}{\text{r.m.s.}} \right)$ is large. Under these circumstances the load interaction effects are
also large and the very elaborate methods outlined in (a) and (b) are necessary.
In some situations, however, although averaging over a long time period would show
a large clipping ratio the signal may be broken down into shorter periods where the
clipping ratio is lower. These periods do not exhibit the same sort of interaction
effects and are amenable to an analysis based on some form of statistical averaging
rather than a cycle by cycle approach. These signals would correspond to Type C,
Fig.2. The original proposal for dealing with Type C, (5) employed matching of the
spectral density function and control of the amplitudes by means of the r.m.s.

The frequency content of a signal is usually determined by breaking down the

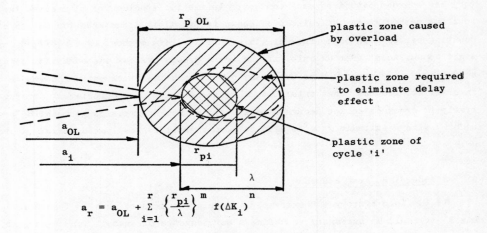

$$a_r = a_{OL} + \sum_{i=1}^{r} \left\{ \frac{r_{pi}}{\lambda} \right\}^m f(\Delta K_i)^n$$

Fig.3 Wheeler model for crack retardation.

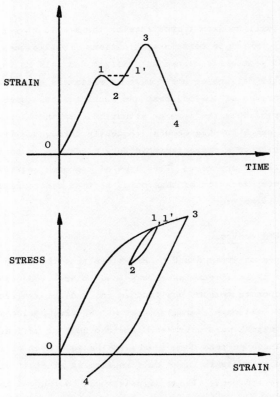

Fig.4 Cycle counting using 'Rainflow' large cycle 0134 etc.,
        small cycle 121'. Range count would give 01 and 23.

signal into a series of separate signals of different frequency content (the discrete Fourier Transforms) and measuring the mean square of each of these signals. The data is then presented as a plot of the mean square, or power, against frequency. These plots are known as the power spectral density or spectral density function. The total area under the S.D.F. plot would be equal to the mean square of the original signal. It was proposed that if the exact form of the S.D.F. was reproduced in the laboratory by a function generator then the damage rate could be measured as a function of time. However, the possibility of phase differences between the service signal and the laboratory test signal indicate the necessity for some form of range/cycle counting to ensure the essential features of the service signal are reproduced.

r.m.s. is a form of averaging commonly used in engineering. However if one wishes to use the fatigue data more generally r.m.s. is not necessarily the most appropriate form of averaging. Fatigue is known to be dependent on the stress range and usually to a power greater than two. r.m.s. however is dependent on waveform, the peak distribution, and is a second order average. Under corrosion fatigue conditions waveform will influence the crack growth rate. It would be preferable, however, to keep these two effects separate. This could be achieved by using the r.m.s. of peaks. However if one is going to change from the conventional r.m.s. it might be better to use the weighted average range described in section d. Perhaps the most satisfactory form of this approach is to reproduce the stress range distribution and retain the appropriate frequency content. This approach would not yield data which is generally useful but it could provide accurate data for individual situations.

d)   Weighted average range

This approach was first proposed by Paris (6) and more recently has been modified to the following form (7).

In this analysis it is assumed that an individual rise in the stress, h_s, see Fig.2, will cause damage, da, according to the following expression:

$$da \;=\; C\,(h_K)^n$$

where $h_K \;=\; h_s\, f(a)$

and $\dfrac{da}{dN} \;=\; C\,(\Delta K)^n$

Each rise in stress will cause a small increment of damage and the average over M cycles will be as follows:

$$\overline{da} \;=\; \frac{\sum C(h_K)^n}{M}$$

$$\;=\; C\; \overline{h_K^{\,n}}$$

this average, $\overline{h_K^n}$, can be reinterpreted as an effective stress intensity factor, termed K_h, as follows:

$$K_h = \sqrt[n]{\overline{h_K^n}} = \sqrt[n]{\overline{h_s^n}} \; f(a) , \quad or \quad S_h = \sqrt[n]{\overline{h_s^n}}$$

so that $\frac{da}{dN} = C(K_h)^n$ describes the crack growth under this type of random loading.

This analysis puts the emphasis solely on ranges, weighted by a material property (i.e. 'n'). Thus the effect of the mean stress and any large ranges, that would be shown up by the rainflow counting method, are not included. To get round this problem, which is loosely connected to the frequency content, material data is produced under conditions of frequency matching (i.e. s.d.f. of matching) so that to some extent the variable mean effects etc. are taken into account. To build this signal back up to the large clipping ratio signal means putting together periods of different S_h and S_{mean} so that the overall statistics of the signal truly represent the service conditions. This rebuilding of the total signal will present some further difficulties as there may be interaction effects between the individual segments. This possibility is illustrated in Fig.5. In this situation one would have to analyse the interaction effects in some deterministic manner, possibly a modified form of the Wheeler model.

The weighted average range analysis has been assessed using several different load time histories, and materials, and seems quite promising for the type of loading where the clipping ratio is about 4 or less. Three of the load time histories currently being examined are displayed in Fig.6. This shows the spectral density functions for a broad band signal, flat from D.C. up to a chosen cut-off frequency, a narrow band signal, the type of signal that could be considered typical of wave loading, and a double peaked signal which has been formulated to represent the loading experienced by an individual member or intersection in a tall offshore platform located in the northern North Sea (8). In this last signal the energy at the lower frequency represents the rigid body response to the wave excitation whilst the higher frequency energy corresponds to a possible dynamic response.

Fig.7 shows the waveform for these signals and for the C.A. sine wave also used in some of the tests. It should be noted that the broad band signal has a damped square waveform whilst the double peaked and narrow band are very similar, only one is shown, and they have a sine waveform.

These signals would not be considered to be representative of the entire load spectra as mentioned earlier. Successive periods of these signals, with different r.m.s. values, could be used to build up to the known amplitude, peak or range distribution in a particular case (9). If one ignores the possible interaction effects it would be possible to do the weighted average range analysis on the complete

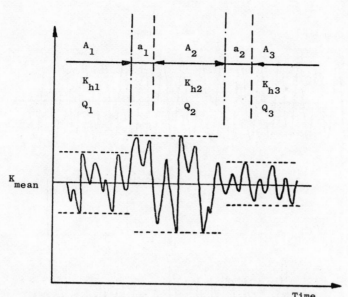

Fig.5 Series of variable amplitude signals of different
       rms and mean stress, ΣA calculated from random load
       data at constant Q, Σa calculated from interaction
       data, $Q = \dfrac{K_{mean}}{K_h}$

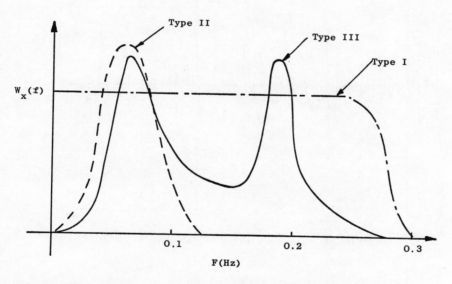

Fig.6 Spectral density functions for three different random load tests
       Type I Broad band, Type II Narrow band, Type III Double peaked.

134

W. D. Dover

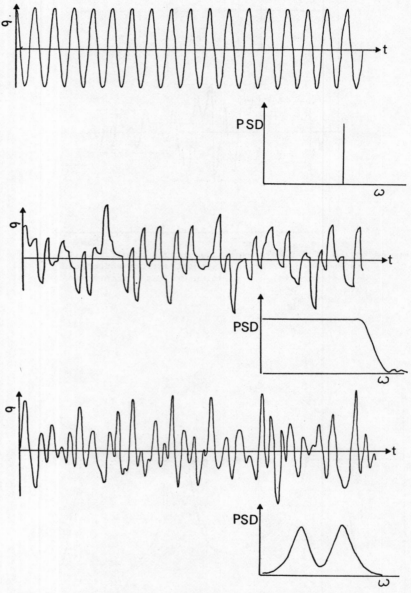

FIG. 7 TYPES OF LOAD SIGNAL USED

distribution of stress ranges. This is the basis of the analysis proposed in the
DNV rules for the design of offshore structures (1977 Appendix C). It is probable
that this would be a conservative analysis for many situations as interaction
effects often produce crack retardation. However one could conceive of circumstances, especially in corrosion fatigue, where interaction effects could accele-
rate crack growth. This possible problem is the reason for the current research
interest in interaction effects such as the incubation period.

In order to compare the effect of these three different signals, Fig.6, on
fatigue crack growth rates it is necessary to examine the statistical properties in
a little more detail. The broad band signal was found to have a Gaussian amplitude
distribution and a Rayleigh range distribution. The narrow band and double peaked
signals were also analysed and found to have the distributions shown in Figs.8
and 9. For the narrow band signal it can be seen that most of the peaks are positive (r = .0606) giving a value for β of 0.48. This should be compared with β = 0
for a true narrow band process and β = 1 for a broad band process. The range distribution seems fairly close to a Rayleigh distribution and the amplitudes distribution again Gaussian.

Fig.9 shows that the double peaked distribution has a slightly higher number
of negative peaks (r = 0.124) so that β is higher at 0.66. The amplitude distribution is again Gaussian but the range distribution seems to deviate from the
Rayleigh distribution. The value of β does not seem to be very sensitive to these
changes which makes it difficult to define when a signal is narrow band (9).

The range distributions and probability density functions for these two signals
are compared in Fig.10. It can be seen more clearly in this figure that the double
peaked distribution has a higher density of small ranges than the narrow band signal and correspondingly less of the larger ranges. This is probably a function of
the counting method but unless the crack propagation is discontinuous it is not
realistic to count using rainflow etc. One possible alternative is to conduct
the rainflow analysis over a short time interval. This would have the effect of
reducing the number of intermediate cycles and increasing the number of the larger
cycles.

Another way of showing the differences between these signals is to conduct an
S_h analysis for each one in order to show how they vary with the value of 'n'.
This has been done and the results are shown in Fig.11 for the three signals shown
in Fig.6, a sine wave and a theoretical Rayleigh distribution. It should be noted
that the broad band signal, with the damped square waveform, would always have a
relatively high r.m.s., so that the ratio of $S_{h/\sigma}$ is low. These differences between the signals should be discernible in fatigue crack growth data if presented
in the form of $K_{r.m.s.}$ vs $\frac{da}{dN}$ instead of K_h vs $\frac{da}{dN}$.

Fig.12 shows some fatigue crack growth data for HY80, a low alloy medium

W. D. Dover

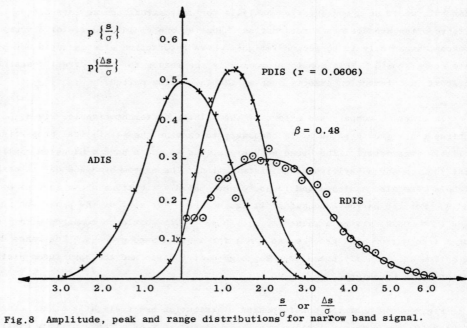

Fig.8 Amplitude, peak and range distributions for narrow band signal.

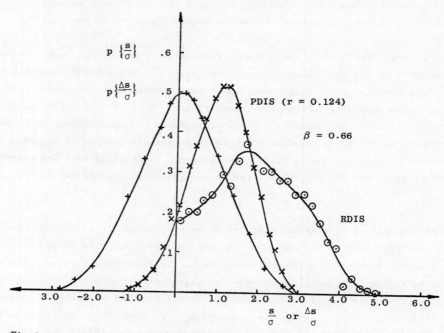

Fig.9 Amplitude, peak and range distributions for double peaked signal.

strength steel, obtained from tests using either a constant amplitude sine wave or
the broad band signal with a cut-off frequency of about 5 Hz. The lower curves in
this figure are the two sets of data in terms of K_{rms} while the top curve represents
the same data but this time expressed in terms of K_h using the information contained
in Fig.11. Other data for this material, and HY100, showing the same good agreement
on the basis of K_h, have been published elsewhere (10). Similar correlations using
these signals on an aluminium alloy, BS2L71, have also been reported (11).

Fatigue crack growth data for a mild steel, used for node sections in offshore
platforms, BS4360 50C, has also been produced. This study is not yet complete but
the results for the broad band and the double peaked signal are available. These
are shown in Fig.13 and again a good correlation is obtained if the data is plotted
in terms of K_h. Also included in this figure are constant amplitude data taken from
reference (12). It looks as if the random load data agrees with this constant
amplitude data but it is interesting to note that the slope varies with the mean
stress. The variation of 'n' with mean stress and the type of load history could
prove to be a guide to the extent of interaction effects. This variation had been
noticed in a previous study (7) and is worth further examination.

The narrow band tests have not been completed yet but from the S_h analysis it
would appear that it is more damaging than the double peaked signal. Thus the increase in cycle frequency, and consequent increase in the time rate of growth,
caused by the dynamic response could be slightly offset by the range distribution
being less damaging. This raises two questions which must be answered. Firstly, is
the system of range counting the correct one and secondly, is the range distribution
measured in the double peaked signal the same as that monitored in service on platforms in the northern North Sea? The latter information has been obtained, but not
released, making it difficult to continue with this particular analysis.

In attempting to produce basic data for the prediction of fatigue crack growth
rates in welded structures it is necessary to use one of the analyses of the load
time history just described and also to retain the other important characteristics
of the real life situations. In welded structures two other factors would seem to
be important and these are crack shape and K history. These two factors will now
be examined separately.

CRACK SHAPE PROBLEMS

The crack in a welded structure may well be a surface crack for most of the
fatigue life. This introduces two possible complications which unless completely
understood could mean that surface cracked specimens should be used for obtaining
material data.

Firstly if the structure is exposed to a corrosive environment, such as sea-
water, there will be movement of corrosion products, into and out of the crack.

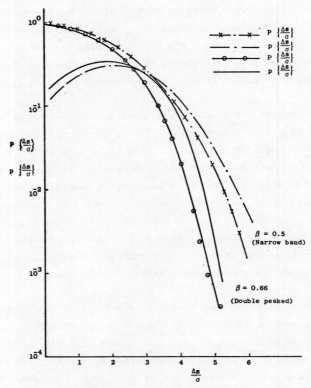

Fig.10   Comparison of range distributions for narrow band
and double peaked signals.

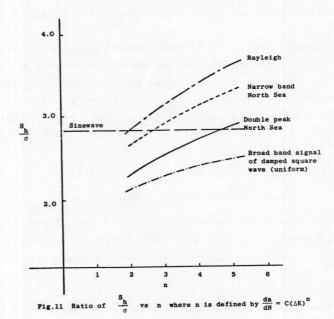

Fig.11   Ratio of $\frac{S_h}{\sigma}$ vs   n   where n is defined by $\frac{da}{dN} = C(\Delta K)^n$

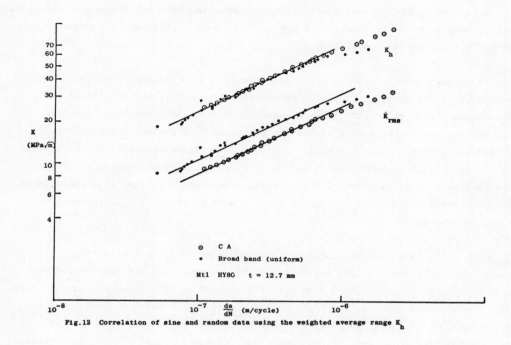

Fig.12 Correlation of sine and random data using the weighted average range K_h

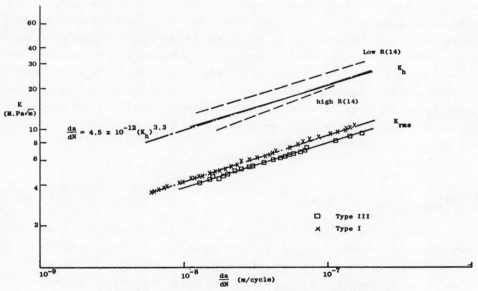

Fig.13 Correlation of random load data using the weighted average range K_h

This movement could be influenced by the crack shape. This in turn would influence
the magnitude of the corrosive effect and the measured material property. One would
either have to correctly model this behaviour or conduct the material property tests
on surface cracked specimens.

A second possible difficulty arises because of the varying plastic constraint
around the crack front. Studies of overload effects have shown that mixed mode
conditions give much greater retardation effects than plane strain conditions. If
the plastic constraint varies around the perimeter of a surface crack one would
expect the amount of retardation to vary around the perimeter resulting in a change
in the crack shape. This problem is currently being studied at UCL and a few preliminary results are available. Firm conclusions cannot be drawn from these tests
but as there is little information in this area it was felt that these results
might be of interest.

The tests have been conducted on surface cracked specimens of BS4360 Grade 50C
steel. A load signal of type III, shown in Fig. 6, was used and the crack depth
monitored by an A.C. potential drop system developed at UCL. Some preliminary tests
were conducted so that the crack growth under stationary random loading could be
assessed (13) and these are being followed by tests involving step changes in both
the mean and r.m.s. stress. Fig.14 shows the results for part of this test where
the mean stress was decreased. The results are plotted as the surface crack length
versus the crack depth. Prior to the change in mean load the ratio of $c/_a$ was
constant and after a delay period coinciding with the mean stress change the ratio
again became constant but at a different value. This shows that the delay effect
is greater at the surface ends than at the bottom of the crack. It has also been
observed that throughout this test, comprising many retardation periods, the crack
shape had a lower aspect ratio than found in earlier tests where r.m.s. and mean
stress were kept constant. It would seem that the size of the retardation effects
are dependent on the crack shape but perhaps more important is that the loading
could control the crack shape. Further tests are needed however before any firm
conclusions are reached on this question.

K HISTORY

One of the features often ignored in C.A. air fatigue crack growth tests is
the variation of the magnitude of the stress intensity factor with crack length
i.e. the K history effect. Under variable amplitude or corrosion fatigue conditions the K history could be important. For the former consider the influence of
a single peak overload on subsequent crack growth for the two situations where

(1) K = constant irrespective of crack length
(2) $K = S \sqrt{\pi a} \; (\sec \frac{\pi a}{W})^{\frac{1}{2}}$

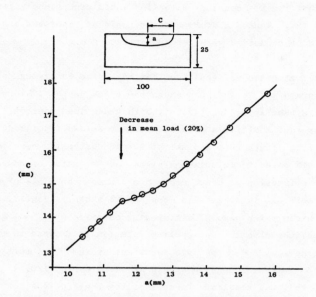

Fig.14 Random load fatigue crack growth test on Grade 50c steel
Surface crack - mean load change.

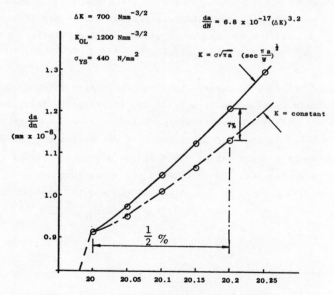

Fig.15 Effect of K history using the Wheeler model
with retardation factor $\left(\frac{r_{pi}}{\lambda}\right)^{1.3}$

If one uses a model, such as that due to Wheeler, to predict the subsequent growth for these two cases one would find the situation depicted in Fig.15. Here it can be seen that the K = constant situation would experience a longer delay period than case (2). Thus K history effects could be important and materials data tests should be conducted with the appropriate K history.

Fig.16 illustrates the difficulties that may arise in trying to do simplified tests in the laboratory. This figure shows the crack depth vs.N. curves for a T-butt weld and a tubular welded T-joint, both under load control. As can be seen the two curves are quite different and the tubular welded T-joint does not show the rapidly accelerating growth rate typical of a load controlled specimen. If one uses the measured growth rates to calculate a value for K, using standard specimen data, and plot this as a function of crack depth one can see the K history experienced by that type of structure. This has been done and is shown in Fig.17, together with the predicted K history for several different geometries and loadings. It would seem that the constant displacement cycling solution is closest to the tubular welded T-joint behaviour. Perhaps more important is that this sort of behaviour would be consistent with a change in stress of the order of 1/3, i.e. the crack is causing a change in local compliance such that the local stress, or load, is considerably reduced in the cracked region by the presence of the crack. This has important consequences for any life calculation or inspection procedure. This observation together with the apparent lack of correlation for large scale fatigue when compared on the basis of local stress (14) has highlighted the importance of understanding how the presence of a crack influences the load distribution at critical regions in structures. It would appear from these large scale test results that using the initial local stress to correlate fatigue data is too simplistic and that a function combining the nominal stress and the local stiffness may be necessary to describe damage accumulation. This possibility is currently being examined at UCL for offshore structures.

It is also of interest to compare this experimentally determined K history with that of specimen types commonly used in the laboratory. This comparison is shown in Fig.18 and it would appear that the surface cracked tension specimen is closest to the T-joint in terms of K history. If one switched to displacement control, or a suitable combination of force and displacement, then the exact K-history could be reproduced. However, when one takes into account the results quoted in the previous section it could be that the surface cracked specimen would be most suitable for this particular application.

CONCLUSIONS

1.   The weighted average range $K_h = \sqrt[n]{\overline{h_K^n}}$ can be used to correlate variable amplitude fatigue crack growth data for load time histories that do not exhibit strong interaction effects.

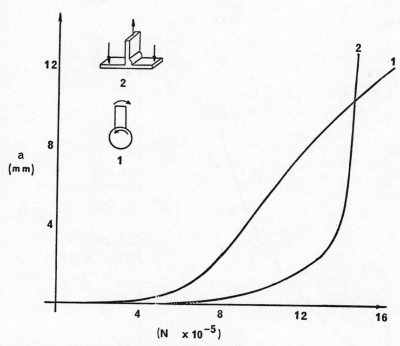

Fig. 16 Comparison of fatigue crack growth plots for T-butt
weld and T-joint specimen

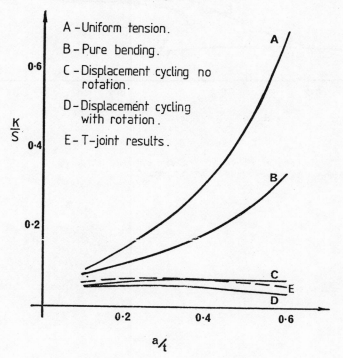

Fig. 17 Theorectical plots of K/S vs. a/t for on edge notch
under different types of loading

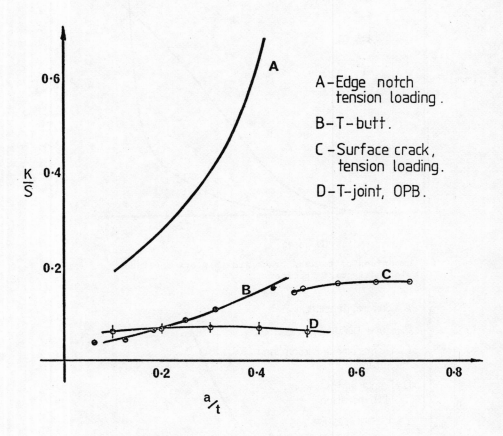

Fig. 18 Experimental plots of K/S vs. a/t for different
         specimen types under load control

2.   Fatigue crack growth data should be determined on surface cracked specimens.

3.   The K history of a crack located in a structure should be determined and re-produced in the laboratory study.

ACKNOWLEDGEMENTS

The author is grateful to Mr. S.W. Attwood for assistance with the signal analysis and the M.O.D. (P.E.) and S.R.C. Marine Technology Directorate for financial support of this work.

NOMENCLATURE

a, A	crack length for a through crack and crack depth for a surface crack (mm)
c	crack length for a surface crack (mm)
K	stress intensity factor (M Pa $\sqrt{m}$)
K_{rms}	($= \sigma\ f(a)$) (M Pa $\sqrt{m}$)
K_h	($= \sqrt[n]{\overline{h_K^n}}$) (M Pa $\sqrt{m}$)
h_K	an individual rise in K
σ	r.m.s. stress (M Pa)
h_s	an individual rise in stress (M Pa)
S	individual stress level (M Pa)
S_h	($= \sqrt[n]{\overline{h_s^n}}$) (M Pa)
S_{mean}	mean stress (M Pa)
ΔS	individual stress range (M Pa)
n	Paris Law exponent
N	number of cycles
$\dfrac{da}{dN}$	crack growth rate (m/cycle)
$\Delta\varepsilon_p$	plastic strain range
δ_p	plastic crack tip opening displacement range (mm)
ΔK	stress intensity factor range for a constant amplitude signal (M Pa $\sqrt{m}$)

K_{mean} mean value of stress intensity factor (M Pa $\sqrt{m}$)

a_{OL} crack length at overload (mm)

$r_{P\ OL}$ plastic zone size at overload (mm)

a_i crack length 'i' cycles after overload (mm)

r_{Pi} plastic zone of cycle 'i' (mm)

λ distance from current crack tip to overload boundary (mm)

m shaping factor for Wheeler model

a_r crack length 'r' cycles after overload (mm)

Q $\dfrac{K_{mean}}{K_h}$

$W_x\ (F)$ Spectral Density Function (S.D.F.)(P.S.D.)

F frequency (Hz)

w frequency (rad/sec)

PDIS   Peak distribution

ADIS   Amplitude distribution

RDIS   Range distribution

$p\{\frac{s}{\sigma}\},\ p\{\frac{\Delta s}{\sigma}\}$ probability density function $= \dfrac{s}{\sigma} \exp \left\{ -\dfrac{s^2}{2\sigma^2} \right\}$

$P\{\frac{s}{\sigma}\}$ probability distribution function $= \exp \left\{ \dfrac{-s^2}{2\sigma^2} \right\}$

R stress ratio $\dfrac{S_{min}}{S_{max}}$

da crack growth increment (mm)

β defined by $\beta^2 = 1 - (1 - 2r)^2$

r proportion of maxima that are negative

REFERENCES

(1) Dover, W.D. Eng. Frac. Mech., 5, 11, (1973).

(2) Wheeler, O.E. Trans. A.S.M.E. J. of Basic Eng.; 94, 181, (1972).

(3) Watson, P. and Dabell, B.J. Symp. Stat. Aspects of Fat. Test. S.E.E., Warwick, (1975)

Warwick, 1975.

(4) de Jonge, J.B., Schutz, D., Lowak, H. and Schijve, J., NLR Report No.
     TR 73029U, (1975).

(5) Swanson, S.R. Mat& Res. & Standards, $\underline{8}$, 10, (1968).

(6) Paris, P.C. Fatigue - An Interdisciplinary Approach. Proc. 10th Sagamore
     A.M.R.C., 197, (1964).

(7) Hibberd, R.D. and Dover, W.D. ICF4, Waterloo, Canada, $\underline{2}$, 1187, (1977).

(8) Dover, W.D., Holdbrook, S.J. and Hibberd, R.D. Eur. Offshore Steels. Res.
     Sem. Welding Institute, (1978).

(9) Pook, L.P. N.E.L. report No. 624, (1976).

(10) Hibberd, R.D. and Dover, W.D. I. Mech.E. conf. "The influence of the environ-
     ment on fatigue", (1977).

(11) Dover, W.D. and Boutle, N.F. J.Strain Analysis, $\underline{13}$, 129, (1978).

(12) Scott, P.M. and Silvester,D.R.V. Interim Tech. Rep. No. UKOSRP 3/02, (1977).

(13) Holdbrook, S.J. and Dover, W.D. Eng. Frac. Mech. accepted for publication.

(14) de Bak, J. Eur Offshore Steels Res. Sem. W.I., (1978).

PROBABILISTIC FRACTURE MECHANICS

A. B. Lidiard

Theoretical Physics Division, A.E.R.E., Harwell,
Oxfordshire OX11 0RA, U.K.

Abstract

This article reviews the theoretical calculation of the probabilities of failure
of engineering structures. The formulation begins with the failure criterion
provided by fracture mechanics (crack size greater than some critical crack size,
defined by material characteristics, geometrical characteristics of the section and
applied stresses) and shows how the probability of failure of the structure can be
related to the statistical distribution of material parameters, crack sizes and
applied stresses (§3). Present knowledge of these distributions in nuclear reactor
pressure vessels and piping is reviewed and their empirical basis is emphasized (§4).
Despite these limitations the calculations which have been made lead to a number of
useful and satisfactory conclusions: viz. they confirm the safety of these nuclear
structures, they determine which quantities the failure rates are sensitive to and
indicate which are the more vulnerable parts of the structure, they enable us to
quantify the benefits of in-service inspection, etc. (§5). More generally, the
heuristic value of these calculations is emphasized.

1.   INTRODUCTION

The mechanical integrity of engineering structures such as pressure vessels,
pipelines, nuclear reactors, offshore platforms, etc., is a matter of great practical
importance for both economic and safety reasons. In practice this integrity must be
assured by careful attention to many aspects of design, materials, manufacture,
inspection. etc. An important uncertainty is the possible presence of cracks in the
structure; such cracks can, under appropriate circumstances, extend unstably and thus
cause the failure of critical sections of the structure and of the structure itself.
It is the task of fracture mechanics to establish what these circumstances are, to
understand them and to provide an appropriate, quantitatively accurate phenomenology
– aspects which are considered in other papers at this conference. The design and
operation of these structures must therefore take account of the possible presence of
cracks. The conventional approach is one based upon a set of conservative
assumptions – about the maximum size of crack, the nature and frequency of transient
loadings of the structure, the material properties, crack growth rates, etc.
However, many of these quantities are statistically distributed and we can never be
absolutely sure that values worse than the chosen conservative limits will not be
encountered. This must be true of relevant material properties, for instance, as
long as we do not understand the factors controlling the occurrence of cracks, the
material toughness, the rates of crack growth by fatigue and so on; even when we do
understand them it may still not be possible to apply this to obtain absolute control
during manufacture. It must likewise be true of transient loadings resulting from
natural phenomena such as winds, waves and earthquakes.

These uncertainties therefore oblige us to take a statistical or 'probabilistic'
approach to the question of structural integrity. There are two ways of going about
this, one by the collection and analysis of 'historical' data on failures in related
systems, the other by the theoretical synthesis of failure probabilities from a
knowledge of the statistical distributions of the quantities which act together to
cause failure. The first way is illustrated by the careful studies of the failure
statistics of industrial pressure vessels by Smith and Warwick[1] and by various
other authors[2] and the consideration of their implications for the failure
probability of the pressure vessels of light-water reactors[3,4]. The
difficulties inherent in this approach are well illustrated by the discussions in
refs. 3 and 4 and centre round the difficulty of representing quantitatively the
relation between the population analysed (in this case industrial pressure vessels)
and the one whose failure rates we want to estimate (the particular population of
reactor vessels). The best that can be done is to estimate the ratio of the failure
probabilities in the two populations by consensus. There has therefore been a
growing interest in recent years in the prediction of failure probabilities by
synthesis from the knowledge of the statistical distribution of the various
underlying factors. (For general background to this field see refs. 5 and 6). It is
these calculations which are the subject of this paper.

The aims of these calculations are at least threefold:
(i) By calculating failure probabilities (either cumulative probabilities or

failure rates) to verify the safety of the structure in question, i.e. to verify that these probabilities are less than some acceptable limit (which will generally be determined by the assessed consequences of failure).

(ii) To indicate the factors to which these failure probabilities are sensitive and thus to point to any areas where present knowledge should be improved in order to obtain greater confidence in the demonstrated safety.

(iii) To estimate the gains in reliability, i.e. the reductions in failure probability, which may follow from particular programmes of in-service inspection or of other changes (e.g. in design, materials, manufacture, etc.). These calculations are thus simply a way of quantifying effects which otherwise would be assessed only qualitatively or intuitively.

It is the object of this paper to review these calculations, which in essence are quite simple but which can appear complex and rather diverse in their development. The next two sections therefore consider the general physical aspects and the basic mathematical formulation. The following section (§4) then briefly considers some of the details of the component distibution functions, while §5 summarizes some of the conclusions and results of applying these methods to the pressurized 'primary circuit' of light-water reactors (L.W.R.'s), i.e. to the pressure vessel itself and to the associated pipework. Although much of what we have to say is general, we shall, in fact, draw all our detailed illustrations with these applications in view, hoping thereby to give a sharper and more meaningful picture. Even here, however, the current literature is so extensive that we cannot be comprehensive. For a wider-ranging bibliography see the recent review by Johnston[7].

2. GENERAL PHYSICAL ASPECTS

The essential uncertainty is that introduced by the possibility that the structure may contain cracks in sections whose integrity is critical to that of the whole. Cracks are most serious when the plane of the crack is normal to a principal tensile stress (so-called mode I); the concentration of stress in the material at the crack edge or 'tip' can become so great that the crack extends across the section, which thus breaks. Fracture mechanics provides the criterion for this situation[8] and this is taken over into the probabilistic theory too.

Now although great care may be taken during manufacture to avoid the production of defective structures and to eliminate any which are produced by subsequent (non-destructive) examination, it is impossible to assert that there can be no cracks in the structures entering service. We must, therefore, assume that a certain fraction of the structures will contain one or more cracks or, equivalently, that for any one particular structure there is a certain probability that it contains one or more defects. Unfortunately, present understanding of the ways in which cracks arise is very limited, although the indications are that cracks occur most frequently, though not exclusively, in welded regions (Nichols[9]). Even empirical evidence of the probabilities of occurrence of cracks is very sketchy and this imposes a basic limitation to the reliability of probabilistic fracture calculations. Nevertheless, this situation will not persist indefinitely; furthermore it is of value to know what our present knowledge of the occurrence of cracks implies for the statistical reliability of structures.

Although the occurrence of cracks introduces the essential uncertainty, this
is not the only quantity which may have to be treated statistically. First, there is
the resistance of the material to unstable crack extension, i.e. its toughness, which
we shall here describe primarily by the K_{Ic} as defined by linear elastic fracture
mechanics[8]. We shall assume that $f(K_{Ic})dK_{Ic}$ is the probability that the
toughness in any structure in any location lies between K_{Ic} and $K_{Ic}+dK_{Ic}$.
This distribution is assumed normalized to unity, i.e.

$$\int_0^\infty f(K_{Ic})dK_{Ic} = 1 \tag{1}$$

(In order to prevent the mathematical notation from becoming too cumbersome we shall,
in fact, use $f(x)$ to denote all such probability distribution functions as long as it
is clear from the argument x which function is intended). The mean value of the
toughness, $\overline{K}_{Ic}$, of course, depends upon the nature of the alloy and will vary
with temperature, metallurgical composition, structure, etc. For particular alloys,
e.g. steels, there is limited information about other characteristics of the
distribution, e.g. mean-squared deviations about $\overline{K}_{Ic}$. In applications simple
unimodal forms are generally assumed for $f(K_{Ic})$.

The second important material property which may be statistically distributed
is crack growth by fatigue. This plays an important part in these probabilistic
calculations since the growth of cracks under variable stresses caused by vibrations
or other transient loadings will lead to structural failure probabilities which
increase with time. Unfortunately, the laws of fatigue crack growth at present are
purely empirical and rather uncertain. The simplest is the so-called Paris law; for
a periodic application of stress giving an associated stress-intensity amplitude
ΔK_I at the crack tip the rate of growth of the crack of depth a with the number of
stress cycles, N, is represented by

$$\frac{da}{dN} = C(\Delta K_I)^n . \tag{2}$$

Although this equation is widely used, there are clear indications that there is a
threshold value of ΔK_I below which no crack growth occurs, while at high values of
ΔK_I one would expect instability where the maximum value of K_I during the cycle
approaches the toughness K_{Ic} (see e.g. Scott[10]). Statistical fits to more
complicated laws which possess these characteristics do not appear to have been made,
although there are several analyses based on eqn. (2). The statistical approach to
fatigue crack growth is thus not well developed and in practice therefore most
calculations of such growth are deterministic and use 'upper bounds' to experimental
crack growth data.

Thirdly, we need to consider the transient loadings upon the structure. In
general, these divide into two classes, (i) those which are expected to occur either
regularly or randomly and with a certain frequency in normal service and (ii) those
accident or emergency loadings which are provided for, but which are only expected to
occur with a frequency of much less than once in the lifetime of the structure. The

frequent transient loadings of the first class, of course, are those which are responsible for fatigue crack growth. But it is possible for the more severe among them also to lead to failure of the structure. Thus we have both the possibility of failure under normal operating conditions and the additional possibility of failure under the much more severe, though improbable, accident and emergency conditions. The calculations are formulated differently in the two limits. In principle, it is, of course, possible to have intermediate cases too.

3. <u>GENERAL MATHEMATICAL FORMULATION</u>

We shall now consider the general formulation of the failure probability, given that failure occurs whenever a crack is present which is larger than the critical size for unstable crack extension (at the location considered and under the other conditions prevailing). To do this we consider a population of structures designed, manufactured, inspected and operated according to the same specifications, rules and conditions. These constrain the characteristics of the structures and the transient loadings to which they are subjected but do not determine them absolutely. We are therefore interested in the fraction of the population which fail over some definite period of time (cumulative failure probability) or in the fractional rate at which failures occur in the population (failure probability per unit time or failure rate). To do this we simply evaluate the chances that a structure contains a crack of greater than critical size when the corresponding stresses occur. To make things as clear as possible, we shall represent the crack distribution simply in terms of one parameter, namely the crack depth, i.e. the crack dimension through the section and normal to the tensile stress: see fig. 1. In principle we should also consider

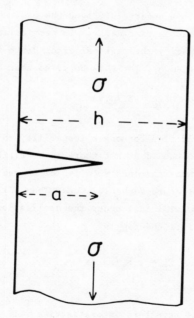

Fig. 1. Schematic diagram of a section of thickness, h, containing a crack of depth, a, and subject to a tensile stress, σ, normal to the plane of the crack.

length and orientation of cracks and their location in the section (surface or
buried), but, as we shall see, present information about the size distribution of
cracks is rather poor and it is probably adequate to consider the distribution in the
depth as an average over these other variables. (For an example of a calculation
where the cracks were classified by their length as well see Harris[11]).

Let us consider one particular critical section in the structure.
(Considerations of stress, weld volume, radiation effects, etc. will select certain
sections as the important ones determining the integrity of the structure; these may
be referred to as the critical sections). Let $N_t(x)dx$ be the average number of
cracks per structure which at time t lie in this section and which have a depth in
the range x to x+dx. Owing to the high degree of perfection obtainable in practice
we may assume that the total average number of cracks per structure of any
(significant) depth is much less than unity, i.e. that

$$\int_0^h N(x)dx \ll 1 \ . \tag{3}$$

where h is the thickness of the section. We shall therefore assume that the chance
of there being more than one crack in any structure (and thus, by implication, in any
one section of a structure) is negligibly small. The probability of failure of a
structure will then be simply the sum, over all sections, of the probabilities of
failure of the separate sections. We shall take this for granted in what follows and
will not encumber the notation by adding a suffix to denote the section. This
simplification can be removed if necesssary; see Nilsson[12].

Suppose first of all that the uncertainty over the presence of cracks is the
only aspect which must be treated statistically. In particular, if the material
properties are unique we can specify the critical crack depth in the section under
the application of a stress system $\underline{\sigma}$; let this be y, so that

$$K_{Ic} = K_I(\underline{\sigma},y) \ . \tag{4}$$

This expresses the critical condition for crack instability in the notation of linear
elastic fracture mechanics, but the idea that there is a critical crack depth y which
is a function of stress $\underline{\sigma}$ and material constants is, of course, far wider and is
contained in elastic-plastic fracture mechanics too. Then all those structures
containing a crack of depth x⩾y will fail under the application of $\underline{\sigma}$, i.e. the
fraction of the population to fail under $\underline{\sigma}$ is

$$P_f = \int_y^h N_t(x) \ dx \ . \tag{5}$$

Now a crack of depth a when the structure enters service will grow by fatigue as a
result of the fluctuating stresses associated with the transient loadings occurring
during normal operations. If both the material properties and the effect of the
transient stresses can be taken as unique, then there will be a definite relation
between the depth, a, of the crack at t = 0 and the depth at time t later. We take

this to be

$$x = \xi\ (a,t)\ . \tag{6}$$

An example of this function is obtained by integrating the Paris law (2) for the case where the stress-intensity factor ΔK_I is proportional to the square root of the crack depth, viz.

$$x = \xi(a,t) = \frac{a}{(1-\mu a^{\mu}\gamma t)^{1/\mu}}\ , \tag{7}$$

in which $\mu = \frac{n}{2}-1 > 0$ and where the coefficient γ is a simple combination of the numerical coefficients (C, n, etc.) and the rate of application of the transient stresses.

We ignore the generation of new cracks, since these will generally remain very small in the lifetime, and can therefore set

$$N_t(x)\ dx = N_o(a)\ da \tag{8}$$

in which x and a are related via eqn. (6). It is convenient then to replace (5) by

$$P_f = \int_{\xi^{-1}(y)}^{\xi^{-1}(h)} N_o(a)da \tag{9}$$

since the time-dependence of P_f then appears in the limits of the integral and not in the integrand. The function ξ^{-1} is the inverse function to ξ, i.e.

$$a = \xi^{-1}(x,t) \tag{10}$$

is the initial depth of a crack which is of depth x at time t. Corresponding to the example (7) we would have

$$a = \xi^{-1}(x,t) = \frac{x}{(1+\mu x^{\mu}\gamma t)^{1/\mu}}\ . \tag{11}$$

We note the following consequences of (9).

(i)   The growth of cracks by fatigue has the inevitable consequence that P_f increases with t. In many situations the upper limit of (9) is effectively infinite and thus constant but the lower limit decreases as t increases.

(ii)   In cases where the structure has been subjected before service to a proof test which imposes greater stresses than are afterwards experienced in service the initial values of P_f will, of course, be smaller but the relative time-dependence may be more marked.

(iii) The failure probability, P_f, depends on the toughness K_{Ic} through the lower limit $\xi^{-1}(y)$ and hence through (4). However, when crack growth is rapid the dependence of $\xi^{-1}(y)$ on y and hence on K_{Ic} can be rather weak. An example of this situation is provided by the pipework in the primary circuit of a pressurized water reactor[11].

The failure probability P_f given by the expression (9) will actually be a function of various parameters characterising the material properties (e.g. K_{Ic}, C, n) and the operating transients (stress amplitudes, $\Delta\sigma_k$, mean frequencies, etc.). Let us call these γ_1, γ_2, ... or, collectively, $\underline{\gamma}$. The probability given by (9) is the value $P_f(\underline{\gamma})$ we would calculate for a particular set of coefficients $\underline{\gamma}$. We often carry out such calculations by choosing 'bounding' values of these parameters, i.e. values which ensure that the calculated P_f is always greater than the true average value (i.e. so that the estimate is 'conservative'). It should be stated explicitly, however, that these bounding values are for the most part, if not always, limits to empirical values and not mathematical or theoretical bounds. For example, we may find by testing that the toughness of a particular class of steels manufactured according to specified rules never falls below, say, 150 $MNm^{-\frac{3}{2}}$. This would then be used as a conservative value of K_{Ic} in these calculations; but there is at present no theory by which we could show that lower values will not be obtained.

If, however, we have enough information to calculate the probability distribution of these parameters so that $f(\underline{\gamma})d\underline{\gamma}$ is the probability that they lie in the range $\underline{\gamma}$ to $\underline{\gamma}+d\underline{\gamma}$, then the failure probability we require is

$$\overline{P}_f = \int_\Gamma P_f(\underline{\gamma})\ f(\underline{\gamma})d\underline{\gamma}\ , \tag{12}$$

where the integration is over the whole of the parameter space, Γ. We note the following points.

(i)   This form assumes that there are no correlations between the occurrence of a crack on the one hand and the parameters governing crack growth rate, toughness, etc. on the other. Metallurgical intuition might suggest such correlations but while empirical information about these quantities remains so limited it is hardly possible to do more than note this as a possible limitation on (12).

(ii)   Obviously we can make intermediate calculations in which some of the parameters are treated as stochastic variables and some are given definite bounding values. Different applications may make different choices. For example, if $P_f(\underline{\gamma})$ proves to be insensitive to a particular parameter γ_i there is little point in incurring the additional mathematical and computational complexity of treating it as a stochastic variable. Uncertainty about the distribution of a variable is another practical reason for using a definite bounding value.

(iii) Equation (12) gives the failure probability under the application of $\underline{\sigma}$ when the integration is taken over the whole of the parameter space Γ. In the next section we discuss the distribution functions but it is necessary to refer here to a point of importance for pressurized components which have passed a pre-service proof test ($\underline{\sigma}^P$). For in this case we know that all structures which have passed such a test should also survive a repeat application of $\underline{\sigma}^P$ at t = 0. In other words for the population of structures in service we have $P_f(\underline{\sigma}^P, t = 0) = 0$. This imposes a limitation on $\overline{P}_f$

and if the proposed distributions $N_o(a)$ and $f(\gamma)$ should lead to a non-zero value of $\overline{P}_f(\underline{\sigma}^P, 0)$ then this quantity must be subtracted from (12) to obtain the correct failure probability for this population of structures. This reduces the region of integration by cutting out that segment which with the given $N_o(a)$ and $f(\gamma)$ would lead to a non-zero $P_f(\underline{\sigma}^P, t=0)$. An illustration is given in fig. 2.

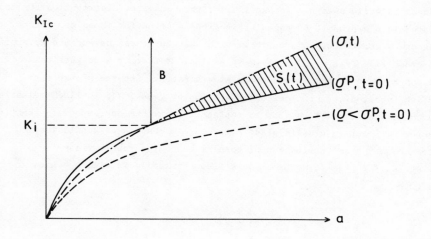

Fig. 2. K_{Ic} - a plane in the (Γ, a) space, i.e. all γ-parameters apart from K_{Ic} are constant in the plane shown. The full line is the boundary defined by the pressure test at $t = 0$, i.e. $K_{Ic} = K_I(\underline{\sigma}^P, a)$. The dashed line is defined by the transient $\underline{\sigma}$ at $t = 0$. There are no contributions to the failure integral (12) from within these curves after the pressure test ($t = 0+$). The dot-dashed line is the boundary $K_{Ic} = K_I(\sigma, \xi(a))$ defined by the transient $\underline{\sigma}$ at $t > 0$; there are contributions to the failure integral (12) only from the shaded region. The range of integration in eqn.(27) is indicated by the line marked B. (This illustration is one for which the larger cracks grow proportionately faster than the small ones. As time goes on the point of interaction moves down the solid curve towards the origin. In this case failures come predominantly from large cracks and large toughnesses.)

(iv) The expression (12) gives the fraction of the total population of structures which fail under the application of $\underline{\sigma}$ at time t, it being assumed that the population is sufficiently large that we are not interested in statistical fluctuations in this failure probability. If this is not the case, then we can evaluate the probability distribution function of P_f. Formally, this can be obtained from the integral of $f(\underline{\gamma})$ over the surface Σ defined by

$$P_f(\underline{\gamma}) = \text{const} \tag{13}$$

i.e.

$$f(P_f) = \int_{\Sigma} f(\underline{\gamma})d\Sigma \ . \tag{14}$$

In practice, Monte Carlo methods with 'importance sampling' provide convenient ways of evaluating the distribution $f(P_f)$: see ref. 11 for example.

While eqns. (12) and (14) provide formal solutions to the problem these can be developed in various ways. In particular, the parameter distribution $f(\underline{\gamma})$ can be separated into a product of the distribution function for those parameters governing crack growth (e.g. C, n, etc.) with that for those parameters governing critical crack size (e.g. K_{Ic}) - at least as long as there are no physical correlations between toughness and crack growth rates. Let the probability distribution function for critical crack size under $\underline{\sigma}$ be $f(y)$; in linear elastic fracture mechanics we shall be able to replace this by the corresponding function for toughness K_{Ic} but in elastic-plastic fracture mechanics we should in principle consider the distribution of both K_{Ic} and of an appropriate critical stress for plastic deformation ('flow stress'). We will now have in place of (5)

$$\overline{P}_f = \int_{o}^{h} dy \int_{y}^{h} f(y)N_t(x)dx \ , \tag{15a}$$

or, equivalently,

$$\overline{P}_f = \int_{o}^{h} dx \int_{o}^{x} f(y) \ N_t(x)dy. \tag{15b}$$

Here the crack size distribution function at time t is now

$$N_t(x) = \int_{o}^{x} N_o(a) \ \Phi_t(x,a)da \ , \tag{16}$$

in which the 'transfer function' $\Phi_t(x,a)$ is the probability that a crack initially of depth a has a depth x after a time t. This distribution arises from both the statistical distribution of material properties (e.g. C, n) and the possible randomness in the transient stresses. Since cracks cannot shrink by fatigue, $\Phi_t(x,a)$ is necessarily zero for x<a. Thus

$$\int_{a}^{\infty} \Phi_t(x,a)dx = 1 \ . \tag{17}$$

The failure integral $\overline{P}_f$ can therefore be written in various ways. Thus from (16) and the second of the two forms (15) we have

$$\overline{P}_f = \int_0^h dx \int_0^x da \int_0^x dy \; N_o(a)\Phi_t(x,a)f(y)$$

$$= \int_0^h da \int_a^h dx \int_0^x dy \; N_o(a)\Phi_t(x,a)f(y) \tag{18}$$

We note that

$$\chi_t(a) = \int_a^h dx \int_0^x \Phi_t(x,a)f(y)dy \tag{19}$$

is the probability that a crack initially (t=0) of depth a is critical under $\underline{\sigma}$ at t. Hence

$$\overline{P}_f = \int_0^h N_o(a)\,\chi_t(a)da \; . \tag{20}$$

Nilsson[12] evaluated this quantity $\chi(a)$ in his formulation ($F_{acr}(a_o)$ in his notation) and hence obtained $\overline{P}_f$.

On the other hand if we start from the first of eqns. (15) we obtain

$$\overline{P}_f = \int_0^h dy \int_y^h dx \int_0^x N_o(a)\Phi_t(x,a)f(y)da \; . \tag{21}$$

If we limit ourselves to linear elastic fracture mechanics, then this can be written instead as

$$\overline{P}_f = \int_0^\infty f(K_{Ic})dK_{Ic} \int_y^h dx \int_0^x N_o(a)\Phi_t(x,a)da \; , \tag{22}$$

where the lower limit of integration over x is related to K_{Ic} through the failure condition (4).

These various expressions (12), (15), (20), (21) and (22) are equivalent to one another but are used variously by different authors.

To complete this section we must now consider more explicitly the relation of $\overline{P}_f$ to the quantities we are interested in. Summed over all sections of the structure considered the quantity P_f is the fraction of the population to fail under the application of the stress system $\underline{\sigma}$. There are two limiting cases to be considered corresponding essentially to normal operations and to emergency or fault conditions. Let us take the emergency conditions first. In this case we may suppose that the conditions occur very rarely indeed. For example, the conditions classified as emergencies or faults with light water reactors have been estimated to occur with a frequency, f_E, of only 10^{-4} to 10^{-2} per reactor year[13,14]. The rate at which structures fail will therefore be simply

$$Q_f^E = f_E \, \overline{P}_f \, (\underline{\sigma}^E, t) \; , \tag{23}$$

i.e. Q_f^E is the fraction of the total population to fail in this way per unit time. The aim must be to ensure that very few, if any, structures are subjected to these conditions in their lifetime, but also if they do occur that $P_f \ll 1$.

The situation with the normal operating transients is different. Here we may suppose that effectively every structure in the population will be subjected to the transient stresses $\underline{\sigma}$ in some small but non-zero time interval Δt which is much less than the lifetime of the structure. We are interested in the failure rate, i.e. in the fraction of the original population of structures failing between t and $t+\Delta t$ divided by Δt. This is

$$Q_f^N = \frac{\overline{P}_f(t+\Delta t) - \overline{P}_f(t)}{\Delta t}$$
$$= \frac{d\overline{P}_f}{dt} \; . \tag{24}$$

The argument is elementary. The quantity $\overline{P}_f$, by definition, is the fraction of the population to fail if the <u>first</u> application of σ were made at $t+\Delta t$. But since $\overline{P}_f$ increases monotonically with t it follows that this fraction includes all the structures which would have failed at earlier times if $\underline{\sigma}$ had been applied before time t. In other words, $\overline{P}_f(t)$ is actually the cumulative failure probability, while Q_f^N is the corresponding 'hazard function'. (Strictly the hazard function is $(dP_f/dt)/(1-P_f)$ in which the denominator corrects for the diminishing population, but in the present case since $\overline{P}_f \ll 1$ this can be replaced by (24)). Obviously, from among the various transients it is those causing the most severe stresses and the smallest critical crack depths which are important in determining $\overline{P}_f$ directly; all, however, contribute in some measure through the crack growth.

In intermediate cases we see that the cumulative failure probability will be $\overline{P}_f$ times the fraction of the population to have experienced the transient stresses $\underline{\sigma}$ in time t. If these occur with constant probability f per unit time we have $(1-e^{-ft})\overline{P}_f$. Thus the failure rate will be

$$Q_f = \frac{d}{dt}\left\{(1-e^{-ft})P_f\right\}$$

$$= fe^{-ft}\overline{P}_f + (1-e^{-ft})\frac{d\overline{P}_f}{dt} \quad . \qquad (25)$$

When ft $\ll 1$ this gives (24), while in the opposite limit ft $\gg 1$ it gives (23).

Finally, we note that if the probability distribution functions for material and other parameters are constant in time then by (12) the derivative dP_f/dt is

$$\frac{d\overline{P}_f}{dt} = -\int_\Gamma f(\underline{Y})N_o(\xi^{-1}(y))\frac{\partial\xi^{-1}(y)}{\partial t}d\gamma \qquad (26)$$

The use of this and associated expressions in $\xi^{-1}(y)$, i.e. the crack depth which is just critical at time t, often proves to be convenient. The example (7) allows $\xi^{-1}(y)$ to be obtained explicitly, which is a useful simplification[15-17] If we suppose that the toughness is the only parameter to show significant variations then in place of (26) we should have explicitly

$$\frac{dP_f}{dt} = -\int_{K_i}^\infty f(K_{Ic})N_o(\xi^{-1}(a))\frac{\partial\xi^{-1}}{\partial t}(a)\,dK_{Ic} \quad , \qquad (27)$$

which is the expression we have used in our discussions[15-17] of reactor vessel reliability under normal operating conditions (see fig. 2 for the definition of the lower limit of integration).

4. THE DISTRIBUTION FUNCTIONS

Before this formalism can be applied to a particular structure it is necessary to obtain estimates of the crack-size distribution function and of the probability distribution functions for the various material and other parameters, i.e. of $N_o(a)$, $f(K_{Ic})$ and $\Phi(x,a)$ in eqn. (22) or of their equivalents. The calculated failure probabilities will be more sensitive to some of these than to others depending on the circumstances – although it is obvious from eqn. (5) onwards that the crack size distribution has a direct bearing on the results. Unfortunately, at the present time the information available on all the primary distribution functions is purely observational and empirical and even then it is often only very sketchy; there is no theory to guide the choice of these functions. In this section we shall briefly review the representations which have been used. We deal first with the crack size distribution and the toughness distribution and then consider the calculation of $\Phi(x,a)$ and the functions which enter into it.

162 A. B. Liddiard

4.1 The Initial Crack Size Distribution Function, $N_o(a)$

It is often appropriate to divide the problem into two parts corresponding
to the process of manufacture itself and the subsequent stage of pre-service
inspection. This separation is particularly appropriate when advanced techniques
of non-destructive examination, such as ultrasonic techniques, are used in the
pre-service inspection but not during preceding stages of manufacture. As a
result, we write $N_o(a)$ as the product of two factors, (i) the size distribution
function of cracks resulting from manufacture, $A(a)$, and (ii) the probability
$B(a)$ of not detecting such cracks in the course of the subsequent pre-service
inspections. Thus

$$N_o(a) = A(a) \ B(a) \quad . \tag{28}$$

Let us take $A(a)$ first. It is generally agreed that although cracks may
occur in forged sections and in plates they are much more likely to arise in
welded regions (see e.g. ref. 9). It is therefore reasonable to write $A(a)$ as
the product of the total number of cracks in the section (welded region) with a
probability distribution function in crack depth, a, and consider the two factors
separately. The idea is that the total number of cracks (of all sizes) will be
proportional to the volume of weld (including the heat-affected zone) in the
section while the probability distribution function will be common to a range of
structures made from similar materials. Estimates of both factors differ
substantially. Thus the absolute number of cracks per unit volume of weld region
in large reactor vessels has been estimated as lying between about 0.4 m^{-3}
(ref. 11) up to 40 m^{-3} (ref. 12). Since failure probabilities are directly
proportional to this number it is clearly important to obtain better estimates
and to understand better the factors controlling this quantity.

Most of these cracks will be small and all authors assume that the
distribution function therefore decreases monotonically with increasing crack
depth, generally in some exponential way. The range of forms employed can be
seen by comparing the assumptions in refs. 4, 11, 12, 18-21; these papers are
addressed to similar systems, namely the reactor vessel and associated pressure
circuit of light water reactors, but the proposed functions are very different
from one another: see fig. 3. There is no fundamental way of choosing between
these forms at the present time and in the nature of things it is difficult to
come by data on deep cracks which would allow an empirical choice to be made.
The authors of ref. 4 attempted to include some, very limited, information on
deep cracks in their function for P.W.R. vessels, but their arguments must be
regarded as very tentative. The matter requires considerable further attention.
In these circumstances, Harris's assumption that the characteristic parameters in
his $A(a)$ are themselves statistically distributed seems to us a rather needless
complication. It might be more meaningful to carry out discrete sensitivity
analyses to determine the influence of present uncertainties on the calculated
failure probabilities.

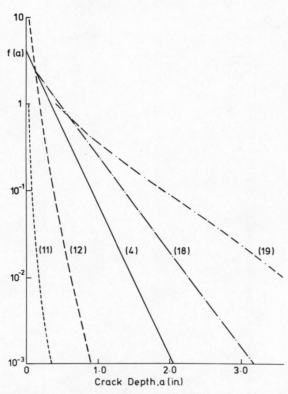

Fig. 3. Comparison of the functions f(a) proposed by various authors
(a in in., f(a) in in.$^{-1}$). References are as shown on the curves.
The curve from ref. 11 is for P.W.R. pipework (various steels) while the
others are intended to apply to reactor vessels (A533B and A508
steels); that from ref. 18 is not strictly comparable to the others as
it is the size distribution after manufacture <u>and</u> inspection but this
evidently sets a lower limit for f(a) after manufacture alone.

The second consideration is the possibility of not detecting cracks during
the inspections following manufacture. We can assume that all cracks detected
are repaired and 'made good' or else shown to be incapable of causing
failure[22]. We are thus concerned with the probability of missing cracks
during inspection as a function of crack depth, a. One may assume that the most
important of the available inspection methods is that of ultrasonic examination
and concentrate on its efficiency. (A quantitative comparison of the benefits of
ultrasonic examination and of radiographic examination which has been given by
Harris[11] for P.W.R. pipework confirms this). The desired function must be
unity for infinitesimally small cracks and decrease as the crack depth increases.
All authors suppose that B(a) decreases monotonically with a but divide into

those who assume that B(a) goes asymptotically to zero at large x (e.g. refs. 11
and 19) and those who assume that the asymptotic value is small but non-zero
(e.g. refs. 4 and 12). Some examples of the assumed forms are given in fig. 4.

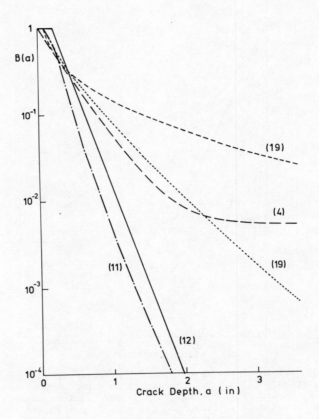

Fig. 4. Comparison of the functions B(a) proposed by various authors
for the chance of missing a crack of depth a during ultrasonic
inspection. References are as shown on the curves.

The differences are substantial. Present experimental and test information is
sketchy and applies to rather diverse situations[23], but the present PISC
series of tests should provide more coherent information for thick
sections[24].

The function B(a) thus with A(a) gives us the size distribution of cracks in
structures as they enter service; $N_o(a) = A(a)B(a)$. We may, however, also
suppose that B(x) gives the chance of missing a crack of depth x during an
in-service inspection at time t. The crack size distribution when the structure

re-enters service after its first in-service inspection will then be $N_t(x)B(x)$.
Subsequent in-service inspections can be modelled similarly.

Lastly, it may be noted that Harris[11], in particular, assumes that the
characteristic parameters in his B(a) (see fig. 4) are also statistically distributed. Presumably this could be made to correspond to the use of a variety of
ultrasonic inspection equipment and methods, but like his distribution of the parameters in A(a) it is apparently intended merely to represent our present uncertainties
over B(a). But these would seem to be best dealt with by discrete sensitivity
analyses.

4.2   The Toughness Distribution

The fracture toughness of ferritic steels, and of many other metals and alloys,
does, of course, vary with temperature in an important way[8]. We are here concerned
not with this temperature variation but with the distribution of toughness at any
one temperature. Actually, we shall have in mind mainly high operating temperatures
where these steels have a high toughness which is insensitive to temperature ('upper-
shelf' region).

For these conditions the fracture toughness, K_{Ic}, is not always easily measured
and it is not therefore surprising that there is not much direct information on
$f(K_{Ic})$. The distribution of K_{Ic} values for a given class of alloy, however, is
expected to arise from uncontrolled variations in composition and metallurgical
structure and we might therefore suppose that a Gaussian or normal distribution
would be a reasonable assumption[4,12,15-17]. This requires only a knowledge of the
mean toughness $\overline{K}_{Ic}$ and of the standard deviation. For the tough steels used in
nuclear applications (A533B, A508 steels) the standard deviation appears to be about
10-15% of the mean value. Another distribution which is sometimes used is the
Weibull distribution:

$$f(K_{Ic}) = 0, \qquad K_{Ic} < K_o$$
$$= \kappa(K_{Ic}-K_o)^m \exp\left\{-\frac{\kappa}{(m+1)}(K_{Ic}-K_o)^{m+1}\right\}. \qquad (29)$$

The additional qualitative characteristic of the Weibull distribution is the cut-off
at $K_{Ic} = K_o$. This can be used to represent the influence of materials selection
procedures during manufacture. Actually, materials selection will be based
on measures not of K_{Ic} but of more empirical quantities, e.g. Charpy V-notch impact
energies, C_V. Such Charpy values can be converted to K_{Ic} through the empirical
relationship first proposed by Rolfe and Novak[25], which, in its usual form, is

$$\left(\frac{K_{Ic}}{\sigma_y}\right)^2 = 5\left\{\frac{C_V}{\sigma_y} - 0.05\right\}, \qquad (30)$$

in which K_{Ic} is in k.s.i.$\sqrt{in}$., σ_y, the yield stress is in k.s.i. and C_V is in
ft.lbs(wt). (To convert to the SI form note that 1 k.s.i.$\sqrt{in}$. = 1.10 $MNm^{-3/2}$,
1 k.s.i. = 6.90 MPa, 1 ft.lb(wt) = 1.36J).

A. B. Lidiard

The practical difficulties of measuring K_{Ic} directly for very tough
steels suggest another approach, namely the calculation of $f(K_{Ic})$ from eqn.
(30) and the measured distributions of C_V and of yield stress, σ_y. This was,
in fact, done by Becher and Pedersen[18] from assumed Weibull distributions of
C_V and of yield stress, σ_y, fitted to measured data. The result for A533B
steel at 'upper-shelf' temperatures is shown in fig. 5 and evidently does not
differ much from a normal distribution. Evidently, other empirical
relationships, such as that between K_{Ic} and nil-ductility-temperature, can
also be used in a similar way[26].

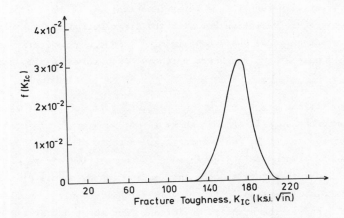

Fig. 5.   The distribution function of the upper-shelf fracture
toughness, K_{Ic}, of A533B steel as obtained by Becher and
Pedersen[18] from distributions of Charpy V-notch energy and of yield
stress.   (1 k.s.i. $\sqrt{in.}$ = 1.10 $MNm^{-3/2}$).   (After Becher and
Pedersen[18]).

Lastly, it should also be noted that, although most calculations assume that
these material distributions are independent of time, there are physical effects
which can cause reductions in toughness, e.g. strain ageing and radiation
embrittlement.

4.3   The Function $\Phi_t(x,a)$

The calculation of the transfer function requires the integration of the
crack growth law (e.g. eqn. (2)) and the averaging of the solution over all
possible transient stresses and all possible values of the material constants
(e.g. C and n in eqn. (2)).   An example of the results of doing this numerically
by Monte Carlo methods is shown in fig. 6, taken from Becher and Pedersen's
calculations[18] for the pressure vessel of a Boiling Water Reactor (B.W.R.).
On the other hand it is difficult to make much progress with the analysis of

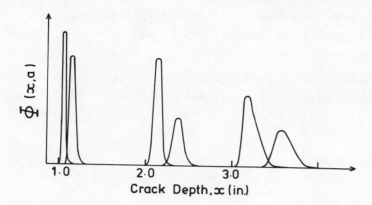

Fig. 6. The transfer function $\Phi_t(x,a)$ for cracks initially (a) 1, 2 and 3 in. deep at t = 10 and 40 yrs. operation of a B.W.R. vessel as calculated by Becher and Pederson[18]. Observe the function is skewed towards larger crack growth, presumably as a result of the assumed log-normal distribution of the parameter C in eqn. (2). (After Becher and Pedersen[18].)

$\Phi_t(x,a)$ when the constants in the crack growth equation and the occurrence of the transient stresses are statistically distributed. Some progress can be made, however, when two particular assumptions are allowable:

(i) The constant C in the Paris law (2) is statistically distributed, but the index n is not. In the absence of any sound theoretical analysis of fatigue crack growth it is difficult to know whether this is a good assumption or not. Both Nilsson[12] and Harris[11] make it, but assume differing values of n (2 and 4 respectively): they both fit the distribution of C to a log-normal function, i.e. to a normal distribution in ln C.

(ii) The stress-intensity function ΔK_I is separable into the stress amplitude and a function of crack depth k(a), i.e.

$$\Delta K_I = \Delta \sigma k(a) .$$
(31)

This should be good for transients which are primarily pressure transients but will not be so good when appreciable thermal stresses are also present. (But see Scott[10]).

We can then formally integrate eqn. (2) to give the depth at time t of a crack of initial depth a, as

$$\int_a^x \frac{da}{[k(a)]^n} = C \sum_k^{(t)} \Delta \sigma_k^n ,$$
(32)

where the sum is over all the transient stress cycles occurring in time t.

If now we can obtain the probability distribution function for the right hand side of (32) we can in principle also obtain $\Phi(x,a)$, since (32) implies a functional relationship between a and x in which the r.h.s. appears as a parameter. Let us take the two factors, C and $S \equiv \sum_k^{(t)} \Delta\sigma_k^n$ separately and deal with S first.

Suppose, first of all, that there is only one <u>type</u> of important transient and that, on average, this occurs a large number of times, N_t, in the time t. Then Nilsson[12] has pointed out that we can regard $\Delta\sigma_k^n$ of each transient, k, as a stochastic variable and apply the central limit theorem[27] to the sum

$$S = \sum_k^{N_t} \Delta\sigma_k^n \qquad (33)$$

This theorem states that, in the limit of large N_t, S is normally distributed, i.e.

$$f(S) \rightarrow \frac{1}{(2\pi)^{\frac{1}{2}}\Sigma} \exp\left(-(S-\overline{S})^2/2\Sigma^2\right) , \qquad (34)$$

in which the mean value is

$$\overline{S} = \overline{N_t\Delta\sigma^n} = N_t \int_0^\infty \Delta\sigma^n f(\Delta\sigma) d(\Delta\sigma) , \qquad (35)$$

and the mean square likewise is

$$\Sigma^2 = N_t \int_0^\infty \left((\Delta\sigma)^n - \overline{\Delta\sigma^n}\right)^2 f(\Delta\sigma) d(\Delta\sigma) . \qquad (36)$$

Since $\Delta\sigma$ is an amplitude and thus necessarily positive the distribution $f(\Delta\sigma)$ is zero for $\Delta\sigma<0$. The generalisation to cases where there is more than one type of transient is straightforward. We suppose that in the time t there are N_{it} transients of type i and that the corresponding distribution function is $f^{(i)}(\Delta\sigma)$. In place of (35) and (36) for $\overline{S}$ and Σ^2 there will be sums over the various types of transient, but the distribution of S remains normal, i.e. as given by (34).

For the conditions under which it applies, this result is evidently very useful as the form (34) is independent of the form of $f(\Delta\sigma)$ - which enters only into the parameters $\overline{S}$ and Σ. (But note that the existence of higher moments of the distribution is a condition of the application of the result). It is not necessarily a simple matter to verify that N_t is large enough for the limiting form to apply, however. Thus the effect of having a relatively high index n ($\sim$4) in the crack growth law is that relatively infrequent transients of large stress amplitude can be more important contributers to S than much more frequent

transients of only small stress amplitude. In these circumstances, which may
apply to light-water nuclear reactors, the important transients may not in fact
be sufficiently frequent for (34) to be correct. An example of this kind is
provided by Harris's calculation for the growth of cracks in reactor
pipework[11]. Fig. 7 shows the probability distribution, f(S), for one
particular location, at t = 40 years, as obtained numerically by a Monte Carlo
method. The distribution is quite visibly skewed and, in fact, Harris was able
to fit these results to a log-normal distribution. Although details are not
given, this skewness is presumably a result of the relatively small number of
important transients (1 a year or less). If this explanation is correct it may
indicate a general limitation on the use of (34), since in practice the dominant
transients will often be the relatively few types of severe transient.

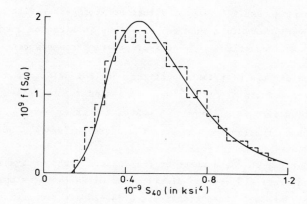

Fig. 7. The probability distribution function, f(S), for the factor S
in the crack growth equation of the joint between the outlet nozzle and
the steam line of a P.W.R. after 40 years' service (S in (k.s.i.)^4;
to obtain S in (MPa)^4 multiply by 2267). The histogram is obtained
from a Monte Carlo calculation while the full line is a log-normal
distribution having the expected (independently calculable) mean and
mean square values. (After Harris[11]).

This matter is worthy of further analysis.

    The above has assumed that definite fixed numbers of the various types of
transient occur in the time t. In fact, these numbers will also be distributed
statistically. If a given type of transient can be supposed to occur randomly
but with a fixed average frequency per unit time then the probability that m
transients occur in time t is given by the Poisson distribution,

$$f_m = \frac{(\alpha t)^m}{m!} e^{-\alpha t} \quad .$$

                                                                    (37)

This distribution is normalised, i.e.

$$\sum_{m=0}^{\infty} f_m = 1 \qquad\qquad (38)$$

However, for the transients which arise in normal operations (as distinct from emergencies) we are generally concerned with quite high average frequencies of occurrence so that both αt and m are much greater than unity. Stirling's approximation may then be used for m! and for the region around the most probable value of m , f_m can then be replaced by

$$f_m \sim \frac{1}{\sqrt{2\pi\alpha t}} \exp\left(-(m-\overline{m})^2/2\alpha t\right) , \qquad\qquad (39)$$

where the most probable value $\overline{m} = \alpha t - \frac{1}{2} + O(\frac{1}{\alpha t})$. If we regard $m/\alpha t$ as a continuous variable then in the limit of $\alpha t \gg 1$ the function (39) tends to a Dirac δ-function $\delta(\frac{m}{\alpha t} - 1)$; in other words, fluctuations in m about the average value αt can be neglected. This limiting result for large values of αt together with the smaller sensitivity of S to variations in m than to variations in $\Delta\sigma$ can be used to justify the neglect of fluctuations in m in appropriate circumstances[11].

We must now consider the distribution of the coefficient C in the law of crack growth. Several authors[11,12,18,21] have suggested that C follows a log-normal distribution (though different values of the index n are used). The long tail on such a distribution can make the distribution of C more important than the distribution of S in determining $\Phi_t(x,a)$. However, if we can ignore fluctuations in the numbers of the various types of transient which occur in time t we can relate Φ_t to the distribution of CS rather simply. Firstly, we note that for the normal transients S is closely proportional to the elapsed time, t, i.e. $S = S_0 t$. Thus the depth x of a crack at time t is determined by its initial depth a and the product $CS_0 t \equiv \gamma t$, thus

$$x = \xi(a, \gamma t). \qquad\qquad (40)$$

The distribution function $\Phi_t(x,a)$ is then determined by the distribution of γ. Thus, regarding Φ_t as a function of x, we have

$$\Phi_t(x,a)dx = f(\gamma)d\gamma, \qquad\qquad (41)$$

$$\Phi_t(x,a) = \frac{f(\gamma)}{\left(\frac{\partial\xi}{\partial\gamma}\right)} \qquad\qquad (42)$$

Equivalently, if we regard Φ_t as a function of a,

$$\Phi_t(x,a) = \frac{f(\gamma)}{\left(\frac{\partial\xi^{-1}}{\partial\gamma}\right)} \qquad\qquad (43)$$

By using these expressions (42) and (43) one can easily calculate $\Phi_t(x,a)$ as a

function of x and of a and thereby show that the denominators have the effect of
'spreading out' $\Phi_t(x,a)$ further than would be the case if the factor $f(\gamma)$ were
alone present. However, for the range of crack growth rates likely in reactor
vessels $f(\gamma)$ dominates. In reactor pipework the denominators will be much more
important.

In this section we have reviewed the distributions of crack size, toughness
and crack growth rates. It is clear that further understanding of these is
required and, in particular, that analysis of full scale numerical (e.g. Monte
Carlo) calculations for derived functions such as $\Phi_t(x,a)$ is very desirable.

5. <u>APPLICATIONS</u>

In this section we shall briefly review some applications of these
calculations to light water reactors (pressure vessels and pressurized circuits).
Such applications have been reported in refs. 4, 11, 12, 15-21, among others.
Both B.W.R.'s and P.W.R.'s have been considered. One object of the calculations
has been to verify the safety of these reactor vessels and pipework by drawing
together the diverse elements in a safety analysis into a quantitative model.
Another has been to indicate the factors to which the reliability is sensitive
and to point to areas where present knowledge is inadequate. To estimate the
gains in reliability expected from in-service inspection is yet another.

In terms of the general formulation considered in §3 most of these
calculations are limited in some way. That is to say, they are only partially
probabilistic, some of the relevant quantities being treated as stochastic
variables, others being given definite values. The most complete of the
published studies in the sense of the range of stochastic variables considered
are those of Becher and Pedersen[18] on the B.W.R. pressure vessel,
Nilsson[12] also on the B.W.R. vessel, Wilson[21] on B.W.R. pipework and
Harris[11] on P.W.R. pipework. Except for Nilsson these all use Monte Carlo
techniques. The drawback to these more extensive calculations is partly that a
large numerical computation may provide little insight into what determines the
result and partly the expense of making direct sensitivity studies. The results
of Becher and Pedersen and of Nilsson on B.W.R. vessels are thus limited to
cumulative failure probabilities at 10 years and at the end of life (40 years).
Failure rates as a function of time in service were not obtained. Nor did these
calculations give direct indications of the sensitivity of the results to the
assumptions made. Although they led to satisfactorily low cumulative failure
probabilities they did not therefore indicate where it was most important to
increase our knowledge in order to strengthen confidence in the predictions.

It is therefore useful and even necessary to make more limited calculations
first. The stochastic variables can be chosen to be those which are believed to
be the most important and for which there is sufficient information to form an
estimate of the distribution function. The importance of a given variable can be
judged by experience, by previous deterministic calculations (e.g. of critical
crack sizes, crack growth rates, etc.) and by tests on the basic eqn. (5).
Harris's extensive study of P.W.R. pipework[11] illustrates this approach.

Our own calculations[15-17] on the P.W.R. pressure vessel gave expression
to the consideration of the Marshall Study Group on the factors influencing the
reliability of these vessels; their principal limitation is that they did not
consider crack growth rates to be distributed, although they recognised the wide
uncertainty over crack growth rates likely in practice[4].

    From these various studies we can draw a number of broad conclusions.

    (i)   The absolute values which have been obtained for the cumulative
failure probabilities and for the failure rates of B.W.R. and P.W.R. reactor
vessels and associated pipework are extremely low even for quite conservative
assumptions and confirm quantitatively the safety and reliability of these
components.

    (ii)   The failure rates, although always very small, increase rapidly and
roughly exponentially with time in service. This is partly a consequence of the
assumption that cracks grow by fatigue and particularly in the case of vessels at
early times these consequences are enhanced by the presumption that the vessel
population has passed a pre-service pressure test ("cold hydro test") which
imposes stresses more severe than those likely to be encountered in service.
(N.B. In the case of pipework this is not so).

    (iii) Failure probabilities are sensitive to the crack-size distribution
function, $N_0(a)$. As a result they are sensitive to factors which determine
$N_0(a)$, e.g. manufacturing procedures and the efficiency of inspection. Further
information on $N_0(a)$ is undoubtedly desirable.

    (iv)   Failure probabilities are relatively insensitive to details of the
toughness distribution and even to the mean toughness $\overline{K}_{Ic}$. One reason is
that in circumstances of large crack growth the quantity $\xi^{-1}(y)$ in (9)
depends on the critical crack size y rather slowly (cf. eqn. (11)). This applies
particularly to P.W.R. pipework and to a lesser extent to the thick P.W.R. vessel
as well. From fig. 8 it can be seen that quite large reductions of $\overline{K}_{Ic}$
increase the failure rates at later times by less than one order of magnitude.
At earlier times the effects are not quite so simple and reflect details of the
stress-intensity function and the fact that the population of vessels may be
presumed to have passed a pre-service pressure test.

    (v)   Likewise, the failure probabilities are not particularly sensitive to
the accuracy of the stress-intensity function, K_I. Thus for P.W.R. vessels in
the second half of life it makes only roughly an order-of-magnitude difference
whether we take all the cracks to be continuous line cracks (at the surface) or
to be semi-elliptic cracks (at the surface) and use the corresponding
K_I-functions. Plasticity corrections or enlargement of the failure criterion
to include the possibility of plastic collapse of the ligament similarly makes
relatively little difference in the second half of the vessel life[17]. At
early times the relative effects may be larger but the predicted failure rates
are then often so minute as to be without significance.

    (vi)   As would be anticipated from (ii) failure probabilities are sensitive
to crack growth rates. For the circumstances of P.W.R. vessels it was found[15]

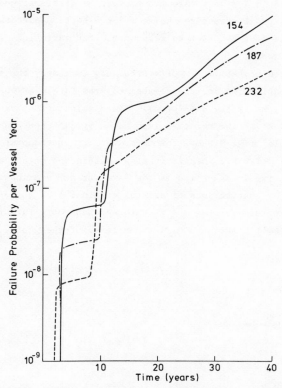

Fig. 8. Comparison of the failure rates of model P.W.R. vessels under
normal, upset and test conditions calculated for different mean
toughnesses as indicated (K_{Ic} in MNm$^{-3/2}$). The failure
criterion is that provided by linear elastic fracture mechanics
including the Irwin plastic-zone correction and supplemented with an
ultimate load criterion (yield stress of 50 k.s.i. = 345 MPa and
ultimate tensile stress of 80 k.s.i. = 552 MPa); see ref. 17 for
details. Other assumptions are (i) $N_o(a)$ from ref. 4, (ii) all
cracks assumes to be edge line cracks, (iii) Gaussian distribution of
toughness with a standard deviation of 10% of the mean, (iv) mean
toughness during the cold hydro test equal to that assumed during
service, (v) crack growth described deterministically with coefficients
γ as given in Table 1 of ref. 29. (After Harrop[30]).

that the failure rate at later times increased roughly as a power of the crack
growth coefficient, i.e. $γ^m$ where m ∿ 2 or 3 depending on other details. The
effects of taking a distribution of γ-values have not been made explicit for
reactor vessels, but such effects can be seen in Harris's calculations for P.W.R.
pipework[11]. The distribution was of log-normal form, highly skewed about the
most probable γ and with a long tail at large values of γ (as assumed here in
fig. 8). In consequence, the distribution of a = $ξ^{-1}(y)$, i.e. of the
argument in (9), had a tail at very small values so that Q_f, which is
determined by $N(ξ^{-1}(y)) \, dξ^{-1}(y)/dt$ and thus depends roughly exponentially
on $ξ^{-1}(y)$, had a very wide probability distribution indeed, one which
extended over many orders of magnitude and decreased slowly at large failure
rates. The reliable estimation of the mean failure rate, which is what one is

principally interested in for very rare events, may be difficult under these
circumstances. These results confirm the need for a better understanding of the
laws of crack growth and of the factors responsible for variations in the
parameters in these laws.

(vii) The failure probability of a structure is simply the sum of the
separate failure probabilities for the component parts (at least when all these
probabilities are ≪1, as is the case here). These calculations can therefore be
used to give indications of the relative importance of different parts of the
structure. For example, fig. 9 shows the separate contributions of the various
critical locations of a P.W.R., when it is assumed that the chance of there being
a crack of any given size in a section is the same for all sections. Harris has
similarly obtained the contributions of all the critical sections of pipework in
a P.W.R. system and in this way has shown that the chance of failure within the
reactor cavity is a small fraction (∿ 1/10th or less) of the whole.

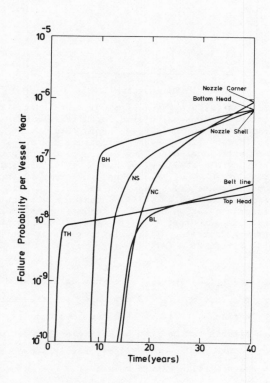

Fig. 9. Contributions to the failure rate of model P.W.R. vessels
under normal, upset and test conditions coming from different regions
of the vessel as indicated. The mean toughness is taken to be 232
MNm$^{-3/2}$ while all other assumptions are as in fig. 8. A very
similar pattern is predicted if all cracks are assumed to be
semi-elliptic edge cracks. (After Harrop and Lidiard[17]).

(viii) These calculations can also be used to quantify the benefits of
in-service inspection including the relative gains from different inspection
schedules. From the estimated B(x) functions we obtain sizeable reductions in
failure rate following an in-service inspection (up to two orders of magnitude on
any one section). Evidently, the reduction in failure rate for the whole
structure resulting from a particular inspection depends upon whether all
sections are inspected and, if not, which ones are. Figs. 9 and 10 show that in
this example the gain from inspecting the nozzle regions and the bottom head
would be very much greater than that from inspecting the beltline and the top

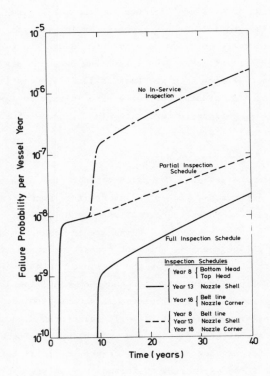

Fig. 10. The effect of different in-service inspection schemes upon the
failure rate. All assumptions are as in fig. 9. The full line shows
the failure rate as a function of time in service for an inspection
schedule which examines all. The dashed line (---) shows the failure
rate for the partial inspection schedule as indicated while the dot
dash line (.-.-.-) shows the failure rate when no in-service inspection
is carried out.

head regions. The gain in reliability will, in principle, be lost after a time, which, of course, depends on the rate of crack growth (in the same way that the benefit of the pre-service cold hydro test is also eventually lost). In the case of reactor vessels this time may be comparable with the lifetime, but for pipework where crack growth rates are higher it may be only a few years. These calculations may therefore be particularly useful in optimising inspection schedules for pipework. Optimisation may not, in practice, be possible for reactor vessels while present uncertainties over crack growth rates and the incidence of cracks remain. Nevertheless the calculations do show that inspection should be during the first 10 years of service if the aim is to reduce the whole life chance of failure as far as possible[28].

   (ix)   Failure as defined here by the criterion of critical crack size does not have the same meaning as 'failure' defined for the collection of statistics on (non-nuclear) vessels[1] where it mostly means potential for failure as judged by an inspector. Considerable care may be needed to relate the two. For example, if we use the model of in-service inspection based on B(x) as already described, then it is not difficult to see that failure rates estimated from the number of vessels rejected or repaired on successive in-service inspections could fall with time in service, whereas failure rates in the sense of this article clearly increase with time in service.

6.   CONCLUSIONS

   In this article we have reviewed the calculation of the probabilities of failure of engineering structures. In so far as fracture mechanics provides a clear definition of failure (crack size > critical crack size for the circumstances prevailing) all these calculations are in essence simple, although their full development can be complex. Present uncertainties in fracture mechanics about the correct description of the region of 'stable crack growth', i.e. the region between first crack extension and mechanical instability, thus also lie beneath these probabilistic calculations. Leaving this on one side we have described the structure of the probabilistic calculations and drawn attention to the need for better knowledge and understanding of the distributions of relevant quantities (occurrence and size of cracks, material toughness, crack growth rates, transient stresses, etc.). Unfortunately at present all this information is purely empirical and often rather incomplete. More attention also needs to be paid to the factors influencing intermediate quantities, e.g. the functions $\Phi_t(x,a)$ and $\chi_t(a)$.

   Despite these limitations the calculations which have been made for nuclear pressure vessels and piping give encouraging results and enable us to draw together many detailed considerations into a quantitative model; (see, e.g. ref. 4). The absolute magnitudes which are predicted confirm the safety of these structures and are broadly in agreement with the limited inferences which can be drawn from statistics on non-nuclear pressure vessels and steam drums[4]. However, we have drawn attention to the distinction between actual failure as modelled here and the potential failure, i.e. rejection by inspection, implied by most statistics. Rejection by inspection has not yet been modelled in detail, but it is not difficult to see that in some circumstances (e.g. relatively slow crack growth and successive inspections truly independent of one another) the behaviour of the rejection rate could be very different from the behaviour of the true failure rate in the absence of inspection. This difference adds to the difficulties of interpreting and transcribing historical 'failure' data and points to the heuristic value of these probabilistic calculations.

References

1. T.A. SMITH and R.G.WARWICK, Int. J. Pressure Vessels and Piping, 2, 283 (1974).

2. See, e.g., the sources cited in refs. 3 and 4.

3. UNITED STATES ATOMIC ENERGY COMMISSION. Analysis of pressure vessel statistics from fossil-fuelled power plant service and assessment of reactor vessel reliability in nuclear power plant service. (USAEC, Washington, 1974) WASH 1318.

4. W. MARSHALL, Chairman. An assessment of the integrity of P.W.R. pressure vessels (U.K. Atomic Energy Authority, Harwell, 1976).

5. G.J. HAHN and S.S. SHAPIRO. Statistical Models in Engineering (Wiley, New York, 1967).

6. E.B. HAUGEN, Probabilistic Approaches to Design (Wiley, New York, 1968).

7. G.O. JOHNSTON in Developments in Pressure Vessel Technology - 1, Ed. R.W. Nichols (Applied Science Publishers, Essex, 1979) p.203.

8. See, e.g. J.F. KNOTT, Fundamentals of Fracture Mechanics (Butterworths, London, 1973).

9. R.W. NICHOLS in Pressure Vessel Engineering Technology (Elsevier, Amsterdam, 1971) p.532.

10. P.M. SCOTT, The Use of Corrosion Fatigue Data in the Assessment of Crack Growth in Large Nuclear Pressure Vessels, A.E.R.E. Report R.8642 (1977).

11. D.O. HARRIS, An analysis of the probability of pipe rupture at various locations in the primary cooling loop of a Babcock and Wilcox 177 Fuel Assembly Pressurized Water Reactor - including the effects of a periodic inspection, Science Applications Inc. Report SAI-050-77-PA (1977).

12. F. NILSSON, in Proceedings of the 3rd International Conference on Pressure Vessel Technology Pt. II Materials and Fabrication (American Society of Mechanical Engineers, New York, 1977) p.593.

13. NUCLEAR REGULATORY COMMISSION, Reactor Safety Study (N.R.C., Washington, 1975) WASH-1400.

14. ADVISORY COMMITTEE ON REACTOR SAFEGUARDS, Regulation of Nuclear Power Reactors and Related Facilities (Washington, 1974) WASH-1250.

15. A.B. LIDIARD and M. WILLIAMS. J. Br. Nucl. Energy Soc. 16, 207 (1977).

16. A.B. LIDIARD and M. WILLIAMS in Tolerance of Flaws in Pressurized Components (I.Mech.E., London, 1978) p.1.

17. L.P. HARROP and A.B. LIDIARD. The Probability of Failure of P.W.R. Pressure Vessels Evaluated Using Elastic Plastic Failure Criteria, A.E.R.E. Report TP.728 (1978) – to be published.

18. P.E. BECHER and A. PEDERSEN, Nucl. Engng. Des. 27, 413 (1974).

19. L.M. ARNETT, Optimization of In-Service Inspection of Pressure Vessels, du Pont Savannah River Laboratory Report DP-1428 (1976).

20. W.E. VESELY, E.K. LYNN and F.F. GOLDBERG in Reliability Problems of Reactor Pressure Components Vol. 1 (I.A.E.A., Vienna, 1978) p.105.

21. WILSON, S.A., Estimating the Relative Probability of Pipe Severance by Fault Cause, General Electric Company Report GEAP-20615 (1974).

22. See, e.g., Section XI of the A.S.M.E. Boiler and Pressure Vessel Code 1974 and Winter 1976 Addenda.

23. See, e.g., refs. 39–46 cited in ref. 11 above.

24. R. O'NEIL, The PISC programme – status report, paper to be presented at the conference on Periodic Inspection for Pressurized Components to be held in London, 8-10 May 1979 at the Institution of Mechanical Engineers.

25. See, e.g., S.T. ROLFE, Int. Metall. Rev. 19,183 (1974).

26. J. DUFRESNE, A. CARNINO, A.C. LUCIA, J.ELBAZ, R. BRUNNHUBER, J. QUERO, J. GRANDEMANGE and A.P. TANON. A model for the estimation of the failure probability of pressurized water reactor vessels, paper presented to the ENS/ANS International Topical Meeting on Nuclear Power Reactor Safety held in Brussels, Oct. 16-19 1978.

27. See e.g., S.O. RICE in Selected Papers on Noise and Stochastic Processes, Ed. N. Wax (Dover Publications, New York, 1954) p.133.

28. L.P. HARROP and A.B. LIDIARD. Enhancement of the reliability of reactor pressure vessels by in-service inspection, A.E.R.E. Report TP.727 (1978); paper to be presented to the conference on Periodic Inspection for Pressurized Components (I.Mech.E., London, 8-10 May 1979).

29. A.B. LIDIARD and M. WILLIAMS in ICOSSAR '77 being the proceedings of the 2nd International Conference on Structural Safety and Reliability, Eds. H. Kupfer, M. Shinozuka and G.I. Schueller (Werner-Verlag, Düsseldorf, 1977) p.449.

30. L.P. HARROP, unpublished results. See ref. 17 for the method used.

ELEVATED TEMPERATURE FRACTURE MECHANICS

B. Tomkins

Springfields Nuclear Power Development Laboratories,
United Kingdom Atomic Energy Authority,
Springfields, Salwick, Preston PR4 0RR, U.K.

SUMMARY

The application of fracture mechanics concepts to cracks at elevated temperatures is examined. Particular consideration is given to the characterisation of crack tip stress—strain fields and parameters controlling crack extension under static and cyclic loads.

INTRODUCTION

Traditionally, the choice of materials for elevated temperature service has been made primarily on the basis of creep resistance. This has usually meant ensuring a limited amount of creep deformation which can be tolerated and is well within the creep ductility of the material at operating temperature. Two factors have seriously questioned the adequacy of this information in some main high temperature application areas (e.g. gas and steam turbines, power plant systems). The first is the presence of transients which introduce the possibility of fatigue as well as creep process development, whilst the second is the presence of defects, particularly in structures. Both these factors involve the possible presence of cracks under stress at elevated temperature and the former raises the problem of the development of failure under combined static and cyclic loading. So, in recent years, considerable effort, particularly in the UK, has gone into an examination of the behaviour of cracks at elevated temperature.

An immediate problem is the characterisation of stress—strain fields in a material which readily undergoes time dependent plastic deformation under stress. The work of Hutchinson and co-workers[1-3] in examining cracks in power law hardening materials is proving useful in this respect as it is directly applicable to a crack under steady load undergoing secondary power low creep. They use finite element analyses to examine standard cracked specimens in tension and bending and similar analyses can be applied to examine relaxed stress fields at crack tips in creep[4] There is clearly a close parallel between cracks in the creep range and elastic plastic fracture mechanics and this has led to the emergence of a time dependent J-integral (C*) as a useful characterising parameter.[5]

As far as components and structures are concerned, an important question regarding cracks is whether they will extend in service. This has led to a study of slow crack extension under a steady load (creep crack growth) as well as under cyclic loads (fatigue) and under combinations of steady and cyclic loads (cyclic creep, creep-fatigue). For creep crack growth, it is now clear that for most circumstances, crack extension involves the development of creep failure in material ahead of the crack tip with subsequent breaking of the intervening ligaments. In this sense there is an analogy with tearing in ductile metals and craze development in glassy polymers. As in ductile tearing, the critical factor is the estimate of finite crack advance step (Δa) in relation to crack tip opening increment ($\Delta \delta$)

which is dependent at a given crack length (a) on either relaxation strain in the
crack tip region or increment of displacement (Δ) distant from the crack. For a
given $\Delta\delta$, Δa will be dependent on the extent of a sufficient stress-strain field,
perhaps definable as a process zone, in relation of material failure behaviour. To
some extent, this local creep fracture damage development will also depend on the
integrated stress-strain history of the region as the crack advances. As this local
failure development is tensile in nature, involving hole nucleation and growth,
albeit on grain boundaries, it is affected by factors which introduce constraint
e.g. crack size relative to section size (a/W) and material thickness in the crack
plane (B). These considerations have encouraged the description of creep crack
growth in terms of a local reference stress (σ_d) just ahead of the crack[6] or in
the net section[7,8] if gross stress redistribution occurs.

Because fatigue crack growth can occur under low applied stress levels, the
linear elastic fracture mechanics concept of a small scale yielded zone at the crack
tip is often applicable even at elevated temperatures. This is true particularly
for cycling at low levels of maximum stress intensity factor, or more accurately low
levels of maximum applied section stress, and for high strain rates i.e. high
frequency cycles. In such cases, conventional fatigue mechanisms operate with
Stage I and Stage II crack growth modes, crack advance being by shear decohesion at
the crack tip. This is essentially the means by which finite crack tip openings (δ)
are achieved and there is no involvement of tensile failure processes ahead of the
crack tip for crack openings of order 1-10 μm and less. Time dependent plasticity
effects can sometimes occur, however, in the plastic zone resulting in variations in
δ and crack growth rate (da/dN).[9]

For low strain or cycling rates and dwell periods under load creep fracture
processes can occur in the plastic zone ahead of the crack tip and some enhancement
of crack growth ensue. This combined creep fatigue situation can in particular
circumstances involve high crack growth rates and in the limit it can be thought of
as incremental creep crack growth.

The paper will examine in more detail these areas of crack stress-strain field
characterisation, creep, fatigue and creep-fatigue crack extension.

CRACK CHARACTERISATION

An essential feature of fracture mechanics is the ability to describe stress-
strain fields in the vicinity of cracks in terms of parameters which enable a
variety of cracked geometries, including specimens, to be compared. Such a
parametric description is important as equivalence in stress-strain field probably
means equivalence in fracture behaviour. For linear elastic conditions, the stress
intensity factor K_I describes the field at a crack tip for mode I tensile opening,
the stresses having the form,

$$\sigma_{ij} = \frac{K_I}{\sqrt{2\pi r}} f_{ij}(\theta) \tag{1}$$

and displacements the form

$$u_{ij} = \frac{K_I}{2G} \sqrt{\frac{r}{2\pi}} F_{ij}(\theta) \tag{2}$$

Even when yielding occurs at the tip, if it is on a sufficiently small scale, K can accurately define the extent of plasticity (r_p) and the crack tip opening (δ). For plane strain crack opening in mode I,

$$r_p \simeq \frac{1}{8}\left[\frac{K_I^2}{\sigma_Y^2}\right]$$

$$\delta \simeq \left[\frac{K_I^2}{2E\,\sigma_Y}\right]$$

(3)

It is this ability of K to define crack tip plasticity that makes it such a useful parameter in relating fatigue crack growth rates when expressed in cyclic terms (ΔK).

The last ten years has seen the development of an equivalent parameter, J, which can describe the crack tip fields in non-linear materials. For simple power law hardening of the form,

$$\frac{\varepsilon}{\varepsilon_o} = \alpha\left[\frac{\sigma}{\sigma_o}\right]^n$$

(4)

Stresses and strains are given as (10,11),

$$\sigma_{ij} = \sigma_o\left[\frac{J}{\alpha\sigma_o\varepsilon_o I_n}\right]^{\frac{1}{1+n}} r^{-\frac{1}{1+n}}\tilde{\sigma}_{ij}(\theta,n)$$

$$\varepsilon_{ij} = \alpha\varepsilon_o\left[\frac{J}{\alpha\sigma_o\varepsilon_o I_n}\right]^{\frac{n}{1+n}} r^{-\frac{n}{1+n}}\tilde{\varepsilon}_{ij}(\theta,n)$$

(5)

Hence, if K or J can be measured or calculated for a crack in an elastic or power law hardening material respectively, cracks in structures and specimens can in theory be compared. In the case of K, its value depends on the geometry of the body containing the crack and the form of loading on the body. These effects are combined in a compliance function Y', where,

$$K = Y'\,\sigma\sqrt{a}$$

(6)

and Y' is $f(a/W)$. For J calculations however, the equivalent compliance function is also a function of the hardening exponent n. Goldman and Hutchinson[1] have considered a centre cracked plate of power law hardening material loaded in tension by a load P (Fig 1) and shown that J has the form

$$J = \alpha\sigma_o\varepsilon_o\left[\frac{ac}{b}\right] g_1\left[\frac{a}{b},n\right]\left[\frac{P}{P_o}\right]^{n+1}$$

(7)

where P_o $(= 4c\,\sigma_o\sqrt{3})$ is the limit load for the plate under perfectly plastic conditions $(n=\infty)$. g_1 is an increasingly strong function of a/b and n as these parameters increase. Hutchinson, Needleman and Shih[3] have also estimated centre crack opening (δ_1) and load point displacements (Δ) for this geometry and expressed these as,

$$\delta_1 = \alpha\varepsilon_o a\, g_2\left[\frac{a}{b},n\right]\left[\frac{P}{P_o}\right]^n$$

(8)

$$\Delta = 2h\varepsilon_\infty + \Delta_c$$

$$\Delta_c = \alpha\varepsilon_o a\, g_3\left[\frac{a}{b},n\right]\left[\frac{P}{P_o}\right]^n$$

(9)

Now as mentioned earlier, these equations can apply to a crack under secondary creep with a rate law of form similar to equation (4). J continues to play the role of crack field characterising parameter but is usually expressed in the rate form C* (rather than the confusing $J \neq dJ/dt$) when related to displacement rates $\dot{\Delta}$. From equations (7) and (9), C* can be expressed in terms of $\dot{\Delta}_c$ (which in the creep case $= \dot{\Delta}$), as,

$$C^* = \frac{P\dot{\Delta}}{b} \left[\frac{\sqrt{3}}{4} \frac{g_1}{g_3} \right] \qquad (10)$$

It is interesting to compare this result with that obtained by Harper and Ellison[12] using limit analysis. This uses a parameter m which is a yield ratio of cracked over uncracked section to estimate the effects of a/b. Their derivation gives,

$$C^* = \frac{-n}{1+n} \frac{P\dot{\Delta}}{b} \left[\frac{1}{m} \cdot \frac{dm}{d(a/b)} \right] \qquad (11)$$

For the simple geometry of Fig 1, $m = (1 - a/b)$, so equation (11) reduces to,

$$C^* = \frac{P\dot{\Delta}}{b} \left[\frac{b}{2c} \cdot \frac{n}{(n+1)} \right] \qquad (12)$$

The values of C* from equations (10) and (12) are compared in Fig 2 for two n values. Good agreement is found for the higher n value of 10 but poor agreement for the lower n value of 3, particularly at smaller a/b ratios. This is not unexpected considering the plastic limit analysis basis of equation (12), which would be much more restricted for smaller n values and short crack lengths. Another analytical attempt to derive C* for a specific geometry of a DCB specimen has been made by Nibkin, Webster and Turner[13] using simple non-linear beam theory. However, the extension of this to other bending geometries[14] relies on the relative invariance of a compliance factor η relating displacement rate and crack size.

So, although the parameter C* does describe the local stress-strain rate field for simple power law creeping material, and could be derived for more complex material constitutive laws,[2] it is difficult to derive analytically and is more readily measured experimentally for various geometries.[5] The experimental method used is that developed for J measurements in elastic plastic fracture mechanics by Begley and Landes[5] and involves measuring changes in potential energy rates for various initial crack lengths. It is worth noting that these estimates of C* are for a crack loaded in a time dependent manner without crack extension. Crack extension would imply some unloading of the local stress-strain field which at first sight is inconsistent with the deformation theory assumptions behind J integral assessments. However, as Paris[15] has pointed out any unloading would be behind the current crack tip and during crack advance the material ahead of the crack is seeing such large increases in deformation that J can continue to characterise the field in this region where material separation is actually occurring. Links between C* and crack advance rate (da/dt) will be considered in more detail in the next section.

The solutions outlined above would in the creep case usually relate to steady extension of material under load by secondary power law creep. However, if the load is first applied rapidly, the instantaneous stress-strain field will follow closely

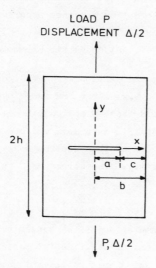

Fig. 1 Centre-cracked plate loaded in tension

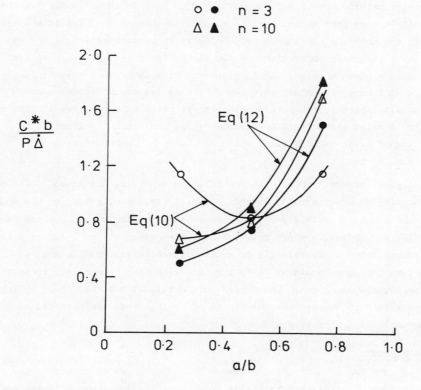

Fig. 2 Dependence of C* on relative crack size

that defined by K if the applied stress is well below the instantaneous yield (σ_Y).
In the time immediately after load application, stress relaxation and redistribution
will occur involving time dependent plastic strain in the crack tip region of order
σ_Y/E.   Only if net section deformation can then occur under steady creep would
further crack tip straining occur. So, it could be that for materials with low
creep ductility, K would be a relevant crack tip parameter for crack extension.

In more ductile materials, and particularly at higher applied stress levels,
crack tip displacements could be very large and the singular crack tip fields lose
their dominance. The crack would then effectively become a blunt notch and subsequent stress redistribution result in much more uniform stresses in the uncracked
section. A reference stress value in this section would then adequately describe
the long term stress-strain history. The stress (σ_d) can be written as (7, 16),

$$\sigma_d = \frac{P}{mBW} \qquad\qquad\qquad (13)$$

where m is the yield ratio parameter and B the specimen thickness. So, it can be
seen that the C* characterisation, as its time independent parallel J, might be
expected to work for materials which are ductile and whose loading history maintains
small crack tip displacements.

Goldman and Hutchinson have described crack displacement variations with n for
the power law material described by equation(4). This is shown in Fig 3. The crack
can be seen to vary from the elliptical shape described by the elastic solution
(n = 1) to the constant opening for rigid-perfectly plastic material (n = ∞). The
form of these curves is independent of the stress ratio $\sigma_\infty/\dot\sigma_o$ so that for
material with a given n value, the displacement at some defined point in the crack
tip region will have a constant relation to the centre crack displacement (δ_1). In
real materials, where equation (4) would tend to break down at large strains and the
higher strain rates which would be experienced at the crack tip itself, δ_1 could
still be a good guide to a critical value of δ (δ_o) which might relate to a
fracture condition.

Finally, it is worth mentioning the solution of Chuang and Rice[17] for a grain
boundary cavity or crack growing by diffusional transport of matter in the boundary
ahead of the crack. For this particular mechanism of crack advance, which is unlike
that considered previosuly where material decoheres ahead of the crack, a relation
can be derived between the velocity of crack advance, crack profile and rate of
material flux into the boundary. Although this mechanism is unlikely to be that of
macrocrack advance along grain boundaries in a metal, it has been shown by Ashby and
Raj[18] to relate to the probable mechanism of cavity growth which would be
occurring ahead of a macrocrack.

CREEP CRACK GROWTH

Having examined some of the parameters $(\sigma_d,$ C*, $\delta)$ which relate to the
characterisation of stress-strain fields induced by loading a crack in the creep
range, we can go on to see how well these parameters define crack advance rates
under a steady load or rate of straining. As mentioned earlier, in most practical
metals and alloys such crack extension involves failure of material ahead of the

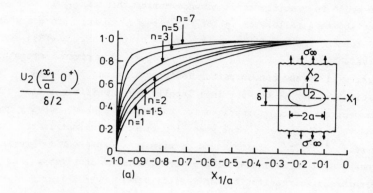

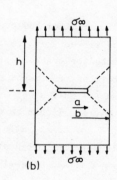

Fig. 3(a)   Crack opening profiles and (b) geometry for finite length
            strip (n = ∞) showing the slip lines for the rigid
            perfectly plastic limit (After Goldman and Hutchinson (1)).

crack. In this respect, there is a similarity with low temperature crack advance under
unidirectional loading in ductile materials, in that, following an initial small amount
of advance, of order δ, due to localised plastic deformation, some tensile material
failure must occur ahead of the crack. At elevated temperature it is likely to be
grain boundary cavitation sometimes related to triple point fracture whereas at lower
temperatures it is usually transgranular associated with cavitation at second phase
particles. In order to quantify crack advance during this stage, it is first
necessary to establish a failure criterion for material in this process zone and
secondly, to determine the resulting crack advance step, Δa. Now Raj and Ashby[19]
and Raj[20] have shown that cavity nucleation in creep at a given temperature is by
vacancy clustering at stress concentrating features in grain boundaries. This
requires sufficient stress to be sustained locally for a sufficient time. Relatively
little displacement or strain is required for nucleation although cavity growth
tends to be controlled by more general power law creep in the matrix and can require
significant strain[21,22,23]. This amount of strain to cause cavity growth and
subsequent linkage will be reflected in a material's creep ductility. For the
elevated temperature case, cavitation can readily extend over larger distances than
the lower temperature analogy where Rice and Johnson[24] have shown that in
ductile metals the process zone for cavity development is often of order of the
crack opening displacement. So, process zone conditions must be related both to
cavity nucleation and growth. In the creep crack situation, growth and linkage
will be strongly related to the displacement field ahead of the crack so the
definition of a suitable nucleation stress condition is not sufficient for crack
advance.

Freeman and Neate[6] have recently examined the process zone stress condition
in terms of a local critical reference stress (σ_{cr}). Their contention is that if
σ_{cr} can be defined, failure of notched or cracked specimens can be related to the
stress rupture curve for uniaxial unnotched specimens. Fig 4 shows some data of
Neate[25] on a normalised and tempered $\frac{1}{2}$Cr-Mo-V steel at 565°C on a basis of plane
stress reference stress vs time to rupture. It can be seen that considerable interpretation problems exist as thickness B and crack ratio a/W vary to give varying
degrees of crack tip constraint. Both apparent notch strengthening and weakening
occur in terms of the reference stress used and determination of the applicable
reference stress in this simple approach presents a considerable problem. Fig 5
shows a similar plot for untempered bainitic $2\frac{1}{4}$Cr-Mo and $\frac{1}{2}$Cr-Mo-V at 565°C which
shows a particularly strong effect of B and a/W. Here a stress factor approaching 3
is observed which is consistent with plane strain crack yield stress concentration
factors due to triaxiality. As Freeman and Neate point out, the variety of effects
in Figs 4 and 5 may be due to material failure criterion variation; shear vs
maximum principal tensile stress. However, in the more ductile steel, more crack
tip blunting would occur which would reduce triaxial effects. This reference stress
approach is clearly limited in this form, in that even when defined correctly it
cannot estimate the amount of crack advance Δa in a given time step. It may give
a good estimate of failure time, t_f, if most of this time is taken up in the development and failure of the first crack tip process zone. In this respect it is a
parallel to estimates of the fatigue life of notched specimens in terms of
endurance, N_f. For crack growth correlations, such a reference stress could form an

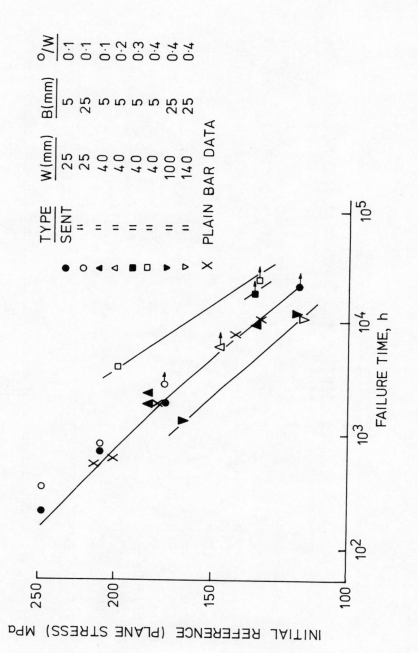

Fig. 4 Failure time data for notched and plain specimens of normalised and tempered $\frac{1}{2}$Cr – Mo – V Steel (565°C). (After Neate (25))

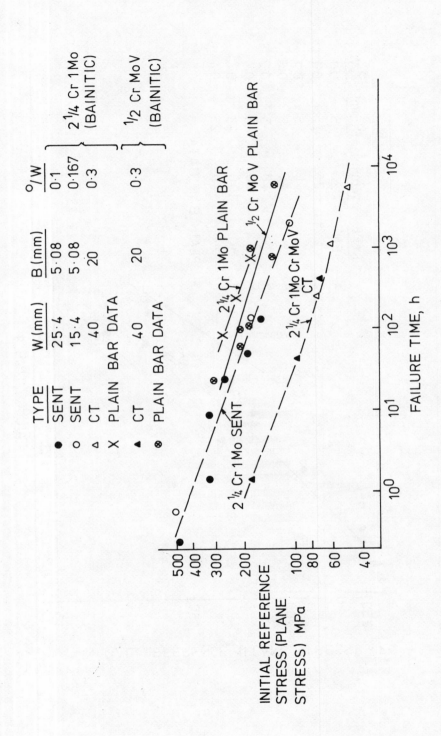

Fig. 5   Failure time data for notched and plain specimens of bainitic (untempered) $2^1/_4$Cr – Mo and $\frac{1}{2}$Cr – Mo – V steels (565°C). (After Freeman and Neate (6))

empirical basis for comparison of crack growth during creep for various geometries but it is likely that the difficulty in estimating a significant value will outweigh its usefulness apart from the case of more ductile materials. One significant problem of the approach is a lack of correlation with overall material displacement which is necessary for section failure. On the other side, however, if definable it could give a lower bound on life of a cracked section.

In that it defines the form and magnitude of the crack tip stress-strain field, C* promises to be a more general parameter than the process zone reference stress. However, it fulfils the same function in being a parameter whose main value is in comparing equivalent crack conditions for a variety of specimens and ultimately component geometries. For crack extension the assumption would be that the same value of C* defines a unique value of da/dt. Harper and Ellison[12] have summarised correlations made to date and Fig 6 shows this for two alloys from their own work[12] and that of Landes and Begley.[26] Some effect of specimen geometry is noted particularly between the CTS and CCP data, even when the C* determinations have been on the basis of experimental measurement, but C* needs testing over a wider range of materials and specimens before its general validity can be established. Harper and Ellison[12] do note, however, that the Landes and Begley tests at constant $\dot{\Delta}$ for CTS specimens did show a decrease in da/dt as a/W increased consistent with a decrease in C* predicted by equation (11). Fig 6 also shows clearly the existence of a slope change at lower values of C* in some specimens. Harper and Ellison[12] relate this to the effects of stress redistribution at early stages in the crack extension process and this does seem the most likely explanation in these tests. However, the possibility of the existence of a creep crack growth threshold in terms of C*, analogous to a ΔK threshold for fatigue crack growth is worthy of mention. If one does exist, it could well relate to a minimum process zone size for cavity development and as such would be extremely small. Low values of C* would indicate low loads and displacement rates and hence more bounded displacements in the crack tip region possibly inhibiting cavity linkage even where larger process zones exist.

One parameter which might be expected to show a close link with the crack advance Δa is an increment of the crack tip opening displacement, $\Delta \delta$. Haigh[27] examined the link between crack opening and da/dt for a normalised and tempered 1 Cr-Mo-V steel tested at 550°C. He found that growth occurred only after an initiation opening, δ_i had been achieved and thereafter da/dt was proportional to $(d\delta / dt)^m$ where m was slightly less than unity. More recent work by Gooch, King and Briers[28] on $2\frac{1}{4}$Cr-1Mo weld metal with various heat treatments has confirmed a proportionality between Δa and $\Delta \delta$ (Fig 7). Neate[25] has shown (Fig 8) that the a vs t curve follows closely the form of the overall displacement Δ vs t curve, so that in general it might be expected that,

$$\frac{da}{dt} \propto \frac{d\delta}{dt} \propto \frac{d\Delta}{dt}$$

which in turn would be proportional to C* for a constant applied load situation. For a given material, the link between $d\delta$ and $d\Delta$ would, however, be expected to vary slightly as it depends on the ratio g_2 / g_3 (equations 8, 9),

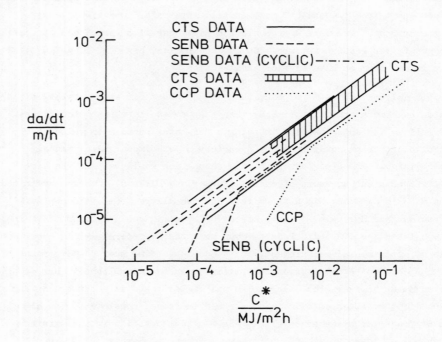

Fig. 6 Summary of creep crack propagation rate vs C* results
        (After Harper and Ellison (12))

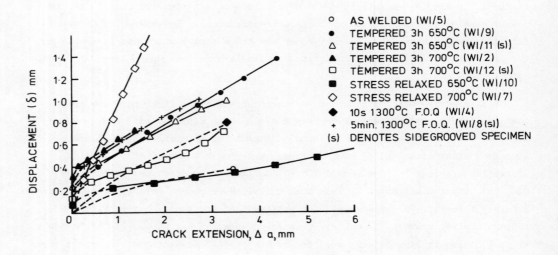

Fig. 7 Edge opening displacement (δ) vs crack extension (Δa) for $2^1/_4$
        Cr - 1Mo weld metal. (After Gooch, King and Briers (28))

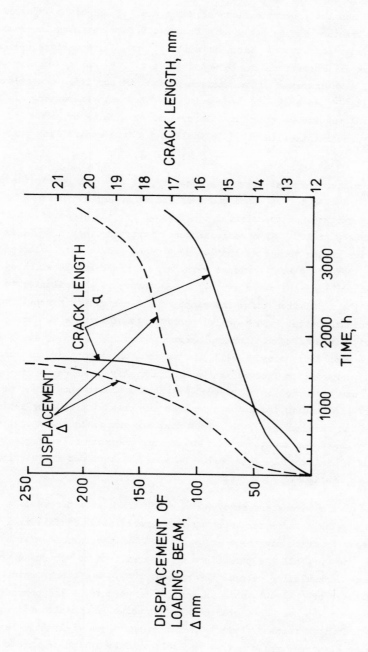

Fig.8 Displacement and crack length as a function of time for normalised and tempered
0.5 Cr – Mo – V steel at 565°C. After Neate (25))

which decreases as   a/W and n increase. The constancy of a crack aspect ratio
$\Delta a/\Delta \delta$ would only be maintained if each crack advance step is seen as involving a
repetition of initiation and failure in the process zone. As material entering the
process zone will have had some stress-strain-time history, for some materials and
loading conditions the proportionality of Δa a and $\Delta \delta$ might be expected to break
down as prior fracture damage could have occurred before entering the zone and
$\Delta a/\Delta \delta$ would increase with a. Also, as with δ and Δ , equations (7) and (8)
indicate a lack of proportionality between $\Delta \delta$ and C* as a/W changes so that
$\Delta a/\Delta \delta$ would also increase as a increases if a C* condition controls Δa.   The
results of Neate[25] do show an increase in $\Delta a/\Delta \delta$ with increasing a. Perhaps
the experimental results showing da/dt correlations with C* or $d\delta/dt$ or $d\Delta/dt$
reflect these uncertainties involved in isolating a true controlling parameter for
growth.

From the microstructural viewpoint, however, it is worth noting the results of
Gooch et al[28] and Neate[25] whose recorded values of aspect ratio $\Delta a/\Delta \delta$ show
a considerable variation with material condition. For the quenched condition, the
ratio is in excess of 100. Thus material sensitivity in creep crack growth is an
important factor making the determination of a crack growth rate relation difficult.
In this sense there is a real contrast with fatigue crack growth which usually
exhibits a lack of material sensitivity. Again, there is a similarity to ductile
tearing where the initiation point and slope of a J R-curve is strongly material
sensitive. Both illustrate the material sensitivity of tensile failure processes
involving cavity formation and linkage. Regarding cavity linkage, the failure of a
a process zone with increasing δ will involve the achievement in the zone of
sufficient displacement to link nucleated and partially grown cavities.
Andersson[29] has attempted to model void growth and coalescence ahead of a moving
crack. Use of his results indicates that once the crack tip opening sufficient for
linkage there has been achieved, the crack displacement field ahead of the crack
will ensure linkage over about one half of the process zone on subsequent
achievement of a similar δ. This mechanism will be discussed further in the
section on creep-fatigue.

A review of the parameters relevant to creep crack growth reveals a complex
picture with no single parameter emerging for general use. If failure in a cracked
section proceeds by crack advance then C* is probably the parameter with widest
application. However, all the parameters considered take no account of possible
fracture damage accumulation outside the process zone. One other factor worthy of
comment when creep crack growth data is applied to structures and components is that
crack advance involves overall displacement (Δ) which in ductile materials can be
considerable. In this respect there is again an analogy with ductile tearing and in
such circumstances structural constraints could readily introduce stress redistribution and inhibition of crack growth.

FATIGUE AND CREEP-FATIGUE CRACK GROWTH

The inclusion of a cyclic component in the load or strain history of a crack
at elevated temperature raises the possibility of significant crack extension by the
fatigue process. This does not involve tensile fracture processes ahead of the

crack tip, but is primarily the creation of new crack surface by shear decohesion, the same process involved in achieving a finite crack tip opening under load in ductile metals. As this is controlled by crack tip plasticity, its magnitude will be influenced by time dependent flow. The presence of a static as well as cyclic component, or a slow enough cycling rate can induce creep fracture as well as deformation effects either in the plastic zone or net section, leading to a possible synergistic effect of creep and fatigue. Two typical loading histories are shown in Fig 9. In this section the effects of temperature, frequency (ν) or strain rate ($\dot{\varepsilon}$) and dwell time under load (t_D) on crack growth will be examined. In addition, some comments will be made on the effect of oxidising environments. A wider review of these effects has been made previously.[9] This section will follow the pattern of that review in examining material flow effects, creep fracture effects and environmental effects on crack growth.

1. Material Flow Effects:

Because the same flow processes are responsible for the accommodation of crack tip opening and the production of new crack surface in fatigue, one might expect some proportionality between da/dN and δ. In the limit, da/dN would equal $\delta/2$ and this condition would be expected for elastic perfectly plastic materials ($n = \infty$). For finite hardening materials, crack tip deformation is spread back along the crack flanks, so that in general

$$\frac{da}{dN} \leq \frac{\delta}{2} \tag{14}$$

Now for small scale yielding which can occur if $\sigma \ll \sigma_Y$, which at elevated temperatures can apply when loading rates are not too slow, δ is given by equation (3). (In fact, in fatigue δ could be up to half this value because at the crack tip previous cycle deformation focusses the crack tip deformation into $\pm 45°$ zones for plane strain conditions). For elastic-power law hardening materials loaded above yield, Tomkins[30] has estimated δ as,

$$\delta \simeq \frac{K^2}{4E\,\sigma_u} + \frac{\pi\,\sigma\,\varepsilon_p\,a}{2\sigma_u\,(1+n')} \tag{15}$$

where σ_u is the material UTS, ε_p the applied plastic strain and n' the work hardening exponent for material obeying the law,

$$\sigma = k\,\varepsilon_p^{n'} \tag{16}$$

The plastic portion of equation (15) compares with the form of equation (8) showing a similar dependence on applied strain and crack size.

Empirically derived crack growth laws show a similarity to equations (3) and (15) having the form,

$$\frac{da}{dN} = \frac{A\,\Delta K^p}{Ef\,(\sigma_u)} \tag{17}$$

for small scale yielding, and

$$\frac{da}{dN} = A_1 \left[\frac{\Delta\sigma}{\sigma_u}\right]^q \frac{\Delta\varepsilon_p\,a}{(1+\beta\,n')} \tag{18}$$

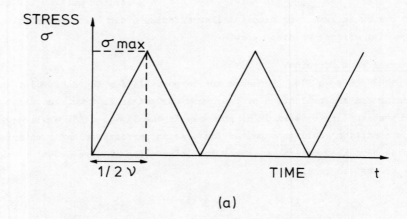

(a)

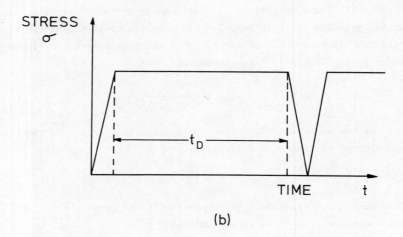

(b)

Fig. 9 Typical fatigue loading histories

where p is in the range 2-4, f is a weak function of σ_u and q and $\beta \simeq 2$.
The weak dependence of f on σ_u reflects the effect of work hardening in spreading
the crack tip flow as often low hardening materials have a high σ_u and higher
hardening materials a low σ_u. Similarly p values greater than 2 are probably
due to work hardening effects.

The effect of temperature (T) on flow properties for cycling at a moderate to
high frequency is to decrease n' and σ_u. This could be expected to result in a
reduction in p and increase in growth rate at a given K level. Fig 10 shows such
an effect on Inconel X-750 cycled at 0.17 Hz for temperatures up to 593°C.[31]
(The data at 704°C will be discussed later.) Similar results have been found by
James[32] on stainless steels and Haigh and Richards on ferritic steels.[7] The
latter in particularly noted the achievement of a ΔK^2 dependence at 550°C.
Although Shahinian has not estimated $\delta/2$ for the data shown in Fig 9, a crude
calculation shows that $da/dN \longrightarrow \delta/2$ at 593°C. In considering environmental
effects later, an alternative explanation will be given for this observation.

James[33] has investigated the effect of frequency on the fatigue crack growth
rate in type 304 stainless steel at 538°C. His results shown in Fig 11 are over
five orders of magnitude in frequency for sawtooth cycles (c.f. Fig 9(a)) with an R
ratio (K_{min}/K_{max}) of 0.05. Over this range, at a given level of ΔK, da/dN is
increased by an order of magnitude as the frequency decreases. Also shown in Fig 11
is an estimate of $\delta/2$ which is approached at the lowest frequency. An examination
of fracture surfaces[34] showed a transgranular crack path over the whole frequency
range. Some increase in δ and therefore da/dN would be expected on reducing
frequency because stress relaxation would be occurring in the plastic zone during
loading. This would give a lower mean effective flow stress in the plastic zone.
However, the factor on growth rate from this source would not be as high as 10,
perhaps indicating the role of an additional accelerating process. This is most
likely to be crack tip oxidation which will be examined in more detail later.

The introduction of a dwell period into the cycle (Fig 9(b)) would also be
expected to lead to stress relaxation in the plastic zone during the dwell with a
resulting additional amount of crack opening. A reanalysis[9] of some of James'
data on type 304 steel shows this effect (Fig 12). Data from a sawtooth cycle is
compared with that of a square wave dwell cycle for the same loading ramp rate and a
distinct accelerating effect of the dwell cycle is shown. At this frequency both
fractures were transgranular so no change in fracture path occurred.

2. Creep Fracture Effects:

The presence of a high enough stress for a long enough time at a high enough
temperature can result in the nucleation of creep fracture damage normally in the
form of cavities but sometimes crack-like linkages of cavities at grain boundary
triple points under high enough stresses. These nucleation conditions can obviously
pertain in plastic zones or the net section for cycles involving low enough strain
rates or frequencies and long enough dwell periods. As in creep crack growth,
linkage of such cavities can be achieved by the crack tip displacement field, but
unlike the steady load or straining condition this field is regenerated each cycle

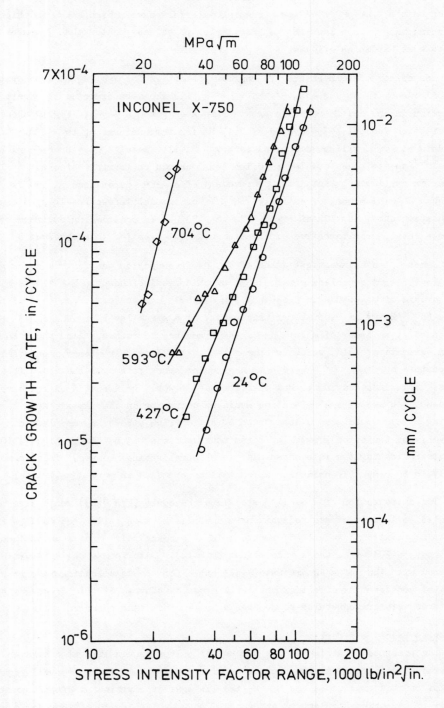

Fig. 10 Fatigue crack growth rates in Inconel X-750 as a function
of stress intensity factor range (ν = 0.17Hz) (After Shahinian (31))

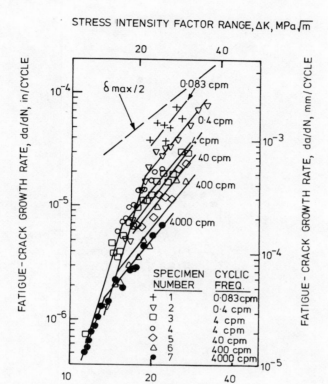

Fig. 11   The effect of frequency on the crack growth behaviour of
          solution-annealed type 304 stainless steel at 538°C (After
          James (33))

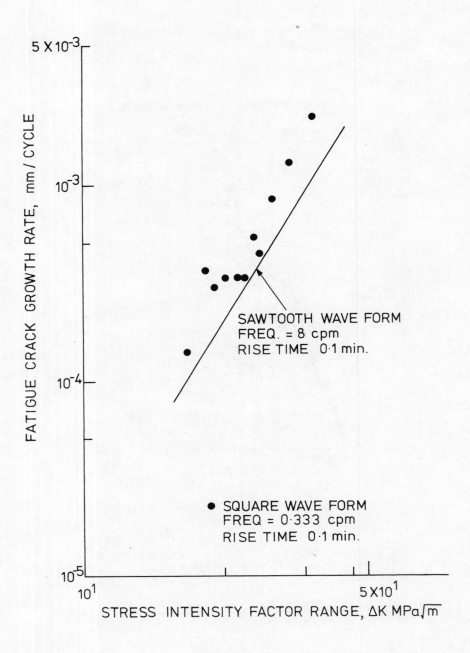

Fig. 12 The effect of loading wave form on the fatigue crack
propagation behaviour of annealed type 304 stainless steel
at 538°C (After James (34))

so that a creep crack growth type of failure can be achieved <u>without net extension</u>
of the specimen or component, but <u>with accumulation of creep strain</u> cycle by cycle.
It is for these reasons that creep-fatigue has emerged as such a difficult problem
to cope with in engineering design. The displacements necessary for cavity linkage
in a process zone can be achieved readily by a subsequent rapid crack opening once
the condition

$$\frac{\delta}{2} \geq (\lambda - p) \tag{19}$$

has been achieved at the tip.[30] λ/p is the ratio of cavity spacing to size,
so $(\lambda - p)$ defines the ligament to be broken for crack advance. However, even
if this instability condition is not achieved, significant cavitation or even just
the comparative weakness of grain boundaries at elevated temperatures can promote the
adoption of an intergranular fracture path with accelerated crack growth rates.

Considering the cycle of Fig 9(a), it is possible to estimate for small scale
yielding the strain rate at points within the zone and the amounts of strain introduced at this rate.[9] A simple calculation is as follows;

Consider a point at distance $r = d$ from the crack tip in elastic-perfectly
plastic material which yields at a stress σ_{min} during the ramp. Then,

$$\sigma_{min} \simeq \sigma_Y \sqrt{\frac{d}{a}} \tag{20}$$

and

$$\varepsilon_r \propto \frac{1}{r} = \varepsilon_Y \frac{\sigma^2 a}{\sigma_Y^2 r} \tag{21}$$

which for $r = d$ gives the strain rate at d for $\sigma > \sigma_{min}$ as,

$$\dot{\varepsilon}_d = \frac{2 \varepsilon_Y \sigma \dot{\sigma}}{\sigma_Y^2} \cdot \frac{a}{d} = 4 \nu \varepsilon_Y \frac{\sigma \sigma_{max}}{\sigma_{min}^2} \tag{22}$$

$(\nu$ is the frequency of the cycle)

From this equation it can be seen that the minimum and maximum strain rates at d
are,

$$\dot{\varepsilon} d_{min} = 4 \nu \varepsilon_Y \left[\frac{\sigma_{max}}{\sigma_{min}}\right] \tag{23}$$

and,

$$\dot{\varepsilon} d_{max} = 4 \nu \varepsilon_Y \left[\frac{\sigma_{max}^2}{\sigma_{min}^2}\right] \tag{24}$$

Thus many points in the plastic zone experience a strain rate of order of the
average plastic zone strain rate $(4 \nu \varepsilon_Y)$. The amount of plastic strain going in at
point d during a load increment at this order of strain rate is given by equation
(21) as,

$$\Delta\varepsilon_d = \varepsilon_Y \left[\left(\frac{\sigma_{max}}{\sigma_{min}}\right)^2 - 1\right] \tag{25}$$

Thus, in lower creep ductility materials, strains of order of the ductility can

readily be introduced at low strain rates in the plastic zone during low frequency
cycles. Ohmura, Pelloux and Grant[35] have found that for a cobalt–base superalloy
HS–188 tested at temperatures in the range 600–870°C, a transition to an intergranular crack path and significant acceleration in crack growth occurred when the
average plastic zone strain rate $(4\nu\varepsilon_Y)$ was reduced to that necessary for intergranular creep fracture in a tensile test. The maximum increase in growth rate
observed due to this effect by Ohmura et al was, however, less than an order of
magnitude indicating a local creep fracture effect close to the crack tip. On a time
base, the crack growth rate da/dt approached that observed under steady creep crack
growth conditions for cycling at the lowest frequency of 0.01 Hz which tends to
confirm the picture of crack advance due to local creep fracture ahead of the crack
renewed each cycle. This might be termed cyclic creep crack growth.

The data of Shahinian[31] on Inconel X–750 shown in Fig 10 also supports this
picture. In going from 593°C to 704°C at the cycling frequency of 0.17 Hz there is
a transition from trans– to intergranular crack advance with an accompanying increase
in slope p (equation 17) and maximum observed increase in crack growth rate of an
order of magnitude. These growth rates are well in excess of estimated $\delta/2$ values,
i.e. $\Delta a/\Delta\delta \gg 1$. James[36] has observed a similar effect in 20% cold worked type
316 austenitic stainless steel tested at 538°C over a range of frequencies at
R = 0.05. In changing from 0.07 Hz to 0.005 Hz there is an order of magnitude
increase in da/dN accompanied by a dramatic increase in p. Although James states
that he observed only transgranular fracture paths, he does not indicate that all
specimens were examined fractographically. In fact the 0.005 Hz data on a time base
lies close to those observed during a static creep crack growth test on the same
steel.[37] James' results on this cold worked steel are in contrast to those shown
in Fig 11 on solution annealed type 304. However, it is now known[38] that testing
under creep–fatigue conditions in this temperature range following cold work can
lead to fine distributions of creep cavitation on grain boundary carbide precipitates.
This gives low values of $(\lambda - p)$ to satisfy equation (19) for linkage by crack
opening at low values of ΔK.

Tension load cycling specimens are obviously susceptible to loss of elastic
constraint and small scale yielding effects at higher values of ΔK; particularly
when cycling is at a high positive R ratio. Haigh and Richards[7] observed a
sharp transition in fracture mode when cycling a 1 Cr–Mo–V steel at 550°C at low
frequency (0.01 Hz) and high R ratio (0.3). Data for WOL specimens are shown in
Fig 13 and Haigh and Richards found that the transition separated fatigue crack
growth at lower levels of ΔK from creep crack growth at higher levels. The creep
crack area showed several of the effects noted ealier; effect of thickness,
increasing overall displacement (Δ), correlation with reference stress (Δ_d) as
defined by equation (13) and slope of ΔK curve in line with the creep exponent n.

Solomon and Coffin[39] have found a similar effect of cycling frequency in
effecting a transition from transgranular fatigue to creep crack growth with
decreasing strain rate in high strain fatigue crack growth tests on the gas turbine
disc iron–nickel alloy A286 at 593°C. Although in these tests plastic deformation
occurred throughout the specimen section, creep fracture damage was observed ahead

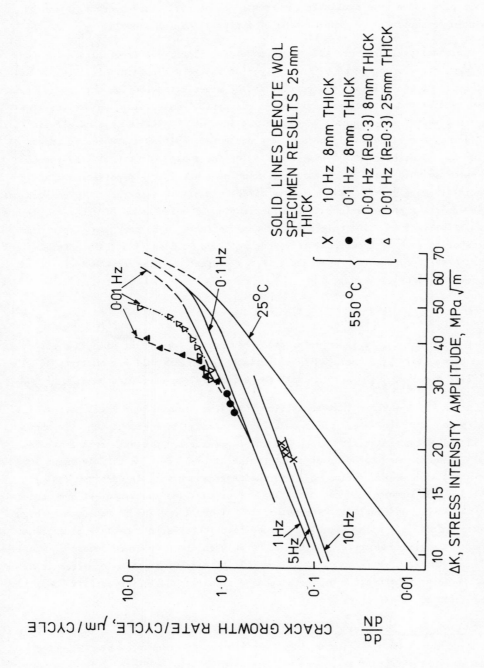

Fig. 13   Baseline fatigue data on 25mm and 8mm thick WOL specimens – 1Cr – Mo – V steel at 550°C
(After Haigh and Richards (7))

of the crack at the lowest frequencies. In this situation, such cracking was first
noticed for applied strain levels of 0.01 imposed at a strain rate of
$2 \times 10^{-6} \text{ s}^{-1}$. So, a consistent picture does exist which shows that for a given
material, a low enough cyclic frequency can induce cyclic creep crack growth by
producing creep fracture damage ahead of the crack tip each cycle.

An equally if not more effective way of inducing creep fracture damage ahead of
a fatigue crack is by means of a dwell period in the cycle (e.g. Fig. 9(b)). In
this case, stress relaxation occurring in the plastic zone during this period can
often readily nucleate creep cavities in susceptible materials. Unlike the slow
frequency tests, the amount of creep strain involved is limited by the elastic field
of order ε_y per cycle and linkage of the nucleated cavities must occur by means of
the crack tip displacement field generated on the subsequent cycle. Andersson[29]
has examined void coalescence ahead of a moving crack in rigid-perfectly plastic
material in some detail. His model is directly applicable to the creep damaged case
as it assumes a pre-existing linear distribution of holes ahead of the crack with a
given (λ/p) ratio. Using this model in conjunction with a crack tip displacement
distribution such as that from Bilby, Cottrell and Swinden[40], it is possible to
estimate this advance (see Appendix). For a typical case, after the first cycle,
the crack advance Δa is,

$$\Delta a \simeq 0.4 \, r_p \qquad\qquad (26)$$

i.e. $\Delta a \propto \Delta K^2$.   This order of crack advance is consistent with that observed
as an upper limit by Michel, Smith and Watson[41] on 20% cold worked type 316
stainless steel at 593°C with a dwell period under load of 600 seconds.

Lloyd[42] has shown that transition behaviour occurs under dwell period
cycling as ΔK increases. Data on solution treated type 316 at 625°C is shown in
Fig 14 and a transition from trans- to intergranular failure with much increased
growth rates is seen to occur at a ΔK value of 12-14 MPa $\sqrt{m}$. This value is
consistent with a $\delta/2$ value equal to the carbide precipitate spacing $(\lambda - p)$.
Metallographic observation has shown that creep cavities in this steel are associated
with carbides. It should also be noted that if dwell cycling is replaced by higher
frequency fatigue cycling beyond the transition there is an immediate reversal to
transgranular fatigue crack growth. So, even when creep fracture damage is simply
nucleated in the plastic zone, it is possible to obtain dramatic increases in crack
growth rate up to the order of the zone size itself once the instability condition
of equation 19 is achieved.

3. Environmental Effects:

The role of an oxidising or inert environment in crack growth at elevated
temperature is difficult to assess because as with creep effects it is dependent on
both material and mechanics. Material effects are related to a range of environment
material interactions; surface chemistry, diffusion and internal reactions.
Mechanics considerations include reversibility of the shear decohesion at the crack
tip, control of environmental access to the tip, oxide blocking or wedging in the
crack and ability to renew the crack tip environment. Data on a few materials
obtained in air and vacuum reflect these complex interactions. As with creep and

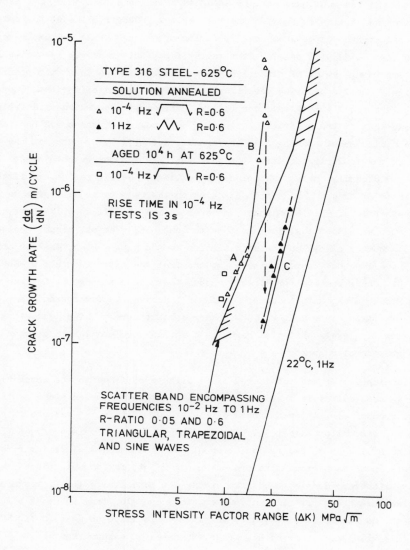

Fig. 14 Transitional fatigue crack growth behaviour in type 316
steel at 625°C (After Lloyd (42))

fatigue effects, perhaps a useful starting point in isolating some factors is to
define again the maximum amount of crack extension attainable by the mechanics of
crack response to load, without fracture ahead of the crack, namely, half the crack
tip opening ($\delta/2$). As mentioned earlier da/dN is often much less than $\delta/2$ because
of the distribution of plastic flow in the tip region. However, it must be realised
that fresh metal surface exposed at the tip during crack opening is extremely active
chemically so that oxide will rapidly form there if sufficient oxygen is available.
At elevated temperature rates of oxidation are increased and the crack tip profile
can change significantly, becoming more blunted the heavier the oxidation. Two
effects on fatigue crack growth rate can follow. Firstly, because the oxide volume
is greater than that of the material, a blocking and wedging of the crack can reduce
the effective cyclic crack opening i.e. the crack opens at a later stage in the
cycle. This is particularly effective for the small crack openings obtained at low
levels of ΔK. Secondly, metal is replaced by oxide in the tip region and if the
extent of this is of order $\delta/2$, oxide cracking on the next cycle will give an
effective growth rate of this magnitude. More excessive oxidation would modify the
crack tip to such an extent that it may cease to behave as a crack, become a notch
and then need a number of cycles for reinitiation at the tip. Haigh, Skelton and
Richards[43] have discussed some of these factors from their tests on a 1 Cr—Mo—V
steel at 550°C. Their results for air and vacuum tests over a range of frequencies
are shown in Fig 15 along with an estimate of $\delta/2$ derived by Tomkins and Wareing.[9]
For tests in air it is clear that oxide blocking inhibits growth with decreasing
frequency at low ΔK levels whilst at higher ΔK levels acceleration in growth
occurs up to growth rates approaching $\delta/2$.

The discussion so far has considered oxide effects confined to the crack tip
surface, but in some materials there is evidence of oxygen diffusion along grain
boundaries to produce embrittlement ahead of the crack. Coffin[44] has shown that
in a cast nickel base alloy Udimet 500 tested at 816°C, grain boundary oxygen
diffusion ahead of the crack led to depletion of the titanium and aluminium rich
γ' precipitate in these regions thus producing a weak path for growth. Such
processes, as with creep damage ahead of a crack, can potentially give large crack
growth rates well in excess of $\delta/2$. However, they can also lead to crack bifur-
cation and hence deceleration as shown by Scarlin[45] in tests on Cast In 738 LC at
850°C. For this alloy, he observed higher growth rates in vacuum than air.
Observations on wrought alloys[45,46] however, show much lower growth rates in
vacuum and here there is an obvious acceleration in oxidising environments by up to
an order of magnitude.

So, it does seem that an oxidising environment can increase growth rates over
rates in vacuum but $\delta/2$ represents a reasonable upper bound to growth rates obtained for continuous cycling even at low frequencies. In this respect, the factors
obtainable by both environment and flow property changes are similar. By far the
most damaging effects so far have been obtained from situations where creep fracture
damage can occur ahead of the crack.

CONCLUDING REMARKS
Elevated temperature fracture mechanics as applied to static and cyclic crack

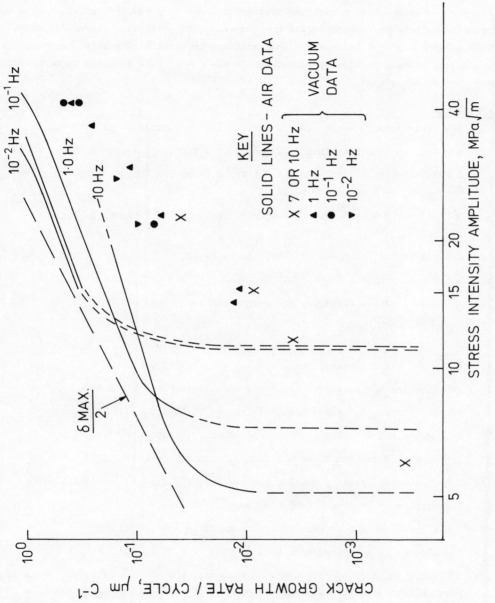

Fig. 15 Effect of environment on fatigue crack growth rate in 1% Cr-Mo-V steel at 550°C
         (After Haigh et al (43))

growth presents a range of problems, many of which still await a solution. No single characterising parameter for crack growth under static loads has emerged to date although use of a time dependent J integral (C*) and to a lesser extent the reference stress has had limited success. Some link seems to exist between crack opening (δ) and crack advance (Δa) but definitions of δ are difficult and the ratio $\Delta a/\Delta \delta$ is material sensitive. Similarities exist between creep crack growth and ductile tearing at lower temperatures. Fatigue crack growth at elevated temperature is consistent with the picture at lower temperatures as far as flow property effects are concerned but environmental and particularly creep fracture interactions can lead to dramatic accelerations in crack growth rate. For fatigue crack growth, however, low cyclic stress levels enable LEFM concepts to be of wider use than in the static case.

REFERENCES

1.   N L Goldman and J W Hutchinson, Int. J. Solids Structures 11, 575 (1975).

2.   C F Shih and J W Hutchinson, J. Eng. Matls. Tech., 98 Series H, 289 (1976).

3.   J W Hutchinson, A Needleman and C F Shih, Proc. ONR Int. Symp. on Fracture Mechanics, Washington D C (Sept 1978).

4.   S Taira and R Ohtani, Proc. Int. Conf. on Creep and Fatigue, I. Mech. E. (1973/74).

5.   J Begley and J D Landes, ASTM STP 514, 1 (1972).

6.   B L Freeman and G J Neate, Mat. Sci. Eng. 36, 241 (1978).

7.   J R Haigh and C E Richards, Proc. Int. Conf. on Creep and Fatigue, I. Mech. E. (1973/74).

8.   G J Neate and M J Siverns, ibid.

9.   B Tomkins and J Wareing, Metal Sci. 11, 414, (1977).

10. J R Rice and G F Rosengren, J. Mech. Phys. Solids, 16, 1 (1968).

11. J W Hutchinson, J. Mech. Phys. Solids, 16, 13 (1968).

12. M P Harper and E G Ellison, J. Strain Anal., 12, 167 (1977).

13. K M Nibkin, G A Webster and C E Turner, ASTM STP 601, 47 (1976).

14. K M Nibkin, G A Webster and C E Turner, Proc ICF 4 (Waterloo) 1977.

15. P Paris, Brown Univ. MRL E-96 (1976).

16. E G Ellison and M P Harper, J. Strain Anal. 13, 35 (1978).

17. T J Chuang and J R Rice, Acta Met. 21, 1625 (1973).

18. M F Ashby and R Raj, Proc. Conf. on Mechanics and Physics of Fracture (Inst. Phys and Metals Soc., Cambridge 1975).

19. R Raj and M F Ashby, Acta Met. 23, 653 (1975).

20. R Raj, Acta Met. 26, 995 (1978).

21. W Pavinich and R Raj, Met. Trans. 8A, 1917 (1977).

22. B F Dyson, Metal Science, 10 349 (1976).

23. F W Crossman and M F Ashby, Acta Met. $\underline{23}$, 425 (1975).

24. J R Rice and M A Johnson, Inelastic Behaviour of Solids, p.641, McGraw Hill (1970).

25. G J Neate, J. Mat. Sci. Eng., $\underline{33}$, 165 (1978).

26. J D Landes and J Begley, Westinghouse Report 74-1E7-FESGT-P1 (1974).

27. J R Haigh, J. Mat. Sci. Eng. $\underline{20}$, 213 (1975).

28. D J Gooch, B L King and H D Briers, J. Mater. Sci. Eng., $\underline{32}$, 81 (1978).

29. H Andersson, J. Mech. Phys. Solids, $\underline{25}$, 217 (1977).

30. B Tomkins, J. Eng. Mat. Tech., $\underline{97}$, Series H, 289 (1975).

31. P Shahinian, Metal Science (to be published).

32. L A James, Proc. ICM I $\underline{3}$, 341 (1972).

33. L A James, ASTM STP 513, 218 (1972).

34. L A James, Nuclear Tech. $\underline{16}$, 521 (1972).

35. F Ohmura, R M Pelloux and N J Grant, Eng. Fract. Mech. $\underline{5}$, 909 (1973).

36. L A James, Nuclear Tech. $\underline{16}$, 316 (1972).

37. L A James, Int. J. Fract. Mech. $\underline{8}$, 347 (1972).

38. G J Lloyd and J Wareing, J. Eng. Mat. Tech. (to be published).

39. H O Solomon and L F Coffin Jnr., ASTM STP 520, 112 (1972).

40. B A Bilby, A H Cottrell and K H Swinden, Proc. Roy. Soc. $\underline{/A/}$ $\underline{272}$, 304 (1963).

41. D J Michel, H H Smith and H E Watson, Proc. Symp. on Struct. Matls. ASME, New York, MPC-1, p.10 (1975).

42. G J Lloyd, UKAEA ND-R-147(R), (1978).

43. J R Haigh, R P Skelton and C E Richards, J. Mater. Sci. Eng. $\underline{26}$, 167 (1976).

44. L F Coffin Jnr., Proc. I. Mech. E., $\underline{188}$, 109 (1974).

45. R B Scarlin, Proc. ICF-4 (Waterloo) $\underline{2}$, 849 (1977).

46. L A James and R L Knecht, Met. Trans. $\underline{6A}$, 109 (1975).

APPENDIX

CAVITY LINKAGE BY A CRACK DISPLACEMENT FIELD

Andersson[29] has examined the relationship between the growth of a void of initial radius $p_o / 2$ in a square cell of side λ and the displacement v of the upper and lower faces of the cell under tensile loading in rigid-plastic material. Fig A1 shows the relationship between p / λ and $2v / \lambda$ for two cases of p_o / λ (0.1 and 0.25). The limiting case for cavity linkage ($p / \lambda = 1$) if several cells were adjacent is achieved at $2v / \lambda \simeq 0.3$. Fig A2 shows the displacement distribution $v / v (c)$ ahead of a plane strain crack under tension using the B-C-S model. $v (c)$ is the crack tip displacement. Also included in the figure is the distribution of p / λ under this displacement distribution for the two cases assuming a linkage condition has been achieved at the crack tip. It can be seen that on the next achievement of this condition following unloading, some 65% of the plastic zone would fail by linkage. On subsequent cycles this settles down to about 40%.

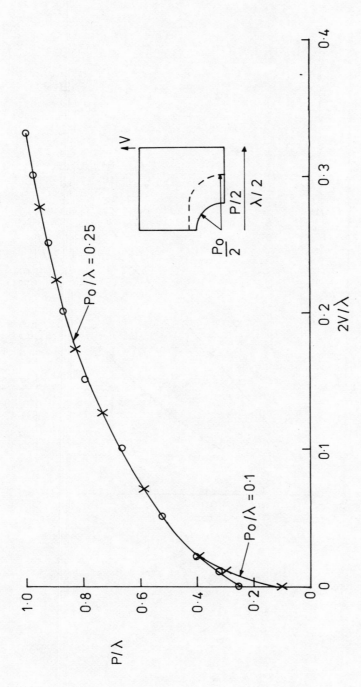

Fig. A1 Relationship between void size and cell displacement (After Andersson (29)).

B. Tomkins

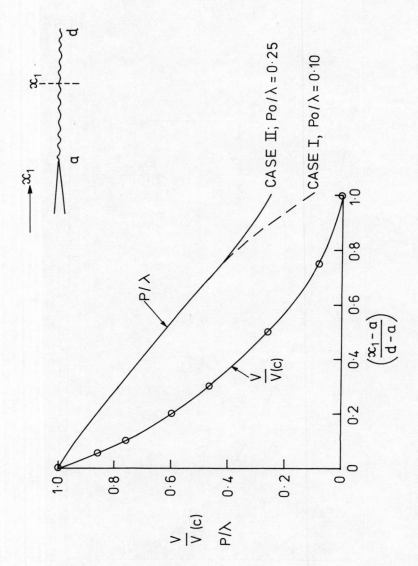

Fig. A2   B-C-S displacement and size distributions ahead of a plane strain crack under tensile loading.

FRACTURE MECHANISMS IN FIBROUS COMPOSITES

P. W. R. Beaumont

Department of Engineering, University of Cambridge,
Trumpington Street, Cambridge CB2 1PZ, U.K.

Abstract

Fibrous composites can fracture in a number of ways; by fibre breakage, by matrix cracking and by fibre pull-out. This paper describes microscopic observations of fibre-matrix debonding, fibre fracture and the pulling-out of broken fibres from a cracked matrix, and presents models for the dissipation of energy in these various processes. Comparison is made between theory and experimental work of fracture data for glass fibre-epoxy, carbon fibre-epoxy and a hybrid composite containing glass fibres and carbon fibres, in order to identify the dominant toughening mechanisms.

1.   Introduction

There exists a number of alternative mechanisms by which a fibrous composite can fail; by matrix cracking, by fibre-matrix debonding, by fibre fracture and by the pulling-out of broken fibres (fig. 1). Models to describe failure processes like these can be derived; they are based on direct microscopic observation using optical and scanning electron microscopy. Three mechanisms will be described by which a fibrous composite can fail, using a sequence in which they may occur. An equation will be selected for each mechanism, based on a physically sound microscopic model, to describe each failure process. Some fracture data for glass fibre-epoxy, carbon fibre-epoxy and a hybrid composite containing glass fibres and carbon fibres will be summarised in cumulative probability diagrams. These diagrams are based on fractographic information on fibre-matrix debonding and fibre pull-out and show the probability of a fibre debonding over a particular distance and having a particular pulled-out length. Each equation is used in turn, together with the information on fibre debonded length and fibre pull-out length to estimate the energy dissipated by the fracture mechanisms. The energy data is summarised in fracture energy diagrams which show fracture energy plotted against fibre volume fraction or number of fibres; in the case of the hybrid composite, fracture energy is plotted against proportion of the two kinds of fibres. Comparison is then made between theory and experimental work of fracture data and the dominant mechanism of toughening is apparent. Each mechanism will undoubtedly depend, in

211

212 P. W. R. Beaumont

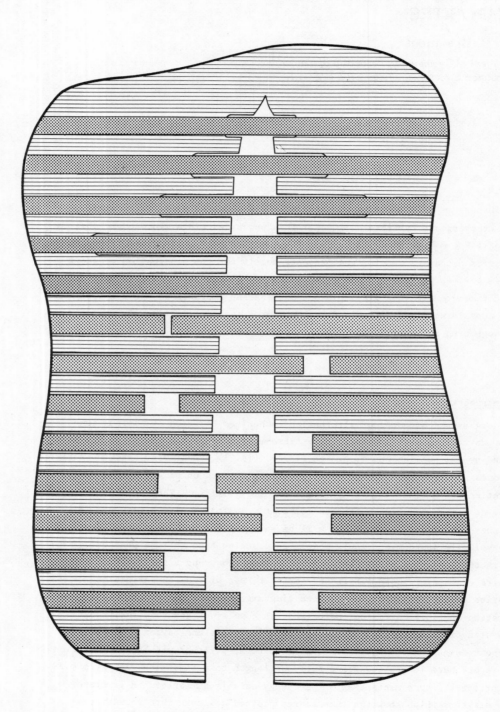

Fig. 1   A schematic diagram showing some possible failure
mechanisms at the tip of a crack.

its own way on environment, temperature and humidity, for example; attention will
be given to fracture under ambient conditions, mentioning some effects of temperature and moisture in passing.

An important point to remember is that when moving from one composite to
another, the dominant mechanism of fracture changes. Another point worth emphasising is that the sequence of microscopic failure events can differ from
composite to composite, and the energies dissipated and their origins can be
quite different in the stages of crack initiation and crack growth.

The properties of glass fibres, carbon fibres and a typical epoxy resin are
listed in Table I.

2. Models of Fracture

In this section, are derived the relevant equations used to calculate the
energy parameters. Theory provides the form of the equation and experimental
data is required to determine the values of the terms and constants which appear
in it.

Consider the propagation of a crack in a brittle matrix, around and beyond
a long, strong fibre, glass fibre in epoxy, for instance, (fig. 2). Localised
stresses at the tip of the crack are likely to cause fibre–matrix debonding.
Under conditions of increasing load, the crack faces open and the interfacial
debonded region on either side of the crack surfaces extends. Differential displacement between fibre and matrix occurs in the debonded region. Provided the
fibre still interacts in some way with the matrix, mechanical keying, for instance, a frictional (sliding) shear force is established soon after the bond
fails. The distance over which this shear force acts is approximately equal
to the product of the debonded length of fibre, ℓ_d, and the differential failure strain of fibre and matrix, $\Delta\varepsilon$. Since the initial frictional shear force,
$\tau\pi d(\ell_d/2)$, acts in each direction from the crack surface over a distance, $\Delta\varepsilon\ell_d/2$,
the work done per fibre is (1,2)

$$W_{pdf} = \pi d\tau\ell_d^2 \Delta\varepsilon/2 \tag{1}$$

$$= \pi d\tau\ell_d^2\varepsilon_f/2 \qquad (\varepsilon_f \gg \varepsilon_m) \tag{2}$$

(d is the diameter of the fibre).

The load on the fibre is a maximum in the debonded region and as it increases
the fibre is likely to break at a flaw somewhere along its debonded length (fig. 2).
The localised elastic work of tensile deformation, W_d, in the fibre over a length,
ℓ_d, is (3)

$$W_d = \frac{\pi d^2}{2E_f} \int_{\ell=0}^{\ell_d} (\sigma_f - \frac{4\tau\ell}{d})^2 \, d\ell \tag{3}$$

assuming a constant frictional shear stress. σ_f is the tensile stress in the un-
constrained fibre; E_f is the Young's Modulus of fibre. Putting $\ell_d = d\sigma_f/4\tau$, the

214   P. W. R. Beaumont

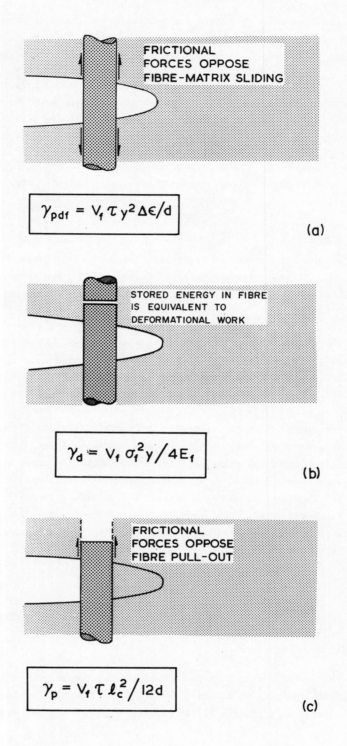

Fig. 2 (a) Sliding of a debonded fibre in its matrix socket.

       (b) Fracture of a debonded fibre.

       (c) Pulling out of a broken fibre from a cracked matrix.

expression for fibre deformational work, often referred to as fibre debonding energy, can be written as

$$W_d = \pi d^2 \sigma_f^2 \ell_d / 24 E_f \tag{4}$$

The exact form of the equation depends upon the way in which the stress builds up in the fibre from the broken end (4,5).

Provided there is some kind of interaction between the debonded fibre ends and the matrix, then a frictional (sliding) shear force opposes any force applied to extract the fibre (fig. 2)(6). The total frictional work of pull-out is

$$W_p = \int_{\ell=0}^{\ell_p} P_f d\ell \tag{5}$$

$$= \pi d \tau \ell_p^2 / 2 \tag{6}$$

The average work to pull out a fibre whose embedded length lies between 0 and ℓ_p is, therefore,

$$\overline{W}_p = \frac{1}{\ell_p} \int_0^{\ell_o} W_o \, d\ell \tag{7}$$

$$= \pi d \tau \ell_p^2 / 6 \tag{8}$$

assuming a constant frictional shear stress, τ. If we assume that the maximum fibre pull-out length is equal to one-half of the critical fibre length*, $\ell_c/2$, equation (8) can be written as

$$\overline{W}_p = \pi d \tau \ell_c^2 / 24 \tag{9}$$

From the above relationships we can identify three contributions to the total work to fracture the composite containing brittle fibres:

$$W_{pdf} = \pi d \tau \ell_d^2 \, \varepsilon_f / 2 \qquad (\varepsilon_f \ll \varepsilon_m)$$

$$W_d = \pi d^2 \sigma_f^2 \ell_d / 24 \, E_f$$

$$\overline{W}_p = \pi d \tau \ell_p^2 / 6 \qquad (\tau = \text{constant})$$

(ℓ_p is the maximum fibre pull-out length). The total work to fracture is, therefore,

$$W_{TOTAL} = (\frac{\pi d}{24})(12 \tau \ell_d^2 \varepsilon_f + d \sigma_f^2 \ell_d / E_f + 4 \tau \ell_p^2) \tag{10}$$

---

*ℓ_c is the smallest length of fibre bonded to a matrix which can be loaded to its breaking point. It can be defined using the expression $\ell_c = \sigma_f d / 2\tau$.

In each model, the work done is directly proportional to the number of fibres
or fibre volume fraction and each one, in its own way, is sensitive to the interfacial shear stress. We assume that the terms which appear in each equation are
insensitive to fibre volume fraction. This may not be true; the frictional shear
stress, for example, depends upon the radial force exerted by the matrix onto the
fibre which is likely to be sensitive to spacing of the fibres.

3.   Statistical Analysis of Fracture

Cumulative probability diagrams can be used to summarise fractographic information on fibre-matrix debonding and fibre pull-out. It involves assembling
data on the failure of model fibrous composites in tension, determining the distances over which fibres debond and pull-out, computing the probability of a
fibre debonding over a particular distance and the probability that the fracture
surface of the composite has a protruding fibre of a particular length. The procedure is as follows. Values of work of fracture, fibre debond length and fibre
pull-out length are tabulated. The fracture data are obtained from flexural
beam tests on model composites in the form of a prismatic bar of epoxy containing a single layer of unidirectional fibre tape (fig. 3). This figure shows a
single tow of carbon fibres containing 5000 individual filaments and two strands
of glass fibres on either side, each strand containing 1600 individual filaments
and loaded in tension. The bundles of glass fibres and carbon fibres can be
arranged in many ways to produce a series of composites ranging from 100 % glass
fibres to 100 % carbon fibres, with many combinations between the two (7).

After fracture, an attempt is made to assign a mode of failure to each group
of specimens, based on fractographic observations of fibre debonding and fibre
pull-out. A precise measurement of fibre debond length and fibre pull-out length
is important. An optical microscope can be used for this purpose. Tracings are
made of each protruding bundle of fibres, carefully following the dark outline of
the pulled-out fibres and the fracture plane of the matrix. Similarly, tracings
are made of the debonded regions which are clearly visible in reflected light.
Figure 3 shows a broken half of the specimen shown previously with the pulled
out fibres and debonded fibre regions visible (7). A tracing of one of the glass
fibre strands is shown with the dark profile of the pulled-out fibres and a light
area representing the debonded region. An average value of the longest fibres
pulled out and an average value of the length of debonded fibres for each bundle
is determined by dividing the area of each tracing by the width of the bundle.
If there are 5 strands of glass fibres in each specimen in a group of 20 specimens,
for example, then 200 tracings are made showing pulled-out fibres and 200 tracings
showing debonded fibres, since both halves of each specimen can be examined.

Summarising the data in plots of cumulative probability versus fibre debond
or fibre pull-out lengths produces useful information (8). Figure 4 shows cumulative probability versus fibre debond length for different numbers of glass
fibres. The data does not overlap but is displaced slightly to the right as the
number of glass fibres increases. The debonding process is sensitive to the number

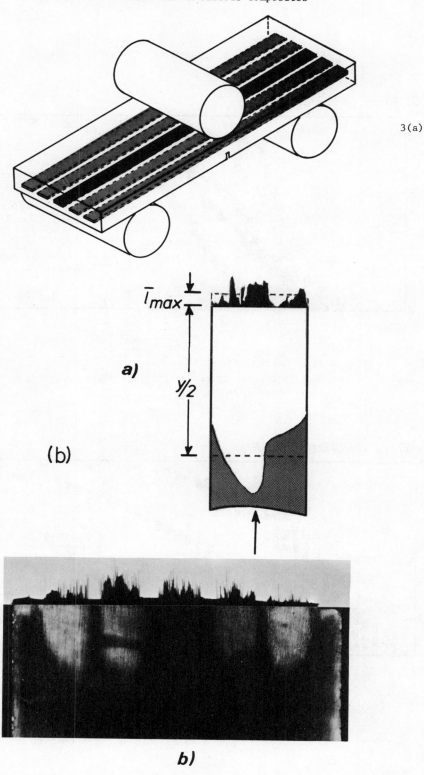

3(a)

Fig. 3   (a)   A schematic diagram of the loading geometry and test-piece
               of a model fibrous composite. In this case, the central
               tow is carbon fibres with two rovings of glass fibres on
               either side.

          (b)   A broken half of the test-piece shown in (a), showing pulled
                out fibres and regions of debonding. Profiles of the pulled
                out and debonded glass fibres of a glass fibre roving are
                shown in the sketch.

CUMULATIVE PROBABILITY (P)

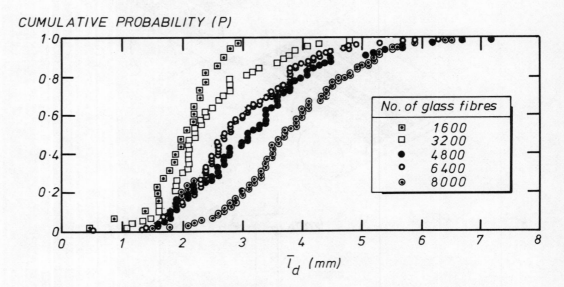

Fig. 4   (a) Cumulative probability versus fibre debond length for
               glass fibres in epoxy.

CUMULATIVE PROBABILITY (P)

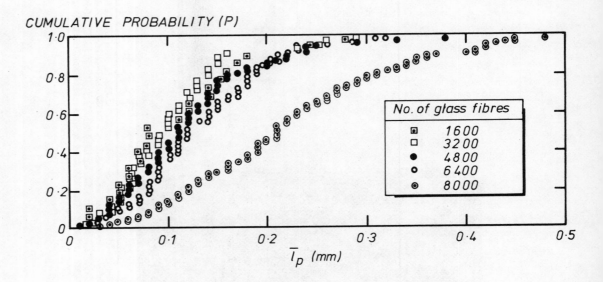

Fig.   4   (b) Cumulative probability versus fibre pull-out length
                 for glass fibres in epoxy.

of glass fibres in the composite. It is interesting to note, (although it is not obvious why), the data for N=8000 fibres falls to the right of the data for N=6400 fibres. This apparent reversal in trend of the cumulative probability data will be referred to later. A similar shift of data towards higher fibre lengths is observed for pulled-out glass fibres (fig. 4). The apparent oddity in this case is the large displacement of data for N=8000 fibres. A Weibull expression can describe each set of data.

$$P\ (\ell)\ =\ \exp\ (\frac{\ell}{\ell_o})^m \tag{11}$$

where $P\ (\ell)$ is the cumulative probability, ℓ is the fibre length, and m and ℓ_o are the Weibull constants. The constants which appear in the exponential equation can be obtained by replotting the data in logarithmic form (fig . 5) and determining the slope and intercept of the linear plot. In both cases, fibre debonding and fibre pull-out data falls on parallel lines each with a slope of between 1.5 and 2.5. Presenting data in this way is useful for observing the subtle effects of environment, moisture for instance, and characterising fracture.

4.   Estimation of Fracture Energy

It is not clear at this stage whether an average value of fibre debond length and fibre pull-out length, together with the models of fracture is sufficient to estimate reasonably accurately the work to fracture the composite or whether a more rigorous statistical analysis needs to be developed.

As a first approximation, let us take the average values of glass fibre debond length and pull-out length. The diagram of fracture energy versus number of glass fibres (fig. 6) shows the estimated energy dissipated during the post-debond sliding mechanism (eq. 2). The relationship is not a simple linear one as one would expect from the form of the equation; the cumulative probability data showed fibre debond length to be sensitive to the number of fibres in the composite. We recall that it is the square of the fibre debond length and number of fibres which appears in the post-debond fibre sliding equation. The plateau to the curve reflects the reversal in the trend of cumulative probability data for N=6400 fibres to which reference was made earlier.

An estimation of fibre debond energy (eq. 4) is shown in the next diagram (fig. 6). At first sight, the shape is linear but closer examination shows a smooth curve with a gradually increasing slope. It reflects the dependence of fibre debond length on the number of glass fibres. The plateau shown in the previous figure is less obvious since fibre debond energy is directly proportional to the length of debonded fibre. The energy dissipated in this way is significantly less than the work done in the post-debond fibre sliding mechanism.

The work to pull broken glass fibres out of a cracked matrix (eq. 8) is of a similar order of magnitude as the fibre debond energy (fig. 6). Both figures have a similar shape; the increase in gradient of the curve at the high numbers of fibres originates from the high values of fibre pull-out length shown previously

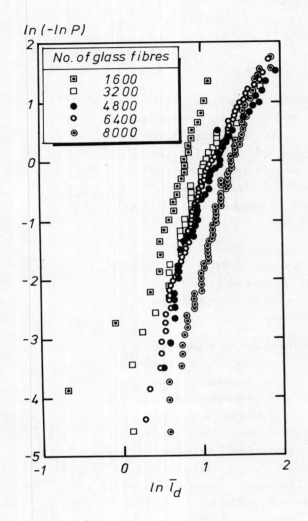

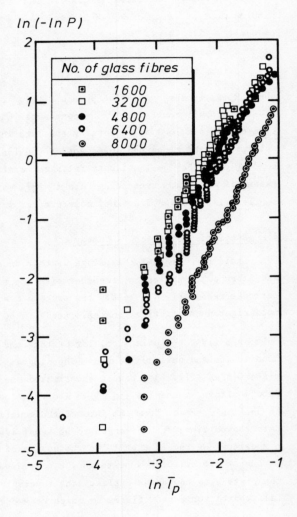

Fig. 5   (a)   A logarithmic plot of the   Fig. 5   (b.)   A logarithmic plot of
                data shown in Fig. 4(a)   the data shown in
                                                                   Fig. 4(b).

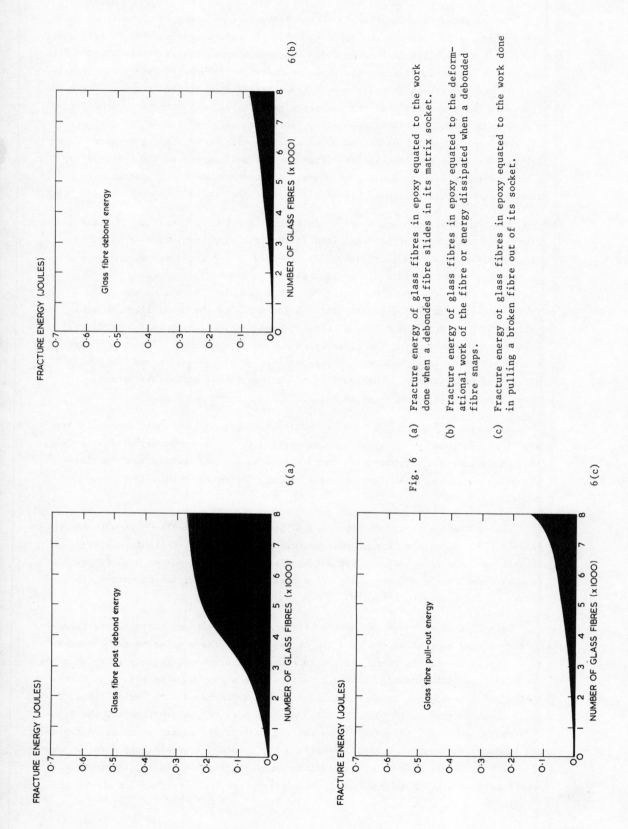

Fig. 6. (a) Fracture energy of glass fibres in epoxy equated to the work
done when a debonded fibre slides in its matrix socket.

(b) Fracture energy of glass fibres in epoxy equated to the deformational work of the fibre or energy dissipated when a debonded
fibre snaps.

(c) Fracture energy of glass fibres in epoxy equated to the work done
in pulling a broken fibre out of its socket.

in the cumulative probability data for N=8000 fibres.

The result of summing these 3 energy parameters (eq. 10) is shown in figure 7. Apart from a small rise in the curve at N=5000 fibres, approximately, it is a smooth curve with a gradually increasing slope as the number of fibres increases. Comparison of the empirical diagram with experimental work of fracture data shows remarkable likeness in shape and magnitude. From observations of the fracture of glass fibres in epoxy we know that the composite exhibits all the common modes of failure; matrix cracking, fibres debonding, fibres snapping and fibres pulling out. The dominant toughening mechanism appears to be post-debond sliding between fibre and matrix; the breakage of fibres and the pulling out of the broken fibre ends dissipates similar amounts of energy and together contribute little more than one-quarter of the total fracture energy of the composite.

Fractographic information of glass fibres in a hybrid composite of glass fibres and carbon fibres is summarised in the following cumulative probability diagrams (fig. 8). The fibre debond length data do not superimpose, and increasing the ratio of glass fibres to carbon fibres may displace the data to the right or to the left (8). For example, increasing the glass fibre content from 30 % (by vol.) to 56 % (by vol.) of the total fibre content shifts the data from low values of fibre debond length to high values of fibre debond length; increasing the glass fibre content a further 7 % (by vol.) moves the data back to lower values. Closer examination of the data shows the subtle effects of composition on the position of the cumulative probability curve. These effects will be referred to later.

In contrast, data of glass fibre pull-out length in the hybrid composite are almost superimposed (fig. 8). The same applies to the data for carbon fibres (fig. 8). Each cumulative probability curve overlaps with one another and the shape and position of the curves are not significantly affected by variations in composition (8).

Taking average values of fibre debond length and fibre pull-out length for the glass fibres and carbon fibres, combined with the equations of fracture energy, we can estimate the energy dissipated during fracture and pull-out of both fibres. In this case, fracture energy is plotted against volume fraction of carbon fibres in the hybrid composite (fig. 9).

This diagram shows an estimation of the energy dissipated during glass fibre-matrix sliding soon after the bond has failed. While there is an overall decrease in energy as the carbon fibre content increases, as one would expect, it by no means forms a linear relationship. Certain features are worth pointing out. The first is that after a sharp drop in energy as glass fibre is replaced with carbon fibre, a plateau is observed up to 40 % (by vol.) of carbon fibre. At that point, the fracture energy actually increases before falling to zero as the remaining glass fibres are replaced with carbon fibres. Recalling the cumulative probability data, we realise that it is the effects of composition on glass fibre debond length and the subtle balance between debond length and fibre volume fraction which is the origin

FRACTURE ENERGY (JOULES)

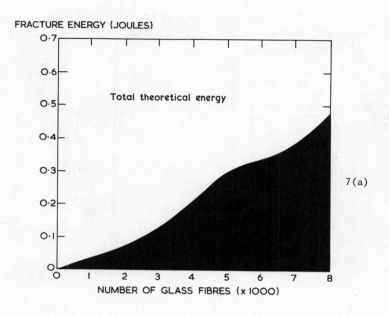

7(a)

NUMBER OF GLASS FIBRES (x 1000)

FRACTURE ENERGY (JOULES)

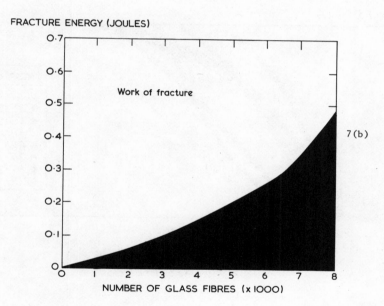

7(b)

NUMBER OF GLASS FIBRES (x 1000)

Fig. 7   (a) Total theoretical fracture energy of glass fibres in epoxy.

          (b) Experimental work of fracture of glass fibres in epoxy.

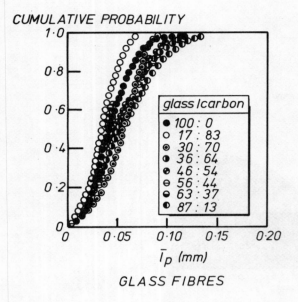

GLASS FIBRES

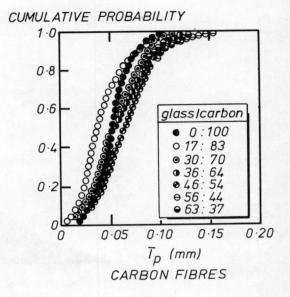

CARBON FIBRES

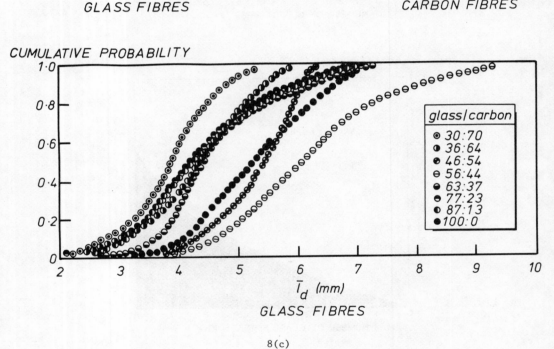

GLASS FIBRES

8(c)

Fig. 8   (a)   Cumulative probability versus pull-out length of glass fibres in glass fibre/carbon fibre hybrid composites.

            (b)   Cumulative probability versus pull-out length of carbon fibres in glass fibre/carbon fibre hybrid composites.

            (c)   Cumulative probability versus debond length of glass fibres in glass fibre/carbon fibre hybrid composites.

of the unexpected shape of the post-debond sliding energy diagram. The small peak
in the diagram at 44 % (by vol.) of carbon fibre coincides with the large displacement
of the cumulative probability data to higher values of glass fibre debond length.

At first sight, glass fibre debond energy decreases linearly with increasing
carbon fibre (fig. 9). Closer inspection shows a shallow curve with a very small
peak at 44 % (by vol.) of carbon fibre. Minor differences in shape and position
of the cumulative probability curves are responsible for the non-linear behaviour.

Slight undulations in the pull-out curve for the glass fibres can also be identified with minor changes in shape and position of the cumulative probability curves
(fig. 10). As a first approximation, the glass fibre debond energy and glass fibre
pull-out energy are directly proportional to the amount of glass fibre in the composite, as one would expect from the form of the equations.

Similar undulations in the carbon fibre pull-out energy diagram originate in
the small differences to be found in the cumulative probability data (fig. 10).
Ignoring these minor effects, the pull-out energy follows a linear relationship
with carbon fibre content, as one would expect.

Summation of these 4 energy contributions gives the total theoretical fracture
energy of the hybrid system (fig. 11). The shape is dominated by the post-debond
sliding mechanism of the glass fibres, but at the carbon fibre-rich end of the
diagram the pull-out mechanism of carbon fibres is important. Comparison between
the theoretical fracture energy and experimental work of fracture (fig. 11) show
remarkable similarities in shape and magnitude. These results show that for the
glass fibre-rich hybrid the glass fibre post-debond sliding energy term is a major
component of the total fracture energy. For glass fibres, the debonding energy
and pull-out energy parameters are comparable in magnitude; together they contribute no more than one-quarter of the total fracture energy of the hybrid.
The work of fracture of the carbon fibre-epoxy can be explained adequately using
the fibre pull-out model (7).

The results of a more rigorous study of the fracture of carbon fibre-epoxy
composites confirm this (9). Fractographic information indicated that no separation had occurred at the fibre-matrix interface and the average fibre pull-out
length was between 3 and 6 times the diameter of the carbon fibre. Assuming
the critical fibre length, ℓ_c, is approximately equal to 4 times the average
length of pulled-out fibres, (fibres pull out over a distance between 0 and $\ell_c/2$),
then the work to pull out broken carbon fibres as a function of fibre volume fraction can be estimated (fig. 12). Experimental work of fracture data fall on a
reasonably straight line which intercepts the axis at the fracture energy of the
epoxy. The solid line in the diagram is constructed by assuming a value of ℓ_c = 15 d
which is remarkably close to the value estimated in the fractographic study.

According to the fibre pull-out model (eq. 9), the work to extract a fibre is in-
versely proportional to the interfacial frictional shear stress, since $\ell_c \alpha \tau^{-1}$. A plot
of fracture energy against frictional shear stress for a series of carbon fibre-epoxy
and carbon fibre-polyester composites is shown in figure 13. The wide solid line re-

FRACTURE ENERGY (kJ/m²)

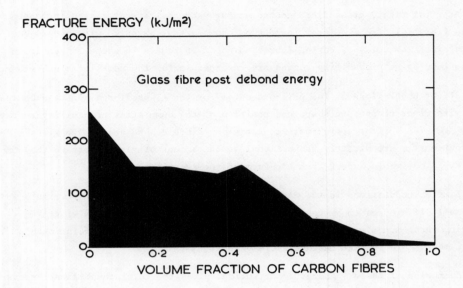

Fig. 9   (a)   Fracture energy or work done when a debonded glass fibre
               slides in its matrix socket in glass fibre/carbon fibre
               hybrid composites.

FRACTURE ENERGY (kJ/m²)

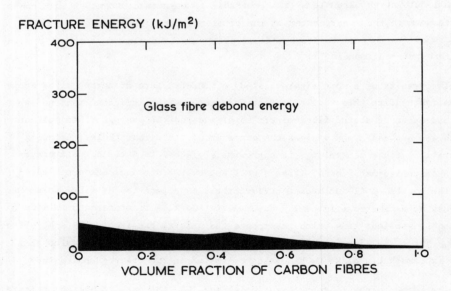

Fig. 9   (b)   Fracture energy or energy dissipated when a debonded glass
               fibre snaps in glass fibre/carbon fibre hybrid composites.

FRACTURE ENERGY (kJ/m^2)

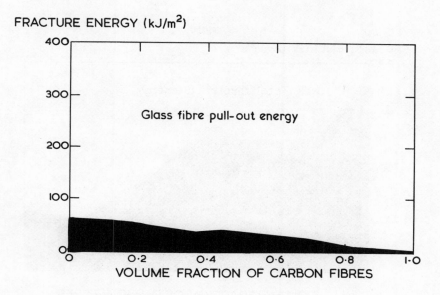

Fig. 10   (a)   Fracture energy or work done in pulling a broken glass fibre
               out of its socket in glass fibre/carbon fibre hybrid composites.

FRACTURE ENERGY (kJ/m^2)

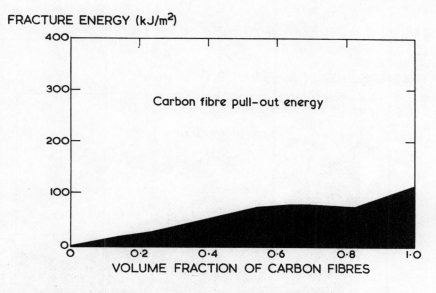

Fig. 10   (b)   Fracture energy or work done in pulling a broken carbon
               fibre out of its matrix socket in glass fibre/carbon fibre hybrid
               composites.

FRACTURE ENERGY (kJ/m^2)

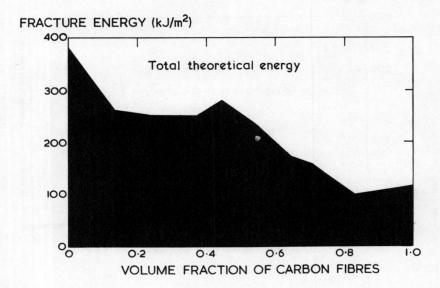

Fig. 11   (a) · Total theoretical fracture energy of glass fibre/carbon fibre
                 hybrid composites.

FRACTURE ENERGY (kJ/m^2)

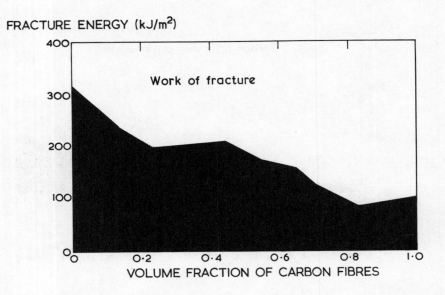

Fig. 11   (b) Experimental work of fracture of glass fibre/carbon fibre
                 hybrid composites.

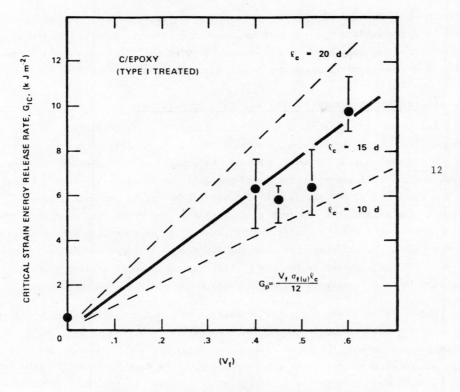

12

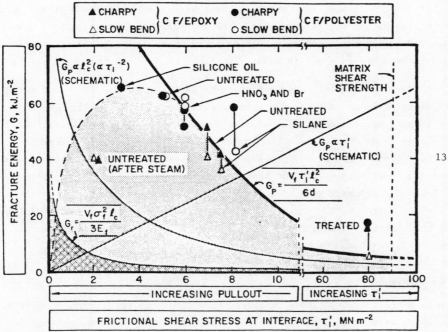

13

Fig. 12   Critical strain energy release rate of carbon fibre-epoxy
           composites as a function of fibre volume fraction. The
           solid line is the fibre pull-out model using an average
           fibre pull-out length to obtain the critical fibre length
           ($\ell_c = 4\bar{\ell}_p$).

Fig. 13   Work of fracture of carbon fibre-epoxy and carbon fibre-
           polyester composites as a function of interfacial shear
           strength. The solid line is the fibre pull-out model
           using measured values of interfacial shear stress.

presents the theoretical work to pull out the fibres from their sockets; experimental work of fracture data agree quite well with the theory. Exposure to steam, however, causes debonding and the absorbed moisture reduces the frictional shear stress. The overall effect is to increase the length of pulled-out fibres and reduce toughness (10).

5.   Energies of Crack Initiation and Crack Propagation

Extension of a crack is a 2 stage process; (1) crack initiation and (2) crack propagation. Crack initiation in brittle fibrous composites occurs by cracking the matrix and breakage of fibres at flaws. The process of crack growth involves displacement of the fracture surfaces and the pulling-out of broken fibres bridging the matrix crack. Provided the length of fibre pulled out of the matrix is small compared to the size of the fracture process zone at the crack tip, then the work done in separating the crack surfaces may be equated to the summation of the various energy terms. On the other hand, if the fibre debond length and fibre pull-out length is large compared to the crack size, the microscopic sliding processes may contribute primarily to the crack propagation stage of fracture.

Figure 14 shows crack initiation energy and crack propagation energy of three carbon fibre-epoxy composites over the temperature range -10 $^{\circ}$C to 150 $^{\circ}$C. The wide solid lines represent the crack initiation energy for each composite and show a slight dependence on temperature. At low temperatures, the fibre pull-out lengths are small and the work done to overcome friction can be included in the crack initiation energy term (11). As the temperature approaches the softening temperature of the epoxy, the length of pulled out fibres increases by as much as 4 times. Crack propagation energy represented by the shaded area increases accordingly. Fibre pull-out length as a function of temperature is shown in figure 14.

The crack initiation energy and crack propagation energy parameters for a glass fibre-polyester as a function of strain-rate is shown in figure 15. Crack initiation energy is essentially independent of strain-rate over 4 decades. A small fracture process zone forms at the crack tip at the initiation of failure in which a limited amount of fibre-matrix debonding occurs. Extensive debonding on either side of the crack surfaces coincides with the stable propagation of the crack. Opening of the crack faces during crack growth causes the fibre and matrix to slide and broken fibres to be pulled out. It may be the rate-dependence of the interfacial frictional shear stress that is the origin of the rate-dependent crack propagation energy parameter (12).

6.   Conclusions

When a crack passes through a glass fibre or carbon fibre-epoxy composite, the fibres which bridge the crack are observed to debond and fracture, pulling out of the matrix as the crack surfaces open. Models based on these observations, predict the energies dissipated when a debonded fibre slides in its socket, breaks in the debonded region and pulls out of the matrix. Detailed comparisons of experimental data with the models show that the post-debond fibre sliding mechanism is primarily responsible for the toughness of glass fibre-epoxy, while the fibre pull-out mechanism accounts for the fracture energy of carbon fibre-epoxy composites.

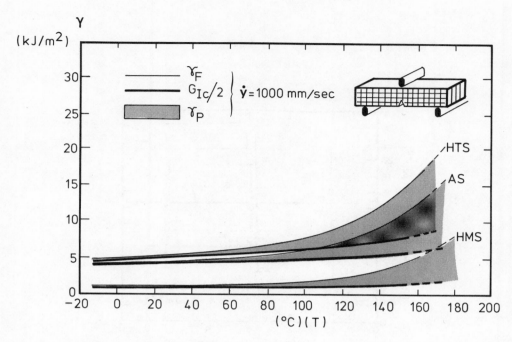

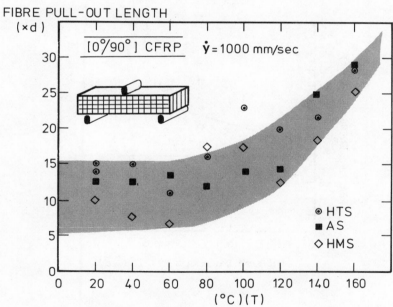

Fig. 14   (a) Crack initiation energy and crack propagation energy
                of three carbon fibre-epoxy composites between
                -10°C and 150°C.

           (b) Pulled out length of carbon fibres as a function of
                temperature.

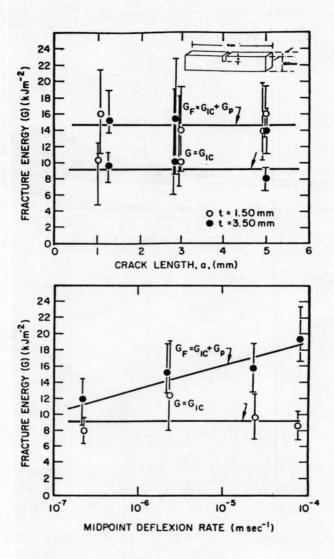

Fig. 15   Crack initiation energy and crack propagation energy of a
glass fibre-polyester composite. In each diagram, the
lower solid curve represents the energy released when a
debonded glass fibre snaps; the upper solid curve is the
sum of the energies dissipated when a glass fibre snaps
and is pulled out of its matrix socket.

References

1. A. Kelly, Proc. Roy. Soc. A319, 95, (1970).

2. B. Harris, J. Morley and D.C. Phillips, J. Mater. Sci. 10, 2050, (1975).

3. J.O. Outwater and M.C. Murphy, Modern Plastics 7, 160, (1970); see also J. Adhesion 2, 242, (1970).

4. M.R. Piggott, J. Mater. Sci. 5, 669, (1970).

5. J. FitzRandolph, D.C. Phillips, P.W.R. Beaumont and A.S. Tetelman, J. Mater. Sci. 7, 289, (1972).

6. A.H. Cottrell, Proc. Roy. Soc. A282, 2, (1964).

7. J.N. Kirk, M. Munro and P.W.R. Beaumont, J. Mater. Sci. 13, 2187, (1978).

8. P.W.R. Beaumont and P. Anstice, unpublished data.

9. P.W.R. Beaumont and A.S. Tetelman, AIME Spring Meeting on "Failure Modes in Composites", Boston, May (1972); see also J. Adhesion 6, 107, (1974).

10. P.W.R. Beaumont and B. Harris, J. Mater. Sci. 7, 1265, (1972).

11. P.W.R. Beaumont and W.L. Server, "Composite Reliability", ASTM STP 580, (1974).

12. P.W.R. Beaumont and D.C. Phillips, J. Mater. Sci. 7, 682, (1972); see also J. Adhesion 6, 107, (1974).

Acknowledgements

I would like to thank the Science Research Council and Air Force of Scientific Research, Washington, D.C., for financial support.

TABLE I   Fibre and matrix properties

Material	No. of fibres per tow	Fibre diameter ($\times 10^{-6}$ m)	Tensile strength (GN m^{-2})	Young's modulus (GN m^{-2})	Failure strain ϵ
Carbon fibre Type II	5000	8	2.40	240	0.010
Glass fibre Type E	1600	13	1.65	70	0.023
Epoxy resin	–	–	0.06	2.5	0.014

FRACTURE CRITERIA IN ELASTIC AND ELASTIC/PLASTIC SOLIDS

A. A. Wells

The Welding Institute, Abington, Cambridge, CB1 6AL.

SUMMARY

The size effect with regard to extension of sharp cracks in technological materials is to a large extent accurately described by linear elastic fracture mechanics. This paper considers some of the anomalies with respect to fracture toughness measurements from standard specimens, commencing with the plastic zone size correction, plane strain/stress transitional effect, and initiation/propagation effect with materials alternatively exhibiting ductile and cleavage behaviour. It goes on to consider the comparison and measurement of crack opening displacement and J integral as fracture toughness estimates under elastic-plastic conditions, further effects of thickness and shape, and resistance curve descriptions of the commencement of slow cracking. Attention is drawn in conclusion to the inadequacies of elastic-plastic analyses with respect to important three-dimensional effects, whereby the measurement of large values of fracture toughness is inhibited, and to an almost complete absence of knowledge of the detailed deformations in crack extension.

INTRODUCTION

Linear elastic fracture mechanics is effective in describing the progressive crack extension properties in relatively brittle materials under most conditions when those materials are homogeneous in a technological rather than microstructural sense. It is also effective in describing slow crack propagation by high-cycle fatigue in most materials, and in many cases by such agencies as stress corrosion, corrosion fatigue and high-temperature creep rupture. Nevertheless, it is well-known that fracture toughness measurements concerned with the onset of unstable rupture using standard specimens are dependent upon straining rate and temperature in many circumstances, and that the specimens each have a measurement capacity dependent upon size and yield strength of the material, such that so-called invalid measurements are affected by non-linearity of the load-displacement curve. In spite of this range of application it remains to be considered as a matter of experience that most common engineering metals have to possess excess fracture toughness in order to accommodate without undue fracture risk average standards of design discontinuities, fabrication faults and over-loading in service, so that they may not be assessed by LEFM methods. Although perhaps 90% of the tonnage of constructions lie within this category, with respect to materials, the difficulty is not as great as might be supposed; the structures themselves are usually large enough so that the crack-like defects within them may be described by LEFM, since few structures are required to resist fracture beyond the stage at which they become unfit for service through loss of shape or dimensional tolerances. It is the fracture toughness measurement specimens that are required to be compact, for reasons of economy, and it is these that also require to be assessed well into the range of non-linear behaviour in load-displacement.

These non-linearities were first categorised in a progressive manner, and a
chronological description of the effects as they were identified is still of value.
The plastic zone size correction and plane strain/plane stress transition may first be
reviewed.

PLASTIC ZONE SIZE CORRECTION

About 25 years ago in characterising fracture toughnesses of thin aluminium alloy
sheets for aircraft applications the author tested centre-cracked panels in three
widths up to 1m, with various crack lengths obtained by slitting and fatigue crack
extension. It was discovered that correlation to produce a fracture toughness
independent of sheet width required an empirical addition of about 20mm to each
critical crack length, and it was immediately hypothesized that this was comparable to
the width of the locally plastic zone, and that the plastic zones had been reduced in
load-bearing capacity compared with the elastic condition. This effect, recognised at
about the same time by several investigators, led to the plastic zone size correction,
which may neatly be expressed in terms of the true fracture toughness K_c as
$K_c^2/(2\pi\sigma_Y^2)$ to be an effective length to be added with respect to each crack tip.

THE PLANE STRAIN/PLANE STRESS TRANSITION

In the same investigation some of the aluminium alloy sheets thicker than about
3mm showed a tendency towards developing flat fractures, in contrast to the oblique
shear-type fractures in thinner sheets, although there appeared to be no observable
change of microstructural mode of fracture, or change of fracture toughness. H.L. Cox
demonstrated the persistence of this effect by testing sheets with oblique slits;
curiously, the fractures started in this way moved back to the flat position.
G.R. Irwin provided a convincing although qualitative explanation after testing a
wider range of materials and thicknesses, in terms of plane strain deformation. The
ideal elastic distribution of stresses at a sharp crack tip exhibits triaxial tensions,
such that the yield stress across the cracking plane is much increased; however, there
must be high stress gradients in the direction of cracking if local thinning near the
crack tip is to be restrained so that the triaxial tension is supported, since the main
part of the specimen is clearly in a state of plane stress. Thus, the plane strain
condition at the crack tip, although never reaching the ideal elastic state, is
extensively relaxed as the plane stress plastic zone size grows and becomes comparable
with sheet thickness. Irwin discovered from experimental evidence that the transition
from flat to oblique fracture occurred in almost all cases at a specimen thickness
comparable to the plastic zone size characterised above, and that the measured fracture
toughnesses for flat fractures diminished considerably in most cases for larger
thicknesses, even although the microstructural mode might not change significantly. It
was later distinguished that such plane strain fracture toughness values, K_{1c}, in order
to guarantee having reached stable lower limits, should be valid measurements only if
both the thickness and the length of the net section of the specimen in the cracking
direction exceeded 2.5 x $K_{1c}^2/(2\pi\sigma_Y^2)$, with K_{1c} and σ_Y in compatible units with respect
to stress and length.

INITIATION AND PROPAGATION

Flat and oblique fractures had long been recognised in certain ferritic steels, associated with a change from the cleavage to the ductile (dimpled) microstructural mode, but usually with a change of testing temperature or straining rate. Irwin's experiments were important, since they demonstrated by consideration of aluminium and titanium alloys in which the microstructural mode change was weak, as well as steels in which it was dominant, that both geometric and metallurgical variables could be involved. However, the change of microstructural mode in the steels did not significantly alter the observed geometric criterion, although the form of the thickness transition differed.

It is now recognised that the transition so described is associated, even at one thickness, with two levels of toughness in ferritic steels, namely a larger one with respect to crack initiation in the ductile dimpled, even quasi-oblique mode, followed suddenly by a lower fracture toughness for fast propagation in the cleavage mode. These fracture toughness values could be contrasted in early tests conducted by the author, using a temperature wave method of measurement of the fracture toughness associated with the fast cleavage mode of crack propagation. In many cases the specimen required to be yielded overall in order to bring about crack initiation, so that it was not possible to make measurements of the initiation fracture toughness by linear elastic methods. In spite of this the measured propagation toughness values often corresponded with those that would have been predicted by LEFM, and they altered as would be anticipated with crack travel and fracture speed. The latter effect was demonstrated even better by photoelastic observations with spark photography, using transparent polymers.

These alternatives should be kept clearly in mind. Some structures can be qualified with respect to service, in terms of given loading and defect populations, by the control of crack initiation, in the knowledge that brittle propagation will follow if initiation occurs. However, if this approach is adopted there is a responsibility not only to conduct fracture toughness tests, but also to perform at least a proportion of them (for design rather than quality control) using specimens having the full section thickness of the material. The use of specimens of reduced thickness can be defended only where the propagation value of toughness is measured, or the test is conducted at a high straining rate so that a conservatively low initiation fracture toughness is depicted, or for purposes of empirical quality control.

THE J INTEGRAL CRITERION FOR FRACTURE

The necessity emerges from the preceding brief treatment for an alternative and a corresponding fracture criterion for the non-linear condition in measurement specimens insofar as the non-linearity is associated with local and general yielding. The crack opening displacement was the first such criterion to be proposed and developed, but the path-independent J integral offers the advantage of greater range as an initial concept[1] and will first be discussed. As conceived by Eshelby, and developed in contiguity with LEFM by Rice,[2,3] the J integral is concerned with a stationary or

incrementally extended crack in a non-linear elastic material, i.e. having a reversible
stress-strain curve. It is appropriate to adhere to the recent comprehensive
exposition of Paris[4] for a planar body such that

$$J = \int_{\Gamma} (Wdy - T_i \frac{\partial u_1}{\partial x} ds)$$

where the path Γ of the integral surrounds and contains the crack tip and is
constrained only to extend from one crack flank to the other. W is non-linear strain
energy density $\int \sigma_{ij} \partial e_{ij}$, T_i is the traction at each location of length ds at and
external to the contour in the direction of the local displacement u_i. x and y are
Cartesian co-ordinates. Rice[1] and Paris[4] demonstrate that J = G, the crack extension
force in the special case of a linear-elastic material, so that J may be regarded as
the projection of G into the non-linear regime.

Since J is a non-linear equivalent of crack extension force it follows, and may
be proved in detail, that J da represents the change in energy contained within the
specimen, arising from the difference in areas of the load-displacement curves
corresponding with otherwise identical specimens loaded from zero to given displacement, having crack lengths different by the amount da.

It also follows that J has these properties if applied to an elastic-plastic
sharply notched body without crack extension, provided that both the stress-strain
curve and the loading of the specimen are monotonic, so that unloading occurs nowhere.
The restriction is necessary since plastic materials have non-reversible stress-strain
curves, so that unloading restores linear-elastic behaviour followed by reversed
yielding, according to a constitutive relation based upon incremental strains and
deviator stresses. Crack extension in an elastic-plastic body produces stress
relaxation in the zones left behind by the crack, and represents the principal non-
conformity with the non-linear elastic assumption.

J may be determined for a cracked planar body in plane strain or plane stress
under any circumstances where an elastic-plastic analysis may be made. Approximations
are easily made for rigid-plastic bodies, but most determinations have made use of the
finite element method, with tests for validity based upon changing element sizes and
mesh configurations in the crack tip zone. Repeated analyses with crack length
increments, adhering in each case to monotonic loading, show that there is good
correspondence between the methods of evaluation of J, 1) by contour integration (path
independence is sustained until coming very close to the crack tip) and 2) by
comparison of load-displacement curves. Moreover, there is a valuable identity
observed in most of the special cases between the accumulation of J and the
accumulation of external work, which proves to be linear beyond the stage which may be
defined as the plastic limit load. Of course, this is self-evidently true for linear-
elastic conditions and constant crack length, but the relations as established by
finite element treatments prove to be bi-linear in general, and continuously linear
only in some special cases. The relation for the deeply notched bend specimen was
established analytically as linear by Rice[5] for non-linear elastic conditions;
unfortunately, the assertion[4] that this property arises in specimen shapes dominated
by one dimension (crack length in the bend specimen) conflicts with the finite element
calculation for the internally notched wide plate, which proves to be strongly bi-

linear, at least in plane strain.

These observations have a bearing upon an alternative elastic-plastic treatment known as Equivalent Energy, which has developed more empirically as an alternative to the J integral treatment. This method relies implicitly upon linearity over the whole range between the adopted fracture criterion (alternative to J) and total energy.

The reservation with regard to J for a loaded, cracked body subjected to incremental crack extension, where there is reversal of strains near the crack, is made evident by finite element studies of Boyle,[6] who modelled incremental crack extension by progressive unpinning of individual nodes at the crack tip. It is appropriate to repeat his conclusions.

"Incremental crack extension, simulated by node release, produces a significantly larger drop of load under the fixed grip condition than would be indicated by estimates of the difference of non-linear compliance, determined in each case for monotonic loading. (Figure 1)

Energy is conserved in the fixed grip crack extension, provided that external work at the opened node is considered. Thus the excess of whole field elastic energy release over potential energy change delineated by J, whether from multipath integration or monotonic loading compliance change, is accounted for alternatively by external work at the opened node or its equivalent as the potential energy release, integrated over the whole field. J determined by multipath integration remained constant during crack extension in the cases studied."

The situation studied by Boyle is not unlike that with respect to unstable propagation of cleavage cracking in a specimen which has survived general yielding before initiation. The result is also similar to that exposed by temperature wave studies for, if the work at the opening node were to be added to the work of local plasticity at the newly created crack tip, whose local and incremental plastic zone is small in extent, the result would be just in excess of the linear elastic crack extension force (Figures 2a and 2b). It is evident that crack extension in elastic-plastic materials is significantly more complex than the J integral approach for a non-linear elastic material would comprehend, useful as the concept undoubtedly is.

THE CRACK OPENING DISPLACEMENT

In the search for a supplementary fracture criterion for elastic-plastic conditions, before the evolution of the J integral, attention was addressed to the finite opening at the crack tip. This simple concept was aided by observations, as for instance with Moiré fringes impressed upon the sides of specimens, which confirmed the discontinuous nature of the opening with large plastic zones. The concept was demonstrated most easily in terms of the rigid-plastic slip line behaviour of notched bend specimens, which predicted the discontinuous displacement, and the fields could also be observed experimentally with the aid of Fry's etch.

Following the lead with regard to the plastic zone crack length correction, the crack opening displacement becomes in the more general terms of plane stress LEFM the

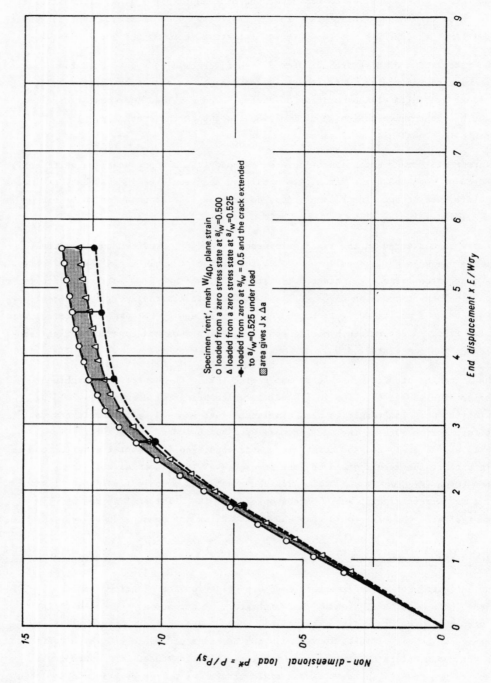

Fig.1. Comparison of incremental compliances for monotonic loading and nodal release.

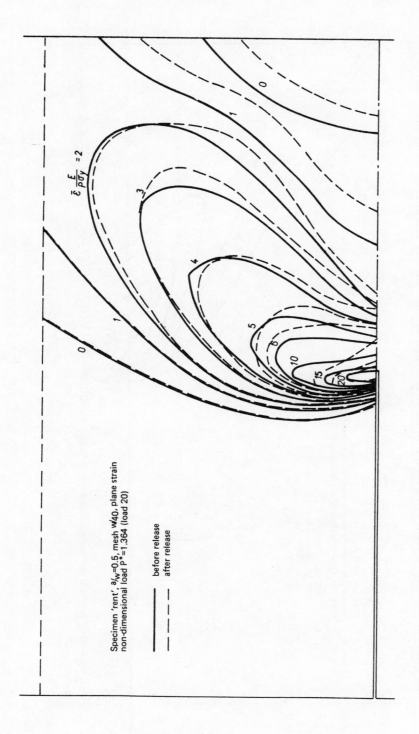

Specimen 'rent', a/w=0.5, mesh w40, plane strain
non-dimensional load P*=1.364 (load 20)

——— before release
– – – after release

$\bar{\varepsilon}\dfrac{E}{p\sigma_y}=2$

Fig.2. Plastic strain fields associated with nodal release: a) before and after.

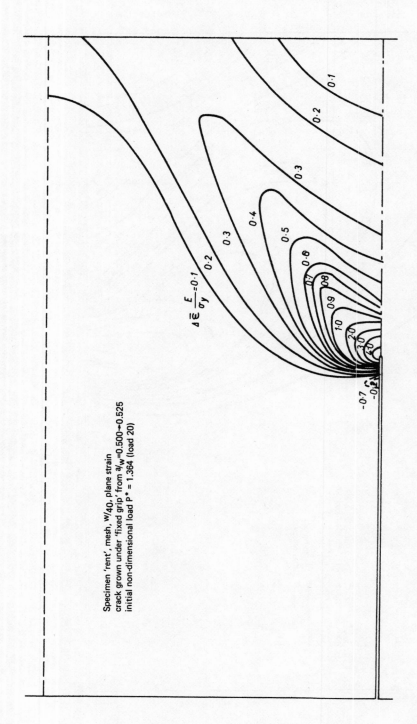

Specimen 'rent', mesh, W/40, plane strain
crack grown under 'fixed grip' from a/w=0.500→0.525
initial non-dimensional load P^* = 1.364 (load 20)

$\Delta\bar{\epsilon}\dfrac{E}{\sigma_y}$=0·1

Fig.2. cont. Plastic strain fields associated with nodal release: b) released strains.

elastic displacement within the crack at a distance from the tip equal to the crack
length correction. It thus becomes proportional to G/σ_Y for plane stress. The strip
yielding model of Dugdale[7] amplified by Burdekin and Stone,[8] then demonstrated the
identity not only for LEFM but also up to general yielding that COD expressed as δ
became equal to G/σ_Y, and a similar relationship for mode III yielding was obtained by
Bilby et al.[9]

Further steps were necessary in order to make it possible to measure COD values
and to apply them to cracked component assessments. Direct measurements at slit notch
tips had to give place to inferences from deflections of notched bend specimens, and
these had to recognise the simultaneous existence of both elastic and plastic
conditions, beyond the crude proportional relationships with bend angle deduced from
rigid-plastic slip line models. The preferred method of BS DD19 recognises the
parabolic relationship between specimen displacement and COD in the elastic-locally
plastic regime up to general yield, and the proportional incremental relationship
beyond. These relationships were experimentally verified, making use of observed
displacements at microhardness indentations within the slit notch flank region. Low
values of COD with elastic loading are made conjectural by local curvatures of the
notch flanks, so that a tangent procedure of definition had to be adopted.

Measured COD values in externally notched wide plates representative of
components were found to be substantially smaller after general yielding than would be
predicted by slip line analysis, and this effect has never been satisfactorily
explained, so that the design curve which is now used is of purely experimental origin.
Some but not all of these difficulties arise from the substantial difference between
postulated COD values in plane stress $\left[\delta = G/\sigma_Y\right]$, and plane strain $\left[\delta = G/n\sigma_Y\right.$, where n
is a factor recognising the local triaxial intensification of stress$\left.\right]$. The existence
of plane strain conditions beyond general yield is in itself a matter of degree, and
there is no assistance to be obtained from two-dimensional finite element studies,
which recognise only the two ideals of plane strain and plane stress. This difficulty
does not exist to the same extent with J integral treatments, although there are quite
substantial differences between J values for the same overall specimen total displacements in plane strain and plane stress (30% for 50% notched bend and compact tension
specimens); these differences are often ignored, as they are more justifiably in LEFM
where the theoretical difference is confined to less than 10%.

Comparisons may be made between J and COD in the elastic-plastic regime using the
finite element method, although the method of extracting COD must be defined taking the
mesh size into account. The method adopted by Boyle[6] for monotonic loading was to
represent the complete displacement profile within the slit notch as a least squares
polynomial, from which the constant term could be extracted. Under these conditions
he established for five different bend and tension specimen configurations in plane
strain, zero strain hardening, with 50% notch depths, that there was strict
proportionality of COD with J over the whole elastic and plastic strain range, with
proportionality factors of $(2.0 - 2.1)\sigma_Y$ except for the centre-cracked plate, for
which the ratio was $1.7\sigma_Y$. The ratios would be different, of course, for plane stress.
It is also possible by integration around the boundaries of rectangular specimens to
prove the proportionality between COD and J under limited circumstances such as those
of incremental full plasticity without strain hardening.

The COD was exhaustively examined as a criterion for the onset of unstable fracture in a 75mm thick carbon steel, using full thickness square bend specimens on the one hand, and 900mm wide externally notched wide plates on the other hand, with notch depths ranging from 20 to 150mm, and slowly applied loading. It is unfortunate, with regard to what has since been learned concerning the virtues of using fatigue pre-cracked specimens, that these specimens employed jewellers' sawn notches of 0.15mm width although with the advantage that the COD values could be measured directly. The results confirmed a general correlation between the two types of specimen at temperatures between 0°C and -40°C, but also revealed consistent anomalies due to geometric effects. These led clearly to a preference, if the lowest possible COD is to be measured at a given temperature or straining rate, for a specimen whether of bend or wide plate form, in which the notch depth is equal to plate thickness. A similar effect was noted when LEFM specimens were first being standardised for measurements of K_{Ic}. There is an important converse, which is that shallow surface cracks in components in service are much less severe than such deep cracks with respect to initiation of unstable fracture (perhaps to the extent of doubling the effective COD) and it would be desirable to quantify this effect further.

Although careful comparisons have also been made between different sizes of geometrically similar notched bend specimens over wide ranges with respect to J as an elastic-plastic fracture criterion, and the most recent position has been declared as fully satisfactory by Paris,[4] no similar attempt has been made to assess comparative effects of relative notch sizes or of bend specimens versus wide plates. If these differences do exist with COD it may be inferred that the same is true of J.

In conclusion, although J has substantial advantages conceptually as a criterion for elastic-plastic unstable fracture, there is little to choose between J and COD with regard to experimental measurements. Both make use of simultaneous measurements of load and displacement between loading points, in specimens which are subject to similar geometric limitations. The differences are confined to the manipulations of raw results. The advantage held by J with respect to its relative independence of the shape of the stress-strain curve for the material is probably counteracted by obscurity of meaning in relation to the behaviour of the fracture process zone. The two alternative criteria will probably continue to coexist, each making its contribution to understanding, as has long been the case with the Von Mises and Tresca yield criteria.

SLOW CRACK GROWTH

It is a common experience with materials which exhibit a useful degree of notch ductility that unstable behaviour is preceded by more or less slow crack growth, even from fatigue precracks, and this slow crack growth can represent the accumulation of a wide range of fracture toughness. At the most elementary level it is possible to distinguish fracture toughnesses between the onset of slow tearing, and maximum load recorded in the test. It is also possible to discriminate logically between these extremes for definition of the toughness by considering the use to be made of the results. In the case of a thin gas pipeline it might be appropriate to take the onset of tearing, since the bulging which accompanies crack extension in thin pressurised shells reduces the requirement of straining compatibility and leads to a rapid rise of crack extension force with crack length. The opposite would be true in the case of a thick-walled pressure vessel, or flat unpressurised component, since its behaviour would be dominated by straining compatibility. Although neither J nor COD retain unambiguous definitions after crack extension has occurred, so that the crack loses its square tip and becomes wedge shaped, it has proved to be a helpful and satisfactory artifice to calculate increments of fracture toughness as though crack extension had not occurred, and then to plot the results progressively against crack extension as an R or resistance curve. The results will often show a more or less steep rise, with the occurrence of unstable rupture at a point of tangency with the curve of increase of crack extension force; this is a principle first proposed by Orowan. Such steps are particularly necessary when the use cannot be foreseen to which the measurement is to be subjected.

THE PRESENT POSITION

Although much has been achieved in the last half century in characterising the onset of unstable fractures, the topic of elastic-plastic fracture and the criteria to be adopted in its treatment are only partially developed. This is more prominently so conceptually than in practice since it has always been possible to adopt empiricisms, but there is an undue dependence upon centres of expertise and experience. The principal conceptual shortcomings are with respect to the three-dimensional character of crack tip stress fields on the one hand, and the changes of deformation and strain which accompany crack growth on the other hand. Better knowledge of the first of these would assist in classifying all manner of secondary yet important shape effects, most of which are associated with triaxiality, in addition to providing a firm basis for a design curve for planar defects in structural components considered as wide plates. The advent of three-dimensional finite element analyses will assist in the near future, since computational methods are rapidly developing in terms of numerical economy, and what were massive problems for main frame computers of five years ago are now coming within the scope of mini-computers. The real advances will emerge as in the past, as patterns of behaviour are revealed which can suggest hypotheses leading to closed solutions, since numerical data are transient in nature, and difficult both to assimilate and to retrieve in detail.

The corresponding understanding of deformations related to crack extension remains in its infancy, and it is doubtful even whether the constitutive relations for plastic flow followed by elastic unloading and reversed plastic strains can yet be set down with certainty. The study of crack extension is recommended to those who wish to achieve, and relish a difficult intellectual problem. There are many remaining opportunities thereby to clarify the fracture problem, which pervades the whole of technology.

REFERENCES

1. J.R. RICE, J. App. Mech., ASME, p. 379 (1968).

2. J.R. RICE, Fracture, p. 191. (ed. Liebowitz). Academic Press, NY (1968).

3. R.J. BUCCI, P.C. PARIS, J.D. LANDES and J.R. RICE, ASTM STP 514, p. 40 (1972).

4. P.C. PARIS, ASTM STP 631, p. 3 (1977).

5. J.R. RICE, P.C. PARIS and J.G. MERKLE, ASTM STP 536, p. 231 (1973).

6. E.F. BOYLE, Calculation of Elastic and Plastic Crack Extension Forces, PhD thesis, The Queen's University of Belfast (1972).

7. D.S. DUGDALE, J. Mech. Phys. Solids, $\underline{8}$, p. 100 (1960).

8. F.M. BURDEKIN and D.E.W. STONE, J. Strain Analysis, $\underline{1}$, p. 100 (1966).

9. B.A. BILBY, A.H. COTTRELL and K.H. SWINDEN, Proc. Roy. Soc. A, $\underline{272}$, p. 304 (1963).

1997